Man and the Planets

Duncan Lunan

Man and the Planets

The Resources
of the Solar System

Illustrated by
ED BUCKLEY and GAVIN ROBERTS

ASHGROVE PRESS, BATH

Published in Great Britain by
ASHGROVE PRESS LTD
26 Gay Street
Bath, Avon BA1 2PD

© Duncan Lunan 1983

ISBN 0 906798 17 5

First published 1983

DEDICATION

To Linda, with love, and because she had to live
with this project for a very long time.

Editing: Paul Barnett (Editorial)

Photoset in 11/12 Plantin by
Saildean Limited, Surrey
Printed and bound by
Biddles Ltd, Guildford and King's Lynn

CONTENTS

PLATES

(After pages 100 and 180)

ACKNOWLEDGEMENTS

As the title implies, this book is about the prospects for future human life beyond the Earth, throughout our Solar System. It is the second book generated by a continuing Solar-System discussion project within ASTRA, the Association in Scotland to Research into Astronautics. The first, *New Worlds for Old*, covered manned and unmanned exploration to date (1979). The present book includes updating material where appropriate, up to the end of December 1981; for great help with Pioneer-Venus, Pioneer-Saturn, and Voyagers 1 and 2 Saturn material I'm especially grateful to Ms Kit Weinrichter.

The first part of the project took place in 1973-75 and the lecturers were Ed Buckley ('Boosters and Deep-Space Ship Designs'), Dr (now Professor) A. E. Roy ('Interplanetary Navigation'), Professor T. R. Nonweiler ('The Rôle and Future of the Space Shuttle'), A. F. Nimmo ('Lunar Colonization'), John Macvey ('Life in the Solar System'), Oscar Schwiglhofer ('Planetary Engineering'), A. T. Lawton ('Outer Solar System Resources'), and Chris Boyce ('Mind-Machine Interactions'). Many ASTRA members and visitors took part in the intervening discussions and their contributions are credited in the text. At the midpoint of this phase an all-day seminar was held at Glasgow University Department of Engineering by courtesy of Professor Nonweiler. Updating meetings continued during the 1970s, and in 1980 the entire project was reviewed within ASTRA chapter by chapter, after which specific discussions were held on Voyager-Saturn, Project Starseed, and space elevators. Some lectures not specifically part of the project were also very helpful, particularly 'The Colonization of the Moon' (Ed Buckley, 1962), 'The Exploration of Mars' (A. E. Roy, 1966), 'The Apollo 13 Mishap' (T. R. Nonweiler, 1970), 'An Artist's View of the Solar System' (Ed Buckley, 1971), 'The Resources of the Moon' (David Antia, 1978), and 'Update on von Neumann Probes' (Chris Boyce, December 1981).

In the initial research phase I had a great deal of help from the Inter-Library Loans Department of Glasgow University Library, and from L. J. Carter of the British Interplanetary Society with NASA and ESRO reports. The exhibitions and publications programme of ASTRA was extensively supported with photographs and literature from 1971 onwards by the Jet Propulsion Laboratory, Pasadena, which manages the Mariner/Viking/Voyager series of probes; and from 1974 on by NASA Ames Research Centre, which manages the Pioneer series. In 1975 I visited Kennedy Space Centre with other ASTRA members, and I must thank Jeri Bell and Bill Slattery of NASA for their help and hospitality then and on my return trip in 1979. That trip was financed by the Third Eye Centre, Glasgow, in connection with the exhibition 'The High Frontier: a Decade of Space Exploration', mounted jointly by the Third Eye Centre and ASTRA; I visited also NASA headquarters, the Smithsonian Air and Space Museum, JPL, Ames Research Centre, Rockwell International Inc. (Space Systems Division) and United Technologies Chemical Systems Division, at all of which the personnel were extremely helpful. Generally I want to thank NASA, the European Space Agency, and all their contractors who supported the exhibition and whose material helped supply background for this book. I also have to thank Glasgow Parks Department, whose Astronomy & Space Education Project I was managing at the time, for leave of absence for my US and European trips.

My thanks also to all the writers, editors, publishers and agents who gave permission for their works to be quoted herein. The following specific acknowledgements were requested:

The asteroid composition table in Chapter 10 is from *Islands in Space: the Challenge of the Planetoids*, by Dandridge M. Cole and Donald W. Cox, copyright © 1974. Reprinted with permission of the publisher, Chilton Book Company, Radnor, Pa.

The quotation from *The Bull of Minos* by Leonard Cottrell in Chapter 6 appears by permission of Mr Cottrell's estate.

The extract from *The Gods of Mars* by Edgar Rice Burroughs in Chapter 7 is copyright © 1913 Frank A. Munsey Company.

I must also particularly thank Dr Krafft Ehricke for permission to use his terminology and reasoning from the paper 'A Strategic Approach to Interplanetary Flight', on which this project has relied heavily. Lastly, on behalf of all the contributors to *New Worlds for Old* and *Man and the Planets*, our thanks to Paul Barnett for bringing both books into the light of day.

Duncan Lunan

ABBREVIATIONS AND ACRONYMS

ALSEP	Apollo Lunar Scientific Experiment Package
ASTRA	The Association in Scotland to Research into Astronautics
atm	atmospheric pressure relative to that at the Earth's surface ($=1$ atm)
A-2	Soyuz launch vehicle
AU	Astronomical Unit: 149.6 million kilometres (approximately the Earth's mean orbital distance from the Sun, which was the original definition of the unit)
cm^3	cubic centimetres
CETI	Communication with Extraterrestrial Intelligence
D	Deuterium (heavy hydrogen), an isotope of hydrogen containing in the atomic nucleus a neutron in addition to the proton
delta-v	velocity change
EMF	Electromotive Force
EML	Electromagnetic Launcher
ESA	European Space Agency
EVA	Extra-Vehicular Activity (e.g., a 'space walk')
g	a measure of inertial forces (gravitational, rotational, or in linear acceleration) relative to Earth-surface gravity ($=1$g)
GeV	giga-electron-volts (the prefix 'giga' indicates a factor of one thousand million)
He-3	lightweight isotope of helium (He) containing in the atomic nucleus one, rather than two, neutrons in addition to the two protons
HISV	Heliocentric Interorbital Space Vehicle (see page 133)
HLLV	Heavy Lift Launch Vehicle (see page 47)

INTELSAT	International communications satellite consortium
JPL	Jet Propulsion Laboratory, California Institute of Technology
K	Kelvins (degrees Absolute)
kph	Kilometres per hour
kps	kilometres per second
KSC	Kennedy Space Centre, Cape Canaveral, Florida
kV	kilovolts (the prefix 'kilo' indicates a factor of one thousand)
LDE	Long-Delayed Radio Echo (see page 113)
LH$_2$	liquid hydrogen
LM	Lunar Module
L1, L2 ...L5	Lagrange points (see page 112-113)
LO$_2$	liquid oxygen
LPO	Lunar Polar Orbiter
l.y.	light years
MEL	Multi-Environment Lander (see page 149)
MeV	mega-electron-volts (the prefix 'mega' indicates a factor of one million)
MIT	Massachusetts Institute of Technology
MW	megawats
NASA	National Aeronautics and Space Administration
NERVA	Nuclear Engine for Rocket Vehicle Application (see page 33-36)
OAO	Orbiting Astronomical Observatory
OTRAG	German rocket company (see page 21-22)
pc	parsecs (1pc = 3.26 light years
pH	a measure of acidity
RJ-5	brand-name for a synthetic hydrocarbon rocket fuel (see page 46)
ROMBUS	Reusable Orbital Module-Booster and Utility Shuttle (see page 46)
RP	Rocket Propellant
rpm	revolutions per minute
SERT	Space Electric Rocket Test (see page 50)
SIOS	Standard Interplanetary Operations Spacescraft (see page 132-137)
S-IVB	Saturn vehicle upper stage (see page 32-33)
SSTO	Single-Stage-to-Orbit (see page 45-49)
S-2	Saturn V vehicle upper stage (see page 39)
USAF	United States Air Force

I

The Case for Deep Space

Down, down, down. Would the fall *never* end?
—Comparison of successive NASA budgets (with thanks to Lewis Carrol)

In the summer of 1978, before my *New Worlds for Old* went to press, I added a farewell tribute to the booster rockets which had opened up the Earth-Moon system and the gulfs beyond: 'Goodbye to Titan III, farewell Atlas, farewell Thor ...' In months the Space Shuttle would be operational and the human presence in space would be firmly established in all operations.

A year later, I was on top of the tower at Launch Complex 39, Kennedy Space Centre, with a NASA guide. The prototype Shuttle *Enterprise* had just been removed after compatibility tests with the tower, which was the same one used in the Apollo lunar launches. On the floors below, major reconstruction was in progress. The elevator the astronauts rode had been reduced by traffic of workmen to a tatty old cargo hoist, while the 'clean room'—open to the elements and streaked with salt and rust—was exactly the opposite of its name. 'We'll be cleaning it up a bit before the missions begin,' George Diller conceded wryly. But the rest of the news was all bad. The *Enterprise*, weather-stained and unattended in a dark bay of the Vehicle Assembly Building, was bound not for space but for the Smithsonian Air and Space Museum. The *Columbia*, hidden in the Orbiter Processing Facility although its fuel tank was already waiting in the high girders of the VAB, was facing problems with the engines and ceramic tiles. From our spectacular viewpoint we looked down the rank of Thor, Titan and Atlas launch pads on Merrit Island—being not dismantled or mothballed but refurbished and extended to launch payloads once booked for the Shuttle. On my trip around the US space centres I heard fears expressed openly that the Shuttle might *never* fly, that the whole space programme might collapse or be handed back to the military. There were conflicting reactions to a proposal that a consortium of aerospace firms might take over Shuttle operations, deep-seated disagreement about what the Shuttle and NASA itself were *for*, and general dissatisfaction with the government and particularly the presidency for lack of an effective lead. I came home convinced that the US space programme needed a major new initiative.

Almost simultaneously, the Eurospace consortium issued a call for new objectives in the European space programme, with spending comparable to the USA's;[1] Soviet spending on space is estimated to be three times the USA's,[2] possibly six times as much in terms of Gross National Product. The Soviet programme and the recommended European one emphasize Earth-orbital, Earth-oriented activities, but with significant deep-space commitments. The European Space Agency has already shown a healthy interest in some of the projects being blocked in the USA, such as the Lunar Polar Orbiter. NASA's LPO has repeatedly been refused 'start funding'; and the ALSEP scientific stations on the Moon were switched off in 1977 in an almost unbelievable act of governmental vandalism. The Galileo Jupiter probe must be redesigned for a later launch, and its political opponents see herein another opportunity for its cancellation. The Venus Orbiting Imaging Radar and Halley's Comet missions should have been started in 1981 and 1982 respectively, at the latest, to be ready on time. There may indeed be no US planetary studies until the 1990s,[3] and the specialized management teams of the Jet Propulsion Laboratory and Ames Research Centre may be disbanded. After all the effort and sacrifice to create a Shuttle-based deep-space potential for the 1980s, it seems it may go unused.

Technical problems with the Shuttle, late in the day, were predicted by T.R. Nonweiler at ASTRA lectures in the 1960s and '70s. Political problems also were foreseen for the '70s, unless there was a post-Apollo initiative comparable to President Kennedy's support for Apollo itself. That support was not forthcoming, and NASA was forced to cancel all manned lunar and planetary plans, as well as major unmanned projects such as the Grand Tour, to retain even a compromise version of the Shuttle design. The compromises in question led directly to the difficulties foreseen by Nonweiler at the outset.

In the US, government projects are subject to review by Congress and Senate each year. The lunar and planetary scientists have made the political task particularly difficult by identifying their programmes so strongly with pure research.

It's idle to point out the relatively huge sums spent by the US government on, for example, defence, or by Americans individually on chewing gum, alcohol, cosmetics or gambling, while the decisions rest with people like Senator William Proxmire, with his notorious 'Golden Fleece' awards to what he calls unproductive research. The belated attempt to relate Mars, Venus and Jupiter missions to Earth-environment studies has cut very little ice.

A totally different approach was advocated by Krafft Ehricke as long ago as 1968. [4] He called for a 'strategic' approach to interplanetary flight in which the basic, nonscientific objective would be acquisition of the Solar System for mankind. Planning should be capability-oriented, rather than mission-oriented as in the Apollo programme: the main object of unmanned exploration would be to study a number of worlds before one of them was studied in detail by human explorers. Manned exploratory missions would be justified by the uniquely human characteristics—e.g., intelligence, judgment, resourcefulness—but with aims beyond scientific inquiry, namely to seek out the potential usefulness of other worlds. Correspondingly, engineering solutions would be related to regular, large-scale transport operations rather than 'marginal performance of a few individual missions', such as the proposed NERVA Mars project, of which Ehricke was highly critical. Following exploration, occupation, utilization and exploitation, long-term objectives would be in the class of making Earth the garden spot of the Solar System, with the rest being its sources of supply.

With Ehricke's permission, the terminology of the strategic approach will be used throughout this book. The planets, their satellites, the asteroids, meteors, interplanetary dust, the Solar Wind, the cometary halo, and the hypothetical dust clouds beyond—all will be evaluated for relevance to spacefaring Man. That last emphasis is important because many of Earth's suppliers may find it difficult or impossible to visit the garden, and their priorities will be different; the settlements in space may regard supplies for Earth as a sideline, and we must be prepared for that. But in the first instance the relevance to Earth is paramount. It may not be long before our overcrowded, polluted and overworked-planet-based civilization not only needs extraterrestrial energy supplies and raw materials, but needs to export its industries to the sites of those sources of supply to preserve a tolerable environment down here. Furthermore, not only may the strategic approach be fundamental to our comfort and prosperity, it *is* essential to our very survival.

In earlier books I have mentioned a 'Politics of Survival', a 300 years' programme intended to guarantee the survival of the human race, to pursue whatever further goals we then see fit.*

Its logical basis is that the major categories of menace are treated as absolutes, not as relatively pressing or remote: the objective is *guaranteed* survival, and therefore the strategy must counter each and every extinction threat. Relative probabilities do not enter into it, and are meaningless in the context of astronomical/biological interaction—if we counter only the immediate threats, we guarantee that one of the 'remote' ones will account for us. Two of the supposedly 'remote' ones occur and recur on every world in the Solar System, and are bound to happen to Earth again unless prevented. Furthermore, the chance that either will happen tomorrow is just the same as for a million years hence; they are therefore, in that sense, the most immediate of all.

There are eight categories in which a single event could wipe out the human race, directly or by a catastrophic chain of consequences. In addition they have the unhappy power to combine synergistically, so that a minor event in one category could overload a previously contained process in another. The breakdown begins: (1) weapons of mass destruction; (2) overpopulation; (3) pollution of the environment; (4) exhaustion of natural resources; (5) genetic breakdown.

Those five are in one way or another man-made, and could conceivably be countered within the confines of the planet—if we were willing to pay the price, which includes total revision of the nature and aims of technological civilization. Some people might find that price sociologically and philosophically acceptable. But the same limiting action can't deal with the three remaining headings, which are external to Earth in origin: (6) giant meteor impact; (7) solar change or nearby supernova; (8) direct Contact with an alien intelligence.

The impact danger is now taken a good deal more seriously than it was in 1969, in ASTRA discussions for *Man and the Stars*. From the Apollo missions and the planetary probes we now

---

* It's my own formulation and some ASTRA members or former members would demur strongly, but many find it generally acceptable.

know that impact events dominated the early history of the planets, and orbital surveys of the Earth, with continuing study of the geological record, have shown that major impacts have continued since. In particular there is now strong evidence that an impact event wiped out the dinosaurs,[5] who were masters of the Earth for much longer than we have been.

However, it seems generally supposed that an incoming asteroid could be destroyed by nuclear missiles launched from the ground. Chapter 10 will show that to be whistling in the dark in a variety of keys; moreover, one might reasonably ask how an alternative-technology society could maintain the missile strength, warheads and computer capability supposedly needed. In fact, to cope effectively with a major impact threat requires a manned-space capability and expertise equivalent to industrializing the inner Solar System.

The other prime suspect for the extinction of the dinosaurs has been a nearby supernova, for which some researchers have believed they had good evidence. 'Nearby' is a relative term: one of the most detailed scenarios postulated a Type III supernova, rare but extremely violent, 1000 parsecs (3260 light-years) away.[6] Such events are estimated to occur in the loosely defined 'solar neighbourhood' on average once every ten million years, with less violent but closer events still more frequent.[7] How much warning we would get depends on the distance, but some aspects of the danger could materialize before publication of this book, if the exploding star were relatively close.

The reliability of the Sun, too, has become a major topic in recent years. There's now strong evidence for the once derided 'Maunder minimum' in sunspot activity between 1645 and 1715, as well as other minima in earlier centuries, apparently correlated with climatic changes on Earth (the evidence relies on tree-ring and carbon-14 counts).[8] It's generally agreed that the Sun has grown about 30% brighter in the last four billion years,[9] and discussion continues as to short-term variations. Observations of the outer planets have suggested fluctuations in the Sun's ultraviolet and X-ray output.[10] Failure to detect the predicted flux of neutrinos from the solar core has led to suggestions that the fusion reactions which sustain the Sun's output are intermittent. However, Mariner 10 has disproved the suggestion that there are occasional flares to 100 times normal intensity: if that happened, the hemisphere of Mercury facing the Sun would melt down, but in fact the surface preserves the bombardment record of its early history. Another possible explanation for the neutrinos' absence is that the Sun's core may differ in composition from the exterior because the outer layers have been 'seeded' as the Solar System passed through an interstellar dust cloud, perhaps generating an ice age. [11] Such events must happen relatively often in the System's history, and we know mankind can survive an ice age. But even a 3% change in the Sun's output, sustained for any length of time, might be more than life on Earth could stand. A 1% change in received illumination, even from one hemisphere to another, is enough to trigger an ice age on Earth. [12]

Man and the Stars argued that colonies in other planetary systems were the best insurance against annihilation by the Sun and, to ensure that some at least would survive a nearby supernova, the colonies should be spread to a radius of at least ten light-years. To achieve that within three centuries would almost certainly need a faster-than-light drive, which seems impossible. We were considering only the effects of direct radiation, however, as in early versions of the dinosaur-extinction hypothesis, and only the least violent supernovae. Relying on distance alone, to be sure that some group would survive shockwaves and fallout from a Type III event we might have to spread over *thousands* of light-years. But we were also assuming that settlements must be on open planetary surfaces—just the assumption challenged in the famous student seminar which led to the space-colony concepts discussed in Chapter 6. On the most ambitious versions of these, we would insure the human race against supernovae within 100 years.

Contact with other intelligence is much less of a certainty. Many experts, such as I.S. Shklovskii, now feel that we're probably the only technological civilization in the Galaxy, [13] and I myself have argued that either we are one of the very first spacefaring cultures or we are already a protected species. [14] The 'conventional' scientific view is that communication by radio is the only possible form of contact, with a small 'c'; and some authorities, such as Sir Bernard Lovell [15] and Professor Zdenek Kopal, [16] believe that even that experience should be avoided.

Much has been made of the supposed intellectual dangers of radio contact; but, for a threat to human survival, direct Contact would surely be necessary. Even then, I imagine that serious risks could arise only by accident. In a programme aimed at *guaranteed* survival, however, we must consider even the remote prospect of high-technology visitors hunting through the Solar System to destroy every self-supporting segment of the human race. 'City-state' colonies in the cometary halo, as advocated by Freeman Dyson, would almost certainly escape such extirpation. Once we've gone thus far, moreover, the spread out to the stars is relatively easy.

That may seem wishful thinking when even a return to the Moon appears out of the question, and trivial or even bizarre when the world faces the frightening problems under headings (1) to (5). So it would be, except that space technology has a significant part to play in solving these problems. Weather satellites, communications satellites and manned and un-manned orbital surveys have opened up techniques of enor-mous potential for our Earth-surface problems. Their applica-tion will be difficult—a fit subject for a third ASTRA project in due course. The rôle of this book is to show how lunar and planetary development can contribute, but also to evaluate that development in its own right, relative to the strategic approach, the Politics of Survival, and the Kardashev analysis below.

The importance of the Politics of Survival, when first formulated, was that it showed there *was* a future, that the human race need not be eliminated in the short historical or even evolutionary term: that there was a class of solutions which could within 300 years lead to guaranteed survival. (The limit was chosen, by the way, from an essay by Sir Fred Hoyle, and as a guess at the extension of human lifespan likely to be available by the end of this century.) It was immediately attacked as dictatorial, as if humanity would rather die out, and as immoral, as if Earth and its underprivileged were to be abandoned after serving as a launch pad for spacefaring Man. If the choice arose, it would be better for an element of the human race to survive and build on what had gone before than for mankind as a whole to be extinguished—but in fact expansion into space can and should be conducted for the benefit of mankind as a whole, and can greatly improve the condition of life for the majority. O'Neill's scenario (Chapter 6) may be over-simple, but his heart is in the right place.

Extending the strategic approach to the cometary halo means that effectively the entire Solar System has been mastered. That would give us a whole-number rating on the scale devised by Professor Nikolai Kardashev: Type-1 civilization is one which has complete mastery of the resources of a planet; a Type-2 civilization controls the matter and energy resources of a planetary system; and a Type-3 civilization is master of a galaxy. [17] On that scale, our current status is often said to be about 0.7. This book charts our development up to Kardashev-2 level.

It might be argued that an alternative-technology civilization on Earth, conserving resources and recycling those used, should be assessed as of Type 1, but the Politics of Survival analysis shows that a stable Kardashev-1 civilization of this kind is a poverty trap. Although it has adequate resources for the chosen lifestyle, it lacks the high technology and expertise to protect itself against dangers (6), (7) and (8), protection against which involves access to much larger resources of matter and energy. Proper use of those resources involves taking the pressure off Earth's environment and reserves, allowing a much needed cutback in the rate of exploitation. Thus we need to advance a long way towards Kardashev-2 status—far enough to go the rest of the way with ease—in ordert to create on Earth a Kardashev-1 civilization which is viable in the long term. And, just because big impacts or supernova shockwaves occur only once in hundreds of thousands or millions of years, doesn't imply that 'in the long term' means a long time from *now*. Those are external events which would give us very little warning, and literally could happen tomorrow.

The ultimate extension of the Kardashev-2 concept is often taken to be Dyson's outline of ways to break up the planets and build a shell around the Sun. [18] Adrian Berry, among others, has looked with apparent enthusiasm at such prospects for our own Solar System. [19] The ASTRA consensus, as explained in Chapter 14, was that we should deliberately hold back from such extremes; and yet it seemed, from Chris Boyce's lectures at that stage of the project, that our civilization is already well launched in that direction. The issue is foreshadowed in contemporary arguments about, for example, the ethics of transplant surgery, genetic engineering and the microprocessor revolution. The decisions taken in these and similar areas may profoundly affect our future decision about the preservation of the planets.

If the big question at the end is to be whether the planets

should be destroyed, then an intermediate one is the preservation of their existing environments. Here, too, some key decisions have already been taken. Despite fears that the Moon and planets might be contaminated by microorganisms from Earth, US and Soviet authorities took the view that they should process with explorations once they had the means to do so, accepting the calculated risks that flyby probes would hit the planets, or that microorganisms would survive on the landers. In Project Apollo, preservation of the biological record had to be discarded for the other advantages of sending human explorers, from whose suits leakage was inevitable.

For each planet, before manned landings, a similar decision will have to be reached. In the strategic approach, unmanned probes would normally be regarded as precursors to manned missions, unless there were compelling and known reasons to hold back. But, as shown in Chapter 5, for example, lunar settlement and industrialization may have profound environmental effects there—enough, indeed, to make the whole exercise self-defeating in some of the possible combinations, and almost certainly enough to prevent some proposed uses of the Moon for scientific programmes.

For each planet in turn, there will come a time to weigh the priorities and take a more-or-less final decision. Beyond the initial one about manned landings and establishing bases or factories, there may be bigger choices about deliberately altering the environment. Enough theoretical work has been done to refer to the possibilities by the general name of 'planetary engineering', with 'terraforming' for the specific case where Earth-surface conditions are approximated.

Oscar Schwighlhofer has defined four types of planetary engineering. They are: (1) structured environments ('half-terraforming'), on the surfaces of planetary bodies or below; (2) mutaforming—adapting human beings by genetic engineering to survive on planetary bodies in existing conditions or some modifications of them; (3) orboforming—altering the rotational or orbital characteristics of a body; (4) terraforming, creating an open environment in which humans can survive with no more protection than on Earth (this last allows considerable variation, but at least requires a breathable atmosphere. As a baseline, the characteristics of the planets and the major satellites are summarized in fig. 1 and Tables 1 and 2.

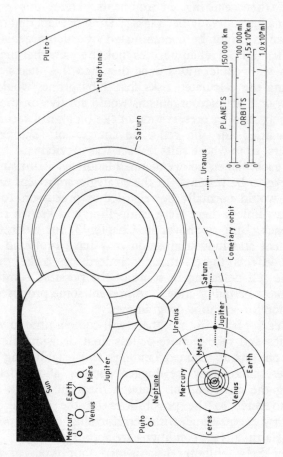

Fig. 1 The planets of the Solar System and their orbits

Table 1: Major Bodies of the Solar Sstem

Body	Diameter (km)	Surface Area (millions of kmw)	Surface Conditions	Gravity (g)	Topography (metres, relative to means surface)
Mercury	4880	75	Regolith in hard vacuum	0.37	+ 2000 to − 2000
Venus	12,104	460	Rock with some dust under great heat and pressure	0.88	+ 10,000 to − 5000

Earth	12,756 (equatorial)	511	70% water; rock, ice, desert and topsoil with vegetation	1.0	+ 8839 to − 10,912
Moon	3478	38	Regolith in hard vacuum	0.164	+ 7620 to − 3658
Mars	6787	145	Polar ice; rock and dust rich in iron oxide	0.375	+ 20,117 to − 3048
Ceres	1003	3.16	Regolith in hard vacuum	0.03?	unknown
Jupiter	142,800 (equatorial)	64,089	No solid surface; gaseous constitution	2.535 (vis. surf.)	+ 7925 to − 18,288 (cloud tops)
Io	3632	41.4	Sulphur crust with active volcanism	0.18	+1000
Europa	3126	30.7	Water ice	0.13	+50 to − 100
Ganymede	5276	87.5	Rock and ice	0.143	cratered
Callisto	4820	73.0	Mixed rock and ice	0.123	cratered
Saturn	120,000 (equatorial)	42,257	Liquid hydrogen over rock, under dense atmosphere	1.15 (vis. surf.)	unknown
Tethys	1050	3.46	ice with cratering	0.015	− 3000 (chasms) − 15000 (crater)
Dione	1120	3.94	ice; one hemisphere cratered	0.022	cratered
Rhea	1530	7.35	frost and ice cratered	0.029	cratered
Titan	5150	83.3	unknown	0.139	unknown
Iapetus	1440	6.51	cratered: ice with one very dark hemisphere composition unknown	0.026	cratered
Uranus	51,800	8433	unknown	1.17	unknown
Miranda	220-1300	0.15-5.31	unknown	unknown	unknown
Ariel	600-3400	1.13-36.32	unknown	unknown	unknown
Umbriel	249-1367	0.195-5.87	unknown	unknown	unknown
Titania	447-2486	0.63-19.42	unknown	unknown	unknown
Oberon	660-3800	1.37-45.36	unknown	unknown	unknown
Neptune	49,500 (equatorial)	7701	unknown	1.18 (vis. surf.)	unknown
Triton	2000-7000	13-154	unknown	unknown	unknown
Nereid	200-1200	0.13-4.52	unknown	unknown	unknown
Pluto	3000-3600	28.3-40.7	unknown	0.042-0.028	unknown
Charon	1200-2000	4.52-12.6	unknown	0.022-0.008	unknown

Man and the Planets

Table 2: Meteorological Parameters Comparison Scale

Body	Length of day (sec.)	Average surface temp. (K)	Surface pressure (atm.)	Atmospheric constituents Major	Minor
Venus	2.09×10^7	750	90-100	CO_2	He_2, H_2SO_4, HCl, CO, HF, H_2O, Ne, Kr, Ar
Earth	8.64×10^4	300	1	N_2, O_2	CO_2, H_2O, O_3, Ne, Kr, Ar, He_2, CH_4 etc, pollutants
Moon	2.55×10^6	145	10^{-13}	none	H and He from Solar Wind
Mars	8.9×10^4	230	6×10^{-2}	CO_2	N_2, H_2O, CO, O_2, O_3, Ar
Jupiter	3.54×10^4	128 (vis. surf.)	0.7 (cloud tops) to 10^8 (core)	H_2, He_2	CH_4, NH_2, NH_4OH, H_2O, C_2H_2, C_2H_6, PH_3, etc.
Io	1.53×10^5	150	10^{-7}	H	S, N, Na, SO_2
Saturn	3.68×10^4	100 (vis. surf.)	details unknown	H_2, He_2	CH_4, NH_3, H_2O
Titan	1.38×10^6	100	0.5-1.5	N_2	CH_4, H
Uranus	suspect	120 (below vis. surf.)	details unknown	?	CH_4
Neptune	suspect	100 (below vis. surf.)	details unknown	?	CH_4
Triton	5.08×10^5	unknown	unknown	CH_4?	?
Pluto	5.5×10^5	unknown	unknown	CH_4?	?

Notes

(1) Planetary and satellite data are subject to continuing revision as radar, optical and spacecraft studies continue.

(2) For all the major moons, the length of day equals the months (i.e., the time taken by the moon to orbit its planet).

(3) The interpretation that Triton has a methane atmosphere and that Pluto has methane ice may soon have to be reversed (see Chapter 11).

II

The Rôle and Future of the Space Shuttle

Up and down, up and down, I will lead them up and down ...
—Shakespeare, *A Midsummer Night's Dream*

'Ferry rockets' were thought of in the 1950s as multistage personnel or cargo carriers, whose massive lower stages could be recovered by parachute, while the winged upper stage would return as a low wing-loading* glider, circling the Earth several times to shed speed before its final descent. The systems were primarily to raise cargoes into space, to build space stations and Moon rockets, rather than to return payloads to Earth. Experiments in the '60s showed that much of what went into space in a reusable vehicle would come back in it, sooner or later, and a heavy-duty transport would be required. Behind the scenes, another major factor was military use: in many cases the armed forces would require rapid return to Earth, calling for high wing-loading or even some form of heat-shield entry. USAF plans in the early '60s, cancelled only as the Shuttle concept emerged,[1] at first involved a high wing-loading glider (Dyna-Soar) and later a Manned Orbiting Laboratory reached by Gemini capsules. The military requirement would be well served by a large, reusable manned vehicle, capable of operations in polar orbit and able to serve as a stable instrument platform for days at a time, yet return to Earth at short notice.

Shuttle designs are summarized in a convenient five-letter code in which, for example, a vehicle which took off and landed vertically would be classed VTOVL – Vertical Take-Off Vertical Landing. From 1967, proposals for the first-generation Space Shuttle were all VTOHL-Vertical Take-Off Horizontal

* Wing-loading: the total lifting area divided by total vehicle weight.

Landing—with either a winged orbiter or a lifting body (a wingless aircraft whose lift was generated by the shaped underside of the vehicle). Small lifting bodies were extensively tested in manned flights at Edwards Air Force Base and in unmanned missile launches from Vandenburg; [2] two or three large identical vehicles could be mounted in parallel, with one rising into orbit while the other(s) peeled off and returned to Earth. Similar designs were advanced for more conventional wing shapes—at least one goes back to the mid-50s [3]—and in the end were preferred for the Shuttle. As of early 1971, the Orbiter was to be launched by a delta-winged, piloted, reusable booster; proposals later that year aimed to cut costs by substituting an unmanned first stage based on Saturn V. [4] But, by July 1972, the design had been reduced to the still cheaper '2½-stage' configuration to be built by Rockwell International, Inc., Space Systems Division.

The Orbiter was now to lift off and be carried to orbit by its own engines, fuelled from a gigantic external tank, and assisted in the early minutes of the lift by two clip-on solid-fuel boosters, which would be recovered from the sea for later re-use. The external tank, however, would be jettisoned before orbit was reached; and smaller rocket motors would complete the Orbiter's boost phase and later return it to Earth, to land on the natural dry-lake beds at Edwards or special 4.57km runways at Kennedy Space Centre and Vandenburg AFB. The payload to be lifted to close-Earth orbit was more than doubled under pressure from the Department of Defence in 1971, [5] and that requirement, along with design compromises made to keep down costs, has produced a much less elegant vehicle than the Shuttle first envisaged.

Previous Soviet and US spacecraft had been protected by 'heat shields' of material which ablated (i.e., melted and vaporized), carrying away the heat generated by atmospheric friction before it penetrated to the layers below. That solution doesn't work for a winged vehicle, because it would change the shape of the aerodynamic surfaces. Instead, the Orbiter is clad in ceramic tiles which absorb the heat without passing it to the aluminium hull beneath. In their way the tiles (borasilicate glass, impregnated with silicone carbide in the high-temperature regions) are a triumph of materials technology: they can be removed from an incandescent furnace and picked up at once with bare hands. In addition, they have been kept

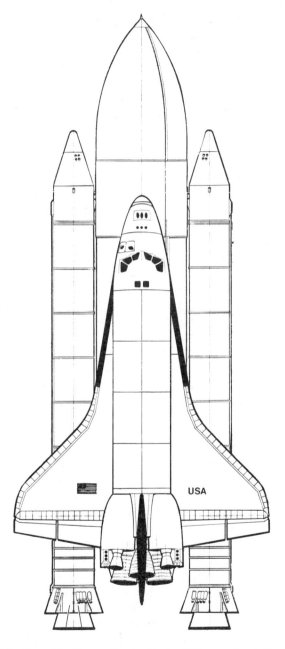

Fig. 2   The Space Shuttle *(Rockwell International, Inc.)*

very light indeed (the Orbiter's nose and leading edges are protected with heavier Reinforced Carbon insulation[4]). But they're fragile—'So fragile,' I was told off the record, 'it's like trying to put an eggshell into orbit.'

Making and fitting the 34,000 tiles individually was a mammoth task, and was far from finished in March 1979 when *Columbia* went to Kennedy Space Centre; a huge temporary staff had to be hired to install the last 7000. The roll-out to Pad 39A, planned for late November 1979, didn't take place until December 1980.

Even a hailstorm on the pad could send the vehicle back to the Orbiter Processing Facility for repairs. Frost and ice on the struts and fuel lines joining the Orbiter to the tank, fuelled with liquid hydrogen and liquid oxygen, break free next to the most important tiles of all, on the underside, where any damage more than 5cm across could make return to Earth impossible. The first tanks had thermal insulation against atmospheric heating (now removed), and extra cladding was added to the struts and fuel lines—all adding weight and reducing the effective payload. Another fear was that flames from the main engines (the largest ever built) and the boosters might be reflected back from the pad to the vehicle despite the huge outlets which were cut for the flame deflectors. $1\frac{1}{2}$ million litres of water are used to damp the flames and the sound waves (which alone could damage the tiles[7])—one-third from the State supply, one-third from the nearby river, and one-third from a huge water tower which has been constructed near the pad.

'If one of those tiles did sustain that kind of damage'—another off-the-record aside—'and the heat of re-entry got through to the alumium underneath, it could spoil your whole day.' It was proposed in all seriousness that the astronauts should 'go EVA' (leave the vehicle) and check the underside for damage.[5] On the only space test of the backpack Manned Manoeuvring Unit (then called Astronaut Manoeuvring Unit), on Gemini 9 in 1966, Eugene Cernan was unable to use it because he was exhausted by the effort of reaching it and putting it on! The system has been improved since and tested 'indoors' in zero-*g* in Skylab, and is to be a mainstay of future activities such as orbital maintenance of the Space Telescope; but to use it to check for 5cm damage under a vehicle the size of a DC-9, on the first operational test, seemed ambitious. The idea of scanning the underside with a TV camera on a boom, held by the cargo bay's Remote Manipulator System, was abandoned; but thought was given to placing a stabilized camera in space and manoeuvring the Shuttle around it.[5] If sufficient underside damage ever *is* found, the crew will have to go EVA with a temporary repair kit.

There's no satisfaction in saying that within ASTRA much of this was anticipated. In lectures throughout the 1960s and early '70s T. R. Nonweiler maintained that the US space programme was going down the wrong line of materials technology, dictated by a design philosophy for which one of his kinder words was 'pragmatic'. The approach had been to start with a relatively straightforward engineering shape (half-cones for capsules, only a little more sophisticated than the Soviet spheres), determine whether it could function aerodynamically as the mission required, then develop the materials to make it operational. In his 1971 lecture on the near-disaster of Apollo-13 Nonweiler said that, under pressure, such an approach was likely to lead to design errors; in the Apollo case, the pressure was Kennedy's commitment to putting Americans on the Moon before 1970. The slow-opening hatch would have been a minor example, had it not caused the deaths of the Apollo-1 crew; a more serious example was the clustering of all tankage for life-support and fuel-cell power in a single bay of the Service Module, with no backup battery power except the 15-minute supply intended for re-entry. The Apollo-13 explosion would have killed the Apollo-8 crew, and likewise the 10, 11, 12 and 13 crews had it happened after separation of the Lunar Module. In both cases, the fire and the explosion, the designers simply had not foreseen the consequences of such events.

In 1974, when the Shuttle design had been finalized, Nonweiler saw the same approach at work. This time the pressure was financial, and the target date was allowed to be postponed (from 1975 to 1981, in fact, creating a six-year hiatus in US manned spaceflight). But the financial constraints also compromised the vehicle design and the objective of a fully reusable system. The Orbiter intended for the second stage was now to become the main-engine platform, married to a throwaway tank and maybe-recoverable boosters not present in the original specifications. Sooner or later, the pragmatic (not to say haphazard) changes would lead to a major technological dead end, probably a clash between materials technology and altered design. The eventual problem indeed lay just where his reasoning had suggested: instead of being shielded by the upper surface of the manned booster, or safely above the unmanned one, in the new design the Orbiter's most vital surface was fully exposed to shockwaves, fire, explosion and flying ice through being placed face-on to the tank.

Other problems which delayed the Shuttle, such as the auxiliary power unit turbines and the failures in the main-engine cluster, are familiar to rocket engineers and, although bigger than ever, were virtually bound to yield to persistent attack; whereas, if the Shuttle proved able to get into space without damaging tiles, apparently that success would be at least partly due to luck. Except for the Apollo-1 tragedy, luck has by and large been with the US space programme, and *Columbia*'s test flights showed that the eggshell could indeed make it to orbit and back. But obviously Nonweiler's criticisms were well founded, and clearly many of the Shuttle's original purposes won't be fulfilled by the four vehicles now being commissioned. In calling for a new initiative in space, the objectives should be reviewed and alternative approaches considered.

Shuttle work in conjunction with space stations, and in supporting lunar and planetary exploration, was to be backed by the Saturn V booster, which was developed for continuous use until 1990 at least. Saturn V was scrapped just when it had become 'cost-effective'—at the point when, if the development cost were spread over the total number of launches, each successive launch would bring *down* the overall cost per vehicle per launch. [8] Even satellites taken up by the Shuttle, unless they were for close-Earth orbit, would have been placed on station and retrieved where appropriate by manned, fully reusable Space Tugs lifted into space by Saturn V. Now payloads bound for higher orbits or beyond must take their propulsion systems with them, and the need to lift those extra rocket stages reduces payload and drastically cuts the effectiveness of the overall space transportation system.

Design changes, extra safeguards and other problems have brought down the payload in any case. It now seems that *Columbia*'s lift capability will initially be 17 tonnes, rising later to 19.5 tonnes, and finally to 23. *Challenger*, the next Orbiter, will be able to lift 27 tonnes, and *Discovery*, the next again,

28.2. With additional strap-on solid motors *Discovery* and *Atlantis*, the last of the series, should be able to lift 32.2 tonnes or more, but not until then (1984) will the Shuttle be able to meet the Defence requirement for 29.5 tonnes in 28°.5 inclination orbit (i.e., due east from Kennedy Space Centre, gaining maximum advantage from the Earth's rotation). That performance is equivalent to 14.5 tonnes in 98° orbit and corresponds to the launch of a Big Bird reconnaissance satellite from Vandenburg. [9] The mission profile for the Galileo Jupiter Orbiter/Entry probe will have to be drastically changed if it is to fly at all: for launch with a solid booster, now cancelled, with a mass in parking orbit of 27 tonnes, the launch window closes in 1982 and stays closed for a decade. The effect on other deep-space missions is academic since, without early 'start funding', none of them will fly in the 1980s.

On many of the Shuttle's research flights it will carry a modular Spacelab built by the European Space Agency; it's primarily for those flights that the Shuttle forepart is able to carry up to seven people. Spacelab fits in the cargo bay and can be assembled in four combinations of pressurized modules and 'EVA pallets'. On normal flights the cargo bay will be open to expose heat-radiating panels on the insides of the doors. An EVA airlock opens into the bay, and, when Spacelab pressurized modules are used, a tunnel will be connected to the lock. Pallet experiments can be operated by remote control or by spacesuited personnel.

Even on Spacelab missions, the Shuttle's stay in orbit will normally be limited to seven days. Flights can be stretched to thirty days, but only by carrying extra 'consumables' (air, food, water, reaction mass, etc.) which cut into the payload. But serious thought is being given to a 'power module' with solar cells and life-support supplies which could make Spacelab independent of the Shuttle services in space. It would then be possible to leave Spacelab in orbit, manned or unmanned, and rotate crews or bring up extra supplies and equipment as appropriate.

While Spacelab will allow a start to be made on matching the Soviet space-station experience in metallurgy, crystallography and medical and biological programmes, a bigger station will be needed to develop practical experience, in which the Soviets are now far ahead. During the extended operation of Salyut 6 from September 1977 to August 1979, for instance,

the station was manned by seven crews, one for 140 days and
another for 175 (two other crews failed to dock); there were
unmanned dockings by seven Progress ferries and one Soyuz;
cargo transfers (e.g., fuel, and equipment such as furnaces and
a radiotelescope) were handled as routine; a Soyuz replaced
another at the end of its mission lifetime; the station was
operated in gravity-gradient mode (long axis towards the
Earth, for stability) to exchange spacecraft between the two
docking ports, [10] and rotated end-over-end for artificial gravity
to help drain a faulty tank. [11] The docked ferries repeatedly
were used as Space Tugs to raise the station's orbit; and in EVA
inspections and repairs, attempted for the first time in the
Soviet programme, the cosmonauts fully matched the work
experience gained by astronauts on Apollo and Skylab. [12]
Salyut missions are to be extended to three years in preparation
for planetary missions, [13] while the Moon Treaty before the
United Nations is partly an attempt to limit the use of celestial
bodies to socialist states. [14] Cosmonauts and Soviet spokesmen
have repeatedly avowed their intention to establish human
settlements throughout the Solar System, as advocated by the
pioneering theoretician Tsiolkovsky, [15] and in the Salyut
programme they are mastering the basic techniques. The
nearest comparable work in the Shuttle programme would be
EVA servicing of the unmanned Space Telescope and the Long
Duration Exposure Facility, for industrial experiments in
vacuum and zero-g.

When serious problems began, space on the Shuttle was
already booked through 1983, and 1984 was filling up. [16] Many
of those payloads will now be launched by Thor-Delta, Atlas
or Titan rockets, and the Department of Defence, originally
one of the major users, [17] will now have to keep using Titan III
until 1984 at least. How many payloads will be lost due to mass
restrictions remains to be seen, but several options on either the
Shuttle or the European launcher Ariane (e.g., for Intelsat v
communications satellites) were confirmed for Ariane after its
first successful firing in December 1979. [18] It does no harm to
think about improving the situation.

One obvious step would be to increase the Shuttle fleet,
already cut down to four Orbiters. The production facilities at
Rockwell International, originally created for Apollo, are
chronically underused: Shuttle sections are being built more-
or-less by hand. The impression is of little knots of men

working here and there within the huge buildings. Manning has to be kept so low that skilled men are reassigned from one section to another as assembly progresses. To make a production line economic, I was told, would need an order for six more Orbiters, but the cost per vehicle would drop by 80%, from $1000 million to $200 million—six new Orbiters for 20% more than the cost of one.

Another strategy would be to move the launch site. The most economical launch from any site is due east, gaining maximum help from the Earth's rotation; but, because the orbital plane must pass through the centre of the Earth, its inclination to the equator equals the latitude of the launch site. Thus the highest payload of the Shuttle is stated in terms of due-east launch, to 28°.5 orbit, from Kennedy Space Centre. In fact, KSC is the furthest north from which one can reach the Moon with a due-east launch. Since all the Soviet launch sites lie well north of 28°.5, they were at a disadvantage which bears on their supposed preference—*at the moment*—for unmanned lunar exploration. Similarly, the USSR didn't begin placing communications satellites in synchronous, equatorial orbit until 1975, [19] and their intended contribution to the World Weather Watch from synchronous orbit was so delayed that an extra US satellite had to substitute for it. [20]

Thus the European booster Ariane, launched near the equator from Kourou in Guyana, has an advantage over the Shuttle in any launch to equatorial orbit, Moon or planets, for all but the largest payloads. A German company, OTRAG, tried to cash in on the equatorial advantage by leasing a large area of Zaire to develop a low-cost launch system. Accusations that the true purpose was to develop a cruise missile, or spy satellites for Third World nations, missed the commercial point of the equatorial site. Ironically, however, the OTRAG proposal was a backward step. Advances in rocket technology, particularly in reliability, had reached a point where a satellite launcher could theoretically be built even by an inefficient process of clustering standardized liquid-fuel rockets. Clustering techniques had been used before, notably in the first-stage tankage of Saturn I, but as a means to developing larger engines, working towards the lunar and deep-space capability of Saturn V. By contrast each unit of the OTRAG cluster would have had its own motor; the biggest complex would have had 600 units and been capable in theory of placing 1500kg in synchronous orbit, or 10,000kg at 300km. [21] Control was to be exercised by throttling the motors in banks—a liquid-fuel analogue to the British Interplanetary Society moonship of the 1930s, with its huge clusters of solid-fuel elements. [22] The OTRAG system was very limited in its potential and unlikely to be man-rated—see Cleator's comment on the moonship at the head of Chapter 4. It had little if anything to contribute to the strategic approach to the Solar System, but threatened to weaken the Shuttle programme still further. The announcement that OTRAG has been asked to leave Zaire [23] came as a relief.

There is, however, a major case for moving orbital, lunar and planetary operations to an equatorial site. The Sabre Foundation, whose advisors include Ehricke and Arthur C. Clarke, has proposed an 'Earthport' a free-trade area on the equator offering launch facilities to all nations. [24] Development of one or more Earthports might counter a less welcome trend, in which some of the equatorial nations consider that synchronous orbit belongs to them. [25] The improvement in the Shuttle's performance with equatorial launches would also help to generate demand for more vehicles.

Another direction to explore is exploitation of the Shuttle tank. The economics of the space transportation system are badly dented by throwing away, every time, what amounts to a Saturn rocket without the engines and electronics. To carry it into orbit would involve a payload penalty of 2.5 tonnes (9% of full load) [4] and would be practicable on many research and satellite launching missions. Marshall Space Flight Centre has studied possible space stations built in and around a Shuttle tank; [26] a summer study at Ames Research Centre proposed a three-tank station with each tank split into ten 2.44m-high sections. Even the central tunnel in each tank would be nearly 2m in diameter. A second cluster, joined to the first by a 140m tunnel, would allow the complex to be rotated at 3rpm for simulated gravity. [27]

Tanks could be converted into lunar shuttles, or ground up to use as reaction mass for a Space Tug propelled by an electromagnetic 'mass driver' [28] (see Chapters 4 and 6). One or more tanks could be more thoroughly insulated and used as an orbital fuel store, restocked with residual liquid hydrogen and oxygen from later missions. In his novel *Kinsman* Ben Bova suggested that the USAF could acquire its own large space station just by taking tanks into orbit and clustering them for future use. [29] Discussions took place at ASTRA even earlier, under the heading 'Project Starseed', on the format and use of such a large station (see Chapter 6).

Clustering of tanks, however, requires either a policy decision or a target for repeated orbital rendezvous. A tank left in orbit would pass over KSC or Vandenburg only once a day; rendezvous would be possible only when the payload to be carried could share the orbital inclination of the first one *and* use that particular launch window. If the station's emphasis were Earth-oriented (weather and Earth resources), near-polar orbit from Vandenburg might be preferred; but short-duration military missions, the most frequent near-polar ones, would seldom if ever fit the timetable. For lunar and planetary purposes, the standard due-east launch from KSC would be better.

Regular missions to an established target in orbit would be much better. The Space Telescope and Long Duration Exposure Facility are to be visited periodically, but in both cases the main idea is to make visits as *infrequent* as the experiment programme allows, to minimize contamination of the area. Better prospects are an experimental Solar Electric Power Station (Chapter 6) and Public Service Platform (a very large communications array), whose prototypes could be assembled in close-Earth orbit, perhaps to be moved to synchronous orbit later. Both projects would require repeated Shuttle visits and might allow clustering of tanks. Nuclear waste disposal in space (Chapter 6) could provide the baseline for a multiple tank station, but probably wouldn't get under way until the 1990s.

Any of these proposals would be enhanced by an equatorial launch site. Even adding tanks to an orbital stockpile, on routine missions, would be much easier from an equatorial site because the cluster would pass overhead every ninety minutes instead of only once a day. Each tank is a 37-tonne cylinder, pressure-braced and at least partly insulated, with a huge internal volume. The early theorists would have been appalled to think that the potential might not be exploited, but then they took it for granted that launch sites would be on the equator. [30]

Because of the Orbiter's high wing-loading, its 'cross-range capability'—the possibility of landing away from the orbital track—is extremely limited. The maximum figure is 2040km: [4] just enough to allow a crew in trouble to abort near the end of the first orbit and return to KSC, despite the rotation of the Earth meantime. On following orbits, return to Edwards or Vandenburg would be possible. Emergency landing facilities are to be available in other parts of the world, [31] but in most KSC launches and *all* Vandenburg launches the Shuttle will normally stay in space for 24 hours if it doesn't come back after the first orbit. For cargo and personnel transfers, and for military missions, that limitation would be removed by operating from the equator—especially if more than one Earthport were to be created.

Separating the personnel and cargo functions would make a high-performance glider possible, delivering crews and small payloads to landing sites much further away from the orbital track. Such a mini-Shuttle would be particularly valuable to the Soviet space-station programme, not just for military reasons but to cut out the risks and major searches when a Soyuz misses its drop zone, or has to be brought back unexpectedly. Allegedly a Kosmolyot winged re-entry vehicle has been tested in air-drops from a Tu-95 Bear bomber, [32] and a runway for it has been added to the space complex at Tyuratam. [33] Earlier Soviet sources described an orbiter with a reusable but unmanned winged booster, and Phillip Parker suggested that the final version may be like NASA designs of the late '60s, with an externally mounted 'tip tank' instead of a first stage. [34] Length would be 25m and payload at least 11 tonnes. From reports that the vehicle is much smaller than the Shuttle and launched by the Proton booster, currently used for Salyut, A.T. Lawton suggests 25.5m but a payload of only 5 tonnes. [35]

Parker's figures, based on a vehicle similar to the Lockheed Starclipper proposal, [4] apparently assume the use of high-energy liquid hydrogen/liquid oxygen (LH_2/LO_2) engines. The US has had that technology since the mid-60s, although it was acquired with great difficulty, [36] and the USSR has yet to demonstrate it. Lawton's lower payload assumes less energetic propellants, but even he may be overestimating the Soviet plan. The Proton booster hasn't been man-rated and, while that doesn't mean that it will *never* be used for manned launches, it seems unlikely on these terms: the suggested payload is only twice that of the unmanned Progress ferry; the launch vehicle is much bigger; only the fifth stage would be reusable, and even that would have an expendable tank. The advantage of reusability for satellite launches would not apply without a major change of policy: for many years the Soyuz/Salyut launch inclination of 51°.6 hasn't been used for other classes of spacecraft.

It seems more likely that the USSR will continue to use its standard boosters for satellite launches, that Progress will continue as a cargo ferry, and that Kosmolyot is much smaller than has been supposed. If it's about the size of Dyna-Soar or the X-24, that would fit far better than the 25m length with reports that it is 'much smaller than the NASA Shuttle vehicle' [34] and was subjected to *drop* tests—from the bomb bay or from under the wing of the bomber rather than from its back? Its rôle would then be to replace Soyuz as a personnel carrier. At present Soyuz craft taking crews to Salyut normally fly without solar cells, and have to make hurried and risky returns to Earth if they fail to dock. A low-wing-loading glider, able to reach a variety of landing fields in the USSR and land under control at low speed, would be a marked improvement. The Kosmolyot launch vehicle may therefore be not the massive and temperamental Proton but the well tried A-2, used for Soyuz, whose first stage is still basically the vehicle used to launch Sputnik 1. With Ariane, Europe is attaining a similar launch capability, and an uprated Ariane may launch a hypersonic glider, Hermes, around 1990. [37] Briefed by Nonweiler, ASTRA has been awaiting such a development for twenty years, and now it seems that Europe could initiate the next major advance in shuttle design.

Nonweiler was until recently Professor of Aeronautical Engineering and Dean of the Faculty of Engineering at Glasgow University, and is well known for his work on man-powered aircraft as well as for studies of atmosphere entry. [38] In the late 1950s he took part in an Armstrong-Whitworth design study of a vehicle to be launched in pairs, mounted on a core booster. Apart from convenience in fitting the shuttles to the booster, the aerodynamic calculations would be simplified if their undersides were hollow: a flat underside generates curved shockwaves which are harder to predict from theory. But it quickly emerged that the simplification was opening up a new principle of flight—the ship, the Waverider, could sit on the straight shockwaves flowing through the underwing cavity, and the upper surface would be aerodynamically inert. The energy of the shockwaves would be channelled, generating lift, instead of dispersing wastefully as a sonic boom.

Until now, re-entry designs have treated descent into the atmosphere, braking by friction, as an ordeal to be survived rather than a functional phase in the life of the ship. The ablating heat-shields of the capsules, the absorbing tiles of the Shuttle, and the refrigerated 'spike' and gaseous heat-shield of the plug-nozzle (Chapter 3)—all rely on destructive processes which (one hopes) end before they go to completion and the hull is exposed to burn-out or melt. The plug-nozzle lands vertically on rocket thrust, whose efficiency is impaired by the dense lower atmosphere: its best uses will be on airless or nearly airless worlds. Capsules use parachutes and shock-absorbing techniques in what can only be termed a 'controlled crash'. Even the Shuttle's rate of descent is faster than the terminal velocity of the human body in air—if you fell out of it, it would be down before you were—and it lands so hard and fast that touchdown has to be controlled by computer.[39] Removing the turbofan engines has made even one circuit impossible, and a large net is proposed for the end of the Shuttle runway.[40] John Braithwaite has remarked of the Shuttle: 'It might be safer to fly the box it came in.'

By contrast the Nonweiler Waverider 'lives' at all stages of descent from first brush with the atmosphere to final touchdown. At near-orbital speed in the upper atmosphere, it's as much in its element as a skier on a downhill run or a surfer on a board—able to prolong the experience for as long as attitude control can be maintained. Its hypersonic glide performance is so high that it can descend from equatorial orbit with a 90° latitude range—it can land at either pole if need be. And at low speed its handling characteristics give a landing speed one-tenth the Shuttle's. For many years it's been an article of faith with aerospace scientists, science-fiction writers and UFO believers that someday we'll have a propulsion system which lets us ignore the atmosphere altogether. Nonweiler's view is that, if a planet has an atmosphere, a wing designed to take advantage of it is more sophisticated than any system which wastes energy in keeping aloft by other means.

The philosophy is to keep oneself in balance with the aerodynamic environment, in terms of temperatures and pressures, instead of smashing one's way through. The Waverider would generate great heat in the shockwaves under the wing, enough to make the underside white-hot, but 'the pilot sitting topsides doesn't have to see it'. The nose and leading edges would also become very hot and absorbed heat is re-radiated from the upper surface, which is in vacuum at high speeds. The hull would be stainless steel, silvered below, blue-black above. The shape of the shockwave, and therefore of the underside cavity, is determined by the leading edge: a straight leading edge, giving a simple delta planform, generates a diamond-shaped shockwave and a double-wedge profile like an inverted V or a printer's caret (Plate 8). A Concorde planform gives a more rounded nose and a 'gothic arch' wing (Plate 7). With a completely rounded leading edge, eliminating the pointed nose (vulnerable to heat), the underwing cavity would be elliptical.

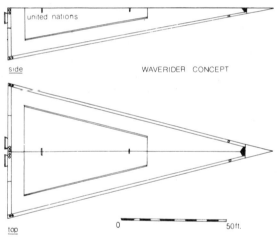

Fig. 3   The 'caret wing' Waverider

The leading edges would have a very small radius of curvature (2-3cm, compared with 2-3m for the shuttle), and would need protection from temperatures of about 1800 K. In the early '70s that was a major problem: graphite or molybdenum might be used, but would be difficult to bond to the stainless steel, and oxidation in the lower atmosphere could destroy the leading edge and make the wing unstable. Now, however, the Reinforced Carbon Carbon of the Shuttle leading edges can stand temperatures up to over 1900 K and, at 35kg per square metre,[4] is dense enough not to share the tiles' fragility problem. It's attached mechanically to the Shuttle wing, to allow for expansion, so presumably attachment to the Waverider could be mastered.

According to Nonweiler, US emphasis on blunt leading edges, which cannot generate plane shockwaves, was a major reason for lack of interest in the Waverider. Another was the materials-technology emphasis on aluminium and ceramics (molybdenum was to be used for Dyna-Soar, but the programme was cancelled[1]). A further curious factor is that, although Waverider was designed for use in re-entry, discussion concentrated on its possibilities as a Mach-6 airliner, for which there's little demand at present. In fact, most engine configurations would interfere with the design. For stability, the centre of gravity has to be in the centre of the wing area, and may well be in the underwing cavity; and in most conditions Waverider functions best in equilibrium with its environment. For that reason Nonweiler turned down a suggestion from Robert Shaw, at ASTRA, that magnetic braking could be applied to the plasma shockwaves under the wing. The whole object is to *avoid* interaction with the plasma and handle as little of its energy as possible within the vehicle. Similarly, in the glide phase and approaching touchdown, engine intakes would interfere with the smooth airflow, high performance and good handling which are the Waverider's strong points. At supersonic speeds, *external* combustion would be possible—injecting fuel into the shockwave to provide thrust and added lift. But getting into cruise mode would be somewhat uneconomic—even if you can get to Australia in an hour and a half, without significant sonic booms along the track, expendable or flyback boosters are unlikely to figure in airline operations.

In 1962-63 Waverider models were tested in rocket flights at Woomera. These and wind-tunnel tests showed that the wing generated more lift than conventional wings of the same area, with less drag, and that low-speed performance was excellent. When the angle of incidence drops far enough for the airstream to make contact with the upper surface, the Waverider takes on the gliding characteristics of a paper dart. It had been thought that a fin below the fuselage might be needed, rendering the vehicle's basic profile an inverted W instead of an inverted V, but that proved unnecessary; as did plans to roll it over and land in a dihedral configuration. Control surfaces and landing gear do pose problems, however, since hinges on the underside would become hot spots during re-entry. Gas jets might be the answer, but to function in atmosphere would have to be much larger than those currently used in space. The ASTRA suggestion was for fully hinged and rotating surfaces, to be extended from the rear of the Waverider after entry.

Shaw suggested that landing gear be similarly stowed. For touchdown, the vehicle would go into a deliberate stall and descend on rocket thrust. Nonweiler wasn't keen on the idea, although it would give the pilot a good Lunar-Module-type view of the descent; the Harrier VTOL fighter manages a smooth transition from horizontal to hovering flight without any 'hiccup' in its motion; it stalls during the approach, 'but not catastrophically'. The Waverider might have Harrier-type vectored-thrust jet engines at the rear, activated only at low speed when the airstream reached their intakes. In general, the further aft the centre of gravity, the easier touchdown would be, and the 'gothic-arch' Waverider's centre of gravity is further back than the caret's; but whether it could be brought back far enough to allow vertical landing (perhaps on an inflated bag) rather than *short* landing is another matter. If, however, it's possible in theory to deploy an inflated bag from the underside, ASTRA suggested lowering a keel, with lateral skids for stability. Since the Waverider's landing speed is low in any case, if it can land horizontally at all then probably engines would be omitted entirely.

Throughout the 1960s Nonweiler argued that Europe should be pursuing low-speed development work, to have a significant contribution to make and to be able to influence design philosophy when the US opted for winged entry vehicles, as he was sure eventually they would. Little interest was taken outside ASTRA, and work on Waverider was limited to Nonweiler's four-man team at Glasgow University, on an Air Ministry contract. The Shuttle decisions were based on Apollo technology, a contrasting line of development. But, in the meantime, facilities for research at high airspeeds have opened up outside the US—e.g., a Free Piston Shock Tunnel in Australia, capable of simulating Earth, Mars or Venus atmosphere entry. [41] With the proposal to develop the Hermes for Ariane-5 launch, Europe could now produce the Waverider independently.

A 1.12 tonne Waverider, capable of carrying one man, would have a length of 15.24m and a wingspan of 6m. It could in theory be launched, even in its original, paired configuration, by Ariane-1 (payload to 200km orbit 5.28 tonnes) if the standard payload fairing were replaced by a suitably shaped mounting cone. Ariane-5's payload will be 10 tonnes in 200km orbit, and the Hermes dimensions have been shown schematically as 12.5m with a 7.6m wingspan. [37] With Ariane-5, Europe could launch Waveriders, singly or in pairs if aerodynamics make that essential, with a payload equivalent to Progress's, if not Kosmolyot's—perhaps carried externally in the cone—and much superior performance during return to Earth.

Waverider is unique at present in that it can be kept in radio contact during atmosphere entry—*from above*. The plasma 'sheath', which envelops any other vehicle and cuts off communications, is channelled to the Waverider underside and leaves antennae on the upper surface free. Cargo-carrying Waveriders could be controlled by spacecraft or space stations overhead, or from ground stations by satellite relay, throughout the descent. Data could be relayed to Earth without a break from spacecraft entering the ionospheres of Mars, Venus, the giant planets or Titan, making it possible to send much more data—especially since the Waverider's stay in the ionosphere would be much longer than for any probe plunging downwards.

Shaw asked whether data-gathering could be still further extended by a 'hypersonic skip' technique, bouncing in and out of the atmosphere, as advocated by Eugene Sanger for a round-the-world rocket bomber or transport. [42] Nonweiler replied that there's no virtue in bouncing a vehicle which controls heat by reradiation: the skip manoeuvre pulls higher *g*s and generates higher heat-loads than the steady glide. In addition, if the glider went over the horizon as seen from Earth, the data would be lost anyway unless an Orbiter or 'bus' vehicle was suitably placed to act as a relay.

Considering Waverider probes after the entry phase, however, it became clear that we had evolved a new class of planetary mission—gliding entry. In an atmosphere, direct-entry probes or floating balloon stations simply could not obtain the data available using Waverider; for Mars and Venus, low-level photography would be valuable, and there are specific targets crying out for glide-mission study (see later). Furthermore, since the upper surface of the Waverider is protected by the high angle of incidence during entry, parachute-landing probes can be released over specific targets, without the design constraint of having to fit within 'aeroshells' like the Viking and Venera landers (Plate 8).

Waverider development could begin with drop tests from balloons or aeroplanes, to be followed by rocket flights and ballistic tests. Research models could be carried into space by the Shuttle, perhaps on the Spacelab EVA pallets, being controlled from above during re-entry; and launched by Ariane, or from the Shuttle with an upper stage, around the Moon or the Earth-Moon Lagrange points (Chapter 6) for entry at interplanetary velocities. Probe missions would provide valuable data during manned-vehicle development, and in the 1990s Waveriders could be delivering personnel and cargo to orbit and returning research products to Earth.

By then, it is to be hoped, industrial activities in close-Earth orbit will be well beyond the experimental stage, and manufacturers will be looking towards the Moon as a possible source of raw materials. In particular, the potential of 'powersats' in synchronous orbit may have been demonstrated, and the use of lunar materials to build them will be a real possibility (Chapters 3-6). But a treaty now before the UN, drafted by the USSR and backed by a number of developing nations, would forbid the exploitation of the Moon unless for the benefit of mankind as a whole. Such a development was foreseen early in ASTRA's discussions, although we didn't expect it in such strength, so soon. Although the US has postponed signing the Moon Treaty pending considerable further study,[43] it represents a trend in international thinking which cannot be safely ignored. An INTELSAT-style lunar consortium is probably the only solution.

By that time, the Space Shuttle's two main functions—delivering payload *to* space and bringing it *from* space—may well have been separated. In bringing down raw materials from the Moon, or finished products from the Moon or orbiting factories, a vehicle which can land on conventional airfields in any latitude may be of great political importance. In Chapters 4 and 5, it will be argued that the future of cargo deliveries to Earth lies with the Waverider.

III

Shuttles and Launch Vehicles

And look at this booster—all that power! Are we supposed to go
up to the Moon, or through it?
>—from *The Conquest of Space* (Paramount, 1955;
> character has just built a winged ars lander,
> believing it to be a Moon rocket.)

In the late 1960s, NASA's plans for manned space exploration
rested mainly on Apollo. Lunar missions in the '70s might
include returning to sites of special interest,[1] with temporary
surface accommodation,[2] and a small rocket which could carry
a man and equipment 80km over lunar terrain[3] or, using
propellant from the Lunar Module Descent Stage, into a high
enough orbit for the Apollo to pick him up without exceeding
its 'delta-*v* margin'—i.e., it would still be able to get home.*
Meanwhile, space stations were to be developed in Earth
orbit, over sixteen missions.[4] The 'Wet' Orbital Workshop was
to be the upper stage (S-IVB) of a Saturn I: the crew (launched
separately) would dock with the station, seal the hydrogen-tank
propellant lines, and pressurize the tank to form a zero-*g*
workshop and habitat.[5] Two of these missions were then to be
followed by a 'Dry' workshop, a more advanced station built

---

*Delta-*v* is shorthand for the velocity change during a particular manoeuvre.
The total delta-*v* required for a given mission is termed the 'characteristic
velocity' of the mission; the total delta-*v* which can be provided by a given
spacecraft is determined by the specific impulse of the propulsion system
(the thrust generated per kilogram of propellant expended), and by the mass
ratio of the vehicle (the ratio of initial mass to mass after all propellant is
used). The spacecraft must have a delta-*v* capability higher than the
characteristic velocity of its mission; the excess is the 'delta-*v* margin'
available for course corrections and additional powered manoeuvres.

into an S-IVB shell and launched by Saturn V. (In modified form, the 'Dry' workshop eventually became Skylab.)

The Orbital Workshop programme was to lead to permanent space stations with twelve-man crews. Such a programme required a reusable Earth-to-orbit transport system,[6] drastically reducing launch costs; and by 1970 NASA's plans were based on the Shuttle *and* Saturn V. Shuttle flights were to begin in 1975, and work in combination with a Space Tug launched by Saturn V (whose payload, over 150 tonnes, was five times that of the Shuttle). The Tug would be refuelled by the Shuttle and used to transfer payloads into higher orbits or to the Moon; it could operate unmanned or have a six-man crew module attached.[7] With landing gear, it could deliver 13.5 tonnes of payload to the Moon (20 tonnes unmanned[8]), allow a crew to stay on the Moon for 28 days, and fly at least ten missions. An extended Apollo programme using four-man capsules was suggested, while the Shuttle/Tug system was being perfected.[9]

In 1977, a twelve-man space station was to be established with a core module launched by an uprated Saturn V (Intermediate-21), and a crew and cargo module brought to it by Shuttle.[10] Further modules would be added using Shuttles and less powerful Intermediate-20s. In the next phase, a Space Base capable of housing a hundred would be created, using seven Intermediate-21s and twelve Shuttle payloads.

Meanwhile, a temporary six-man lunar-orbit space station was to have been established, using the Space Tug.[7] Now the original Earth-orbit space station was to be transferred to polar orbit around the Moon by the Nuclear Shuttle—an unmanned vehicle using the NERVA engine, whose development began in 1961,[11] at the same time as Apollo's. Launched by Saturn V and fuelled by six Shuttle payloads of liquid hydrogen, the Nuclear Shuttle could deliver 20 tonnes of payload to lunar orbit—or 50 if it returned empty. An expendable Tug would set the original six-man space-station module down on the lunar surface, to become a base.[7] The new Lunar Orbit Space Station would support eight men, allowing six three-man 28-day visits to the surface per year.[10]

By 1979, there were to have been more than 200 people in space—150 in space stations (50 in geostationary orbit); 25 in lunar orbit, 50 on the lunar surface, and 12 *en route* to Mars.[12] The synchronous-orbit space station and the enlarged lunar one were then postponed to 1980, and the enlarged lunar base to 1982; but, meantime, the Mars expedition was to have been launched: two ships each carrying six men, but each capable of bringing back all twelve if need be. The living quarters would be standard space-station modules.

Three Nuclear Shuttles would launch each vessel towards Mars, two of them separating and returning under their own power to Earth. The ships would leave Earth in November 1981, reaching Mars in August 1982: three men from each ship would land, spending 30 days on the Martian surface. On the way home, the ships would curve inside Earth's orbit to make a close pass by Venus. Returning to Earth in August 1983, they would rendezvous in high elliptical orbit with a Nuclear Shuttle, and take on enough fuel to bring them down to the Space Base; less ambitious plans would have ended with direct atmosphere entry. In 1983 and 1986 equipment would be stockpiled in Mars orbit and on the planet (a space-station module making a temporary twelve-man Mars base); 1988 would see a semi-permanent Mars base, and 1989 a permanent colony on Earth's Moon.

It was a beautiful programme, destined to vanish like snow in the sunshine. President Nixon's special task force on space outlined three possible Mars programmes, a 1986 mission being recommended by Vice-President Agnew, the chairman.[13] But, in July 1969, the tenth Moon landing (Apollo-20) had been dropped in order to use the Saturn V for Skylab,[14] and in 1970 it was suggested that Apollo-19 might be dropped for a second Skylab.[15] Drastic financial cuts for 1972 were then made by Congress, delaying work on the Nuclear Shuttle by several years and reducing the Tug to an unmanned vehicle, carried into orbit by the Shuttle, to place satellites into higher orbits.[16]

Production of Saturn Vs had already been halted, causing the Apollo-18 and -19 vehicles to be reallocated to the space-station project:[14] funds failed to materialize for the space station, however, and NASA could not even raise the money to launch either the last two Apollos *or* the second Skylab. The Space Shuttle became a single-stage vehicle, with clip-on boosters and throwaway tank. No funds could be raised for the Space Tug; detailed studies of the unmanned version were made in Europe, with a view to completing the project by 1980 with NASA funding in the final years,[17] but NASA couldn't take on even this commitment.[18] With Saturn V gone, the Moonbase forgotten with the manned Tug, and everyone trying to pretend they'd never *heard* of Mars, NERVA's continuing funding [19] began to look like an oversight, and sure enough it was reduced to an unmanned vehicle with 20% of the manned vehicle's thrust; [20] the writing was on the wall, and in January 1973 all work was terminated, [21] after 18 years' work and more than $1400 million spent. [22]

NASA still wants a six- to twelve-man space station with a ten-year lifetime: one design features a station with 17 modules to be launched one at a time by the Shuttle. [23] Solar cells would have to be used instead of the nuclear power originally planned. [10] A considerably larger station (in volume) could be built using an external tank; [4] but unless additional funds become available the modular station will not be in orbit until about 1990. [19]

A manned Space Tug could fit into the Shuttle cargo bay, but three of them would have to be strapped together and launched to lunar orbit for one to make a manned landing. [24] For the lunar space station, the lunar base and the Mars mission no capability remains: Saturn V was required to launch the core modules and the Nuclear Shuttles which propelled them. Eight Saturn Vs were needed to launch the units of the two Mars ships, and that was on the assumption that the four Nuclear Shuttles used as boosters were in space already. [25]

If desperate needs arise, they could be met with chemical fuels. Each Shuttle is to be capable of 500 missions over a ten-year period; consequently nine Shuttles working for a year could build, equip and fuel the three ships of the von Braun 1950s plan for a lunar expedition. [26] That mission was to take fifty men to the Moon, build a lunar base by dismantling the cargo ship, and conduct a 400km overland expedition from Sinus Roris to the crater Harpalus! The original proposals called for 360 launches of 36 tonnes each to 1720km orbit (this was before the discovery of the Van Allen belts), but with better mass ratios and higher specific impulse 1980s designers could presumably launch an equivalent mission from close orbit. Similarly, it would take about 100 Shuttle flights to build the von Braun/Ley 1950s Mars expedition: twelve men in two ships, coming back in one ship with $5\frac{1}{2}$ tonnes of geological samples. [27] But the 1950s figures may be optimistic: a more recent study allowed the same mass (2000 tonnes) for a six- to eight-man Mars mission, even using cryogenic propellants (LH_2/LO_2*), in place of the hydrazine and nitric acid originally proposed. For less favourable oppositions, when Mars is further from Earth, the launch mass from Earth orbit might be doubled.[28] (In the NERVA mission, in the most favourable year, launch mass would have been 1000 tonnes.)

A more critical point is the time involved. Whereas the NERVA 1981 mission had a duration of 450-550 days (640 if Venus flyby were included in the way home), making a high-energy return to Earth, a chemically powered Mars ship would need to travel by minimum-energy Hohmann orbit (an ellipse meeting the orbit of each planet at a tangent). The very long wait on Mars for the planets to be suitably aligned again gives that mission a total duration of two years and nine months.

On missions of such length the health of the crew may be at considerable risk. In 1969 a White House report, 'The Biomedical Foundations of Manned Space Flight', stressed that there wasn't enough information about Man in Space for even the NERVA mission to Mars.[29] On the eight-day Gemini-5 mission it was estimated that the astronauts suffered a 10-20% bone-density reduction; a 30-40% bone calcium loss would be enough for 'spontaneous' fractures to occur in normal activity.[30] Muscular atrophy in space would also increase the risk of fractures on return to Earth, because of reduced support for the bones. The problem with such effects is not continuing survival in space, but readjusting to gravity after an extended period of weightlessness. After 260 days the astronauts on a Hohmann transfer to Mars might not even survive braking manoeuvres, it seemed; nor could they coast back to Earth, because the Hohmann return can't be started for 400 days. If they did survive the departure from Mars (not likely, if they've remained in orbit because they couldn't risk a landing) and Earth-capture manoeuvres, then they might still be condemned to a lifetime in space: perhaps they could be acclimatized gradually to gravity on a space station, but there's no guarantee that the physiological changes won't be permanent.

---

*Combination of liquid hydrogen (LH_2) with liquid oxygen (LO_2) gives the highest exhaust velocity—and hence with suitably designed engines the highest specific impulse—currently available with chemical propellants. Only liquid hydrogen and fluorine offer greater thrust, but fluorine is an extremely reactive, dangerous element.

Other problems specifically affect survival in space, on long missions. On Mercury and Gemini flights the astronauts ate too little, losing weight. On long flights this could become highly dangerous, if they couldn't summon the energy for essential tasks as they neared a planet. In direct contrast to the stereotyped diet of pills, it has proved essential to cater to individual tastes. On longer flights, nutritional programmes will have to cater accurately for enzyme deficiencies, correct any vitamin imbalance, [33] and help counteract bone decalcification[34] —while avoiding allergies and varying sufficiently to prevent boredom. Skylab tests showed that Shuttle crews would need 3000 calories per day, just as on the ground. [81]

Such requirements defy the standard 1950s solution, a tank of algae busily absorbing all biological wastes and purifying the air at the same time. Indeed *Chlorella*, the alga strain whose high oxygen yield has kept it at the forefront of life-support research, seems incompatible with the other plant life necessary for an acceptable space food-chain. [35] Another problem is that algae, being very simple organisms, have high mutation rates even under terrestrial conditions. There has been Soviet research on closed-cycle life-support, including the Oasis system which produces protein by the joint action of two strains of bacteria. [36] Bacteria, however, are yet likelier to mutate under space conditions. Work in the US has concentrated mainly on water and oxygen reclamation by physical means: nuclear-powered systems for recovering water from solid and liquid wastes [37] and electrolysis cells for oxygen from water vapour, [38] while carbon dioxide can be reduced with hydrogen to yield water and methane [39] (methane has potential uses in spacecraft attitude control; as does carbon dioxide, if its oxygen doesn't have to be recovered [40]).

There were improvements on the three Skylab flights, where the astronauts had freedom of movement, exercise and recreational facilities, and a proper wardroom, washroom, and sleeping area. Food preparation took account of the needs indicated on earlier flights, [41] and the astronauts' intake was carefully monitored by Mission Control. [42] Only one of the first crew showed marked disorientation on return to Earth, and he recovered in a few days. [43] Great progress was reported in acclimatization to weightlessness, using motion-sickness drugs, and the 59- and 84-day flights which followed didn't reveal any upper limit to human tolerance of zero-g. [44]

Nevertheless, physical effects were noted. The astronauts didn't lose much weight, but the weight was redistributed —some of them grew markedly taller. The 28-day Skylab crew showed no significant bone-density losses, but on the longer missions effects were again found to vary between individuals as they had done on the Apollo missions. Calcium loss can range from 0 to 20%. [82] Red-blood-cell counts and white-cell reaction to infection were lowered, but recovered rapidly; [83] indeed, after the 59-day mission the effect was less and recovery more rapid. [84] Apparently the red-cell loss is due to muscular atrophy. On the Soviet six-month mission, the longest to date, red-cell loss was the lowest yet, due to increased water intake and exercise. [85]

Skylab crews used lower-body negative-pressure tests (a partially evacuated cylinder, coming up to the wearer's waist) to force increased circulation in the legs, where the major losses in volume take place (the 28-day crew took 20-24 days to regain it [86]). Fluid leaves the legs early in the flight, and slow tissue loss follows: readaptation to gravity involves rapid cardiovascular changes with relatively massive shifts of blood and body fluids. Salyut-6 cosmonauts have worn 'penguin suits' during the working day, to stress those muscles used in standing erect on Earth, [87] and take a metabolism-speeding drug called 'Eleutherocc', especially before return to Earth. [88] Recovery after the Soviet long-duration flights is reported to be excellent, although the 96-day Soyuz-27 crew kept trying to swim out of bed in the morning. [89] Soviet plans have been announced for a space station with a ten-year lifetime, to run simulations of interplanetary missions, [90] and another statement specifically mentioned a three-year stay, [91] which is equivalent to a Hohmann mission to Mars. As far as is known, the USSR doesn't yet have the propulsion technology to attempt anything faster; but whether they intend to keep crews in zero-g for three years at a time is a different question. Designers in the US assumed that gravity-simulation measures would have to be taken.

Only two ways are known to simulate gravity in spacecraft. Continuous acceleration is one; but continuous $1g$ acceleration would get us to Mars in under a week, even allowing for deceleration, so if we could achieve that we would have removed the problem! The other is by centrifugal force, as the ship or part of it is rotated. The concept became familiar in the space-station designs of the 1950s and was incorporated into the design studies for the twelve-man and bigger stations to be launched by Saturn V, using the S-2 upper stage, or part of the station extended on a long boom, [45] as a counterweight. [10] Preliminary experiments were performed with Gemini-11 and -12, using the Agena target vehicle on a 30.5m tether as a counterweight, but only up to small fractions of a *g*.

Flexible couplings are not favoured because of the risk of losing stability. Both Saturn V space stations would have had fixed booms, although considerable weight penalties were involved—particularly where the counterweight was part of the station. The NERVA Mars ships were to be docked nose-to-nose and spun about their common centre of gravity, but only one-sixth *g* (lunar surface gravity) could be generated, because the radius of rotation would be only 15.25m even on the lowest deck. [25] At more than four revolutions per minute on a 15m boom, the crew are likely to be sick. [46] (See Chapter 6.)

For a full, comfortable 1*g* without disorientation caused by Coriolis forces, minimum boom radius is 60-180m. In *2001: A Space Odyssey* there was an inconsistency which couldn't be avoided: the centrifuge in which the crew travelled would have been too big for the *Discovery* even at the 0.2-0.3*g* assumed. [47]) Studies at Rockwell's Space Division indicate that it takes about two days to adjust to a rotating environment; [48] but all ground tests are complicated, of course, by the superimposed 1*g* field of the Earth.

Psychological factors are also important on such long trips. Although in many ways the spaceship problem is analogous to those of nuclear submarines, A. E. Roy has pointed out that, if a ship is six months out from Earth, little if anything can be done to bring it back in less time than a further six months, and the pressures are accordingly greater. Robert Shaw added that good food, good air and living space are the major factors on nuclear subs—the crews are experienced submariners who are used to worse conditions.

Jan Merta, a psychologist working among divers on North Sea oilrigs, reported that in ships and similar installations all-male and all-female crews tend to very rigid discipline, while mixed crews show less tension, greater efficiency and more self-control. Roy remarked that all-male space crews might be run like the Royal Navy in Napoleonic times—but that isn't true of nuclear submarines, Andrew Nimmo replied:

discipline there is not severe, although they don't have mixed crews yet.

If one man will go mad cooped up for six months, said Roy, then two will murder each other as every word and action becomes predictable. With three, two will gang up against one. But mixed crews to relieve such tensions will require still larger ships, so perhaps missions will remain all-male (or become all-female) and tightly run. Merta felt, however, that because in those settings one is completely dependent on the people round about, and cannot survive as an individual, psychological understanding is required as well as physical training. In that sense, Shaw suggested that the US astronauts were over-trained, coming from over-narrow military pilot backgrounds, and would be hit harder than most by the 'Moon experience'. Future exploration would necessarily feature broader personalities.

'Buzz' Aldrin's autobiography makes clear that he was neither prepared nor willing for the celebrity rôle thrust upon all three Apollo-11 astronauts. [92] Aldrin's nervous breakdown and divorce played a big part in the myth that spaceflight imposes an intolerable mental tress. Other elements included Borman and Irwin's religious convictions (which actually predated their flights [93]) and Mitchell's ESP research (again actually an interest of long standing [94]); while the 'stamp scandal' of Apollo-15, a minor incident, was blown up out of proportion. Scott, Irwin and Worden were in fact rescheduled as the backup crew for Apollo-17, despite the furore and Irwin's 'revelatory experience' on the Moon. After his resignation, the other two were dropped, and certainly that represented a change in policy: the makeup and assignments of the crews had followed a fairly regular rotation rather than being determined by psychological factors. But for the deaths of See, Bassett and Williams in training, and of Grissom, White and Chaffee in the Apollo-1 fire, the Apollo-11 crew might well have been Conrad, Lovell and Bean. [95] The Skylab crews were not selected for compatibility as such, although the commander's choice had considerable influence. Shuttle crews, which are to include women as mission and payload specialities, will presumably be selected on similar lines.

In general, Merta thought space was too unlike present environments for psychological prediction to be sensible. 'A new frame of mind' would be required for living in space. That lay outside the scope of our discussion, said Chris Boyce: its nature would be different from what we consider human nature, but we don't yet know in sufficient detail what 'human nature' is. Nevertheless, we can't just ignore the topic.

The last major point concerns dangers from outside the ship. Meteors are steadily being downgraded as a threat: a year of data from the Explorer-46 Meteoroid Technology Satellite showed that earlier studies (Explorer and Discoverer) greatly overestimated the population of small meteors [49]—and even the earlier data hadn't indicated a serious danger. Better still, it was found that the 1950s 'Meteor Bumper' concept—a thin outer shell providing a double hull—did indeed give six times the protection of a single wall. Although a big particle—the size of a marble, say—striking at a velocity up to 64km per second could still disable a spacecraft, the chances of such an event are very remote. Likewise, the once-feared 'cosmic rays' (high-energy atomic nuclei) have not so far produced any harmful effects (but see later).

Initially the problem proved to be the one nobody had greatly feared—the Sun. Beginning with Explorer-1 we've been finding that space is not the non-conducting vacuum we once thought, and that in a sense the Sun can be said to fill all of it. Out from the Sun flows a continuous 'wind' of charged particles, saturating space, and shown by Pioneer-10 to extend much further than expected, [50] probably beyond the orbit of Pluto. Towards the orbit of Jupiter, the Solar Wind becomes increasingly turbulent and, where it impinges on the magnetic fields of Earth and Jupiter, it is channelled into Van Allen belts of trapped radiation—hydrogen nuclei and electrons. The Solar Wind itself does not pose a threat to Man in space, although a manned spacecraft would require heavy shielding to spend any time within even Earth's radiation belts. But the Sun itself is far from constant: huge magnetic storms, visible as sunspots, rage on its surface, with associated outbursts of energy, solar flares.

A flare reveals itself first as a bright patch (in hydrogen-α light) near a sunspot. In 5-20 minutes it becomes up to twenty times brighter than its surroundings, emitting X-rays, ultraviolet radiation and a highly concentrated flow of subatomic particles with energies from thousands to billions of electron volts. In a bad year, up to a hundred of these events can occur: about one in ten of the highly directional particle streams hits the Earth-Moon system, saturating the Van Allen Belts and causing geomagnetic disturbances as particles leak into the atmosphere over the poles, with displays of aurorae. [51]

A spacecraft beyond the Van Allen belts would be subjected to high-energy bombardment from all directions, by particles spiralling in the 'magnetic bottle' of the flare stream. In an Apollo capsule the astronauts' dosage could reach 31-397Rad, depending on the positioning of the spacecraft in the first shockwave, before full insertion in the stream [52]; 5Rad per year is the recommended dose limit for radiation workers. Doses experienced by Gemini astronauts, below the Van Allen belts, ranged from 0.015 to 0.192Rad. Gemini-10's Agena target thrust both vehicles into an orbit reaching 765km; with several passes through the South Atlantic Anomaly, where the inner Van Allen Belt comes closest to the Earth, pilot dosage reached 0.77Rad. [53] On the Apollo missions, doses were 0.5-1.0Rad: [96] the exposed situation beyond the Earth's magnetosphere was partly countered by getting away from the dangerous proximity of the Belts. A flare would make matters very much worse: in extreme cases the proton-radiation dosage could reach the value permitted over twenty years to radiation workers. [97] Heavier atomic nuclei such as those of carbon, oxygen and nitrogen cause more tissue damage than protons or helium nuclei [52] and Pioneer-10 has detected sodium and alumium nuclei in the Sun's high-energy emissions. [54]

Fortunately the most violent events are rare. Between 1950 and 1969, over 1000 weeks, there were only three 'event-weeks'—so called because one flare is usually followed by another after three days—in which the dosage in an exposed spacecraft during each of the six events could have reached or passed 100Rad. [98] A more typical flare would perhaps double or treble the 17Rad exposure to be expected within an alumium-hulled spacecraft during an eighteen-month mission. The flare hazard is more severe at peak times in the sunspot cycle of approximately eleven years: during the three Skylab missions, which were near the time of the Quiet Sun, only one major flare was observed. [99]

On the NERVA Mars mission, the control centre of each ship was to be shielded with food and, later in the mission, compressed waste, providing a 'storm cellar' in which the crew could survive for up to two weeks. [25] It had to be hoped that the ship could run itself meantime (computers are not fond of radiation flux) but, unless transit times can be drastically reduced, warning times would allow little else to be done.

As of 1968, the Solar Forecasting Centre of the US Air Weather Service could give thirty minutes' to eight hours' notice of a flare storm, by a visual watch on the Sun's surface. John W. Evans, Director of Sacramento Peak Observatory, reported that watchers developed 'premonitions' of flares, perhaps due to subconscious recognition of a degree of ordering of the solar surface not yet fully analyzed. Predictions were given 'after some thought (to avoid any unseemly appearance of haste)'. [51] Since then it's become possible to predict which groups will flare, but not when: the prediction record is four times greater than chance, but still only 20% accurate. [100]   Chinese astronomers report that high-energy flares are preceded by spiral patterns in the 'penumbra' around a spot, and that these are transferred from spot to spot by snakelike filaments. [101]   As well as possibly explaining the 'premonitions', these observations may explain the three-day pairing of events, since sunspots themselves often occur in pairs. Skylab studies revealed that flares are accompanied by the expansion of very large structures in the corona (the Sun's upper atmosphere), but it isn't clear whether these come before or after the hydrogen-α explosive phase. The need is for extended study of sunspot groups from above the atmosphere, to establish what happens *before* they flare. [100]

In any spacecraft beyond the protection of Earth's magnetosphere, life-support systems based on bacteria, algae or even plants would be seriously at risk. Thick aluminium shielding around the entire crew compartment would involve major weight penalties, certainly too much for NERVA-type missions, and would pose a secondary hazard of gamma-rays when subjected to electron bombardment. [52] Ehricke assumed that polystyrene shielding could be made effective. [55] Shielding using a magnetic field is theoretically possible, but depends on superconducting refrigerated magnets to generate fields of the required intensity: working models have been produced. [52] Another promising system involves generating a deflecting cloud of electrons around the spacecraft, for the two-day duration of the flare-storm.

Much more shielding would be required, however, to deal with a hazard which accumulates with time in deep space. In the early lunar missions there were puzzling reports by the astronauts of brilliant flashes, apparently within the eye itself. Experiments with hoods on Apollo-17 confirmed that the effect was Cerenkov radiation, an actual flash of light caused by a very high-energy nucleus passing through the fluid of the eyeball. Crescent-shaped flashes at the periphery of vision were apparently caused by direct transfer of energy, while large flashes with dark centres were evidently caused by muons passing through the eyeball from behind. [102] On Skylab, shielded from lower-energy cosmic rays by the Earth's magnetic field, the frequency of flashes was proportional to the station's latitude and highest of all in the South Atlantic Anomaly. [103] Each of these single heavy high-energy particles leaves a trail of tissue damage. Malformations were caused in insects and other creatures carried in the Apollo-16 and -17 'Biostack' experiments. [96] In higher organisms, the biggest risk is destruction of the tissue of the central nervous sytem, which does not regenerate. In only two weeks between Earth and Moon the astronauts may have lost one hundred-thousandth of their brain neurons, and, over several years, the effect could reach several per cent. [104] It was already known that galactic cosmic radiation would become the major factor on long flights, surpassing the accumulated solar dosage after about eighteen months in an aluminium-hulled ship, [98] but the effect is exacerbated because the damage is irreparable.* At the time of Ehricke's paper, [55] the galactic hazard wasn't fully appreciated; but it greatly strengthens his argument that, for manned transfers between planets, fast hyperbolic orbits are necessary for the strategic approach: hyperbolic transfers are needed to reach Venus in less than 35 days, Mars in less than 70 days, and Jupiter in less than 1.1 years.

Artificial gravity, long mission supplies, meteor bumpers, radiation shielding—all increase the masses of ships, making chemically fuelled missions still less attractive. Moreeover, the Hohmann transfer orbit (see page 36) has no reasonable manned application except for travel to Mars, Venus and the

---

*The high-energy galactic cosmic rays are believed to originate in supernovae. If such an event were to occur in the general vicinity of the Sun, the flux of such nuclei penetrating the Earth's magnetic field and atmosphere would be very much increased—the first in a series of threats to higher lifeforms, such as human beings, on the open surface of the planet.

asteroids (see later). Its only advantage is that the ships' components could be taken into orbit by Shuttle, whereas there seems no prospect of breaking up nuclear-powered ships into segments of that size—the segments could probably have been bigger had they not had to be compatible with Saturn V. Suffice it to say that Mars and Venus *could* be reached with a Shuttle-based transporation system, but it's not likely to happen. In any case, such missions would be limited to purely scientific objectives, whereas (as Ehricke pointed out) planetary expeditions should have long-term practical purposes.

At ASTRA in 1974 Ed Buckley said that we were at a crossroads in space exploration: the future lay with big, economical, reusable space transport systems. The present Shuttle is too small, but provides a bridge from 1960s technology (Saturn V), of which the space station/NERVA programme was only an extension, to single-stage-to-orbit (SSTO) launchers and advanced interplanetary propulsion systems. Major reservations had in fact been expressed about the NERVA programme by Ehricke, since it had no growth potential beyond minimal Mars/Venus missions: the expenditure of effort to develop it for those missions was 'difficult to understand'. Plebuch and Martinez of the TRW Systems Group considered that NERVA development was justified only if there had to be a Mars landing before 1990.[56]

It now seems unlikely that the manned Shuttle first stage will ever be built, since that would confer relatively little gain in performance: a vehicle capable of reaching orbit in one piece is more likely. Taking off horizontally on jet engines, switching to rockets at high altitudes, would require major advances in 'lightweight aeropropulsive technologies'[57] such as a scramjet/rocket vehicle powered by a gaseous-core nuclear reactor[58] (see later): this involves a 'light bulb' heat-transfer system in which neither the air (in the jet mode) nor the LH_2 (in rocket propulsion) would come into direct contact with radioactive material. Nevertheless, from the late '60s onwards, space-mission planning has shown a marked reluctance to use nuclear power within the atmosphere. Who remembers the Saturn V-N concept, with its NERVA upper stage, and the Mars missions that it was going to give us?[47]

If LH_2/LO_2 is to be used for SSTO, great design ingenuity will be required. The plug-nozzle or 'aerospike'* reduces structure and engine weight. Re-entering atmosphere tail-first, the ship circulates LH_2 around its 'spike' to keep it cool, then sprays out the hydrogen through the rocket nozzles to form a gaseous heat-shield protecting the rest of the craft. No massive heat shields or wings are required. [28]

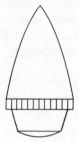

Fig. 4   The plug-nozzle craft

One plug-nozzle global transport design, Hyperion, could lift 20-25 tonnes of payload into orbit (less than the present Shuttle, however) by taking off from a rocket-propelled air-cushion sled. [59] Other studies (Pegasus, ROMBUS [28]) involved very much bigger vehicles, with external separable tanks. Pegasus was to have almost the payload capability of Saturn V, while ROMBUS was designed for lunar-base and Mars-mission lifts—400-500 tonnes to orbit.

While the combination of liquid oxygen and RP kerosene (that is, kerosene of *R*ocket *P*ropellant refinement), as used in Saturn's first stage, generates less energy than LH_2/LO_2 (liquid hydrogen/liquid oxygen), RP kerosene takes up much less *volume* than liquid hydrogen. Consequently, if a shuttle took off on RP kerosene/LO_2 and later switched to LH_2/LO_2, a smaller vehicle could lift a given payload into orbit. Moreover, a synthetic hydrocarbon fuel called RJ-5 (Shelldyne H) gives roughly the same specific impulse as RP kerosene but, being denser, takes up about 25% less room. Such a 'mixed-mode' vehicle might take off with ten RJ-5/LO_2 engines burning; 200 seconds after liftoff, eight of the engines would switch off while the remaining two switched over to

---

*The plug-nozzle is essentially a rocket motor turned inside out: the combustion products play out over a 'spike' at the rear of the craft so that, in an atmosphere, the flame is shaped by the slipstream instead of requiring an outer hull, and in space it assumes an optimum shape.

LH_2/LO_2. Such a craft could deliver a minimum of 41.5 tonnes to close-Earth orbit (Plate 2); [60] a corresponding SSTO winged shuttle, using exclusively LH_2/LO_2, might have to be as much as 80% heavier in structure [61] —and may not be feasible at all.

The mixed-mode shuttle could take into orbit the manned Space Tug or its lunar variant and have payload to spare. If the RJ-5 engines were dropped after use, instead of being carried into orbit and back, then another 20-30 tonnes could be added to the payload. If the shuttle were to glide to a landing instead of using turbofan engines, double or treble the original payload could be carried for 435km orbit, [60] and still more by making *this* vehicle '2½-stage' with external tanks and boosters. Alternatively, close-orbit payload could be raised to 50 tonnes or more by launching from 1500m up; [57] in Peru, for example (when I was a boy, everyone knew the world's first spaceport would be in Peru). Best of all, by using the mixed-mode shuttle as a suborbital booster, payloads equivalent to Saturn V's could be placed in orbit by an LH_2/LO_2 upper stage. In this rôle, the shuttle would re-enter the atmosphere 3850-5150km downrange, so it could be launched from the Pacific coast of the USA and land at KSC without needing turbofans. [60]

The mixed-mode concept allows performance gains for plug-nozzle launchers, too, but seems to favour winged shuttles overall. In any case, the US space programme is definitely pursuing high-thrust conventional rocket motors and winged vehicles rather than the plug-nozzle concept; an aerospike was considered for the Space Shuttle main engine, but NASA didn't adopt it. [63] Consequently, there seems little prospect of giant plug-nozzle boosters; for lunar and planetary-mission elements, mixed-mode launchers are likely to be winged shuttles or giant capsules (see below).

It would be possible to develop a heavy-lift unmanned booster with the tank, main engines, solid-fuel boosters and avionics (inertial guidance, computers, etc.) of the Space Transportation System. The payload to close-Earth orbit would be 70 tonnes, with the tank as a bonus. The engines and avionics could subsequently be returned to Earth in either a shuttle cargo bay or a special 'entry body'; [105] in the latter case (the Intermediate Heavy Lift Launch Vehicle) the engine cluster would be despatched as soon as orbit was reached, and recovered in Australia. [106] Further clustering—e.g., with two tanks, two engine modules, and four solid boosters—could raise the payload to 220 tonnes, as compared with 150 for Saturn V. [105] Dramatic results could be obtained by developing an LH_2/LO_2 booster to replace the solids; clamshell doors would close over the engines to protect them as the units tumbled into the sea. With two such clip-ons, the Shuttle could carry 50 tonnes into orbit; a Heavy Lift Launch Vehicle could take 92.5. With four LH_2/LO_2 clip-ons, HLLV payload would reach 162.5 tonnes, slightly more than for Saturn V; [106] but clustering the present units gives higher payload and more tanks in orbit, for whatever purpose they might be used.

Most proposals for Solar Electric Power Satellites (Chapter 6) involve using raw materials from the Moon: each powersat would have a mass of at least 70,000 tonnes, equivalent to an aircraft carrier. [107] Boeing and Rockwell International both have designs assuming instead that powersats would be assembled from units prefabricated on Earth; the optimum payload per launch is 225 to 500 tonnes. [106] The Boeing concepts feature either a two-stage fully reusable VTOHL booster or a gigantic two-stage capsule, both stages having a ring of rocket engines around the base. In vehicles of this size, mixed-mode techniques offer considerable savings in size and weight. The capsule is visualized as taking off and landing (on rocket thrust) using a big reservoir at Kennedy Space Centre for launchpad and splashdown. [108] An average of ten launches per day would be required [109] to have the first powersat operational by 1996.

Rockwell's proposal is a huge winged shuttle. While transporation on such a scale would make opening up the Solar System relatively easy, there's concern about the effects of so many big rockets on the upper atmosphere; and development of lunar resources would be a more valuable approach in the long term.

The Eurospace report (see page 2) calls for European heavy-lift and powersat studies, while in the USSR development of heavy-lift boosters seems to be bogged down. The series G or 'Lenin' booster (equivalent to Saturn V) has yet to be test-flown successfully; [110] a disastrous launchpad explosion in 1969 delayed the programme for over two years, and launch failures in 1971 and '72 postponed the Moon landing until 1975 at the earliest. [111] In 1976 Washington sources reported that priority had been reduced and no further launches could be expected for two years;[112] in fact, none have yet been attempted. The upper limit for Soviet launches therefore remains at around 25 tonnes for a proposed 'heavy Salyut', to be launched by the Proton (In D-1-E or D-1-E-e configurations).[113] One of the major limiting factors is the Soviet lack of LH_2/LO_2 technology, even [110] for the Lenin.*

In 1974, relating these possibilities to deep-spacecraft designs, Ed Buckley began with a set of modules which could be put into orbit by a massive, unmanned plug-nozzle booster. In systematic exploration of the Solar System, there would have to be standardized core modules for deep-space missions. Research units, landing craft, storage bays and life-support systems would likewise be modular, with different capabilities and endurances for different missions. Centrifuges would deploy from the living modules for gravity simulation; during launch into orbit, and boost from orbit into interplanetary trajectory, the centrifuge arms would be folded back against the sides of the vehicle. The living and support modules would not be much changed by different propulsion systems—indeed, if several systems were in use, it would be an advantage to standardize their payloads—but the overall appearance of the ship would depend very much on the engines selected.

Four deep-space drives have been envisaged for use beyond NERVA, and two of them promise to merge into a system combining the best features of both (see page 55). They are (1) nuclear-electric propulsion (ion-drive), (2) the gaseous-core nuclear reactor, (3) controlled thermo nuclear fusion, and (4) the nuclear pulse rocket. Any of them can in theory meet Dr Ehricke's requirements for fast, hyperbolic interplanetary transfers. Depending on the characteristics of the propulsion system, such trajectories can take four forms: continuous low-acceleration transfer, partial-acceleration transfer, brief-acceleration transfer, and continuous high acceleration transfer (CLAT, PAT, BAT and CHAT).[55] The last two can be attained only by gaseous-core reactor or nuclear pulse rockets, but the first two allow a choice of systems.

Ion-drive units have already been flown successfully in

---

*Hitherto cryogenic propellants have been used only in launch vehicles, but research is going on in the West to develop insulation and refrigeration for big tanks in space.

space, powered by solar cells, although nuclear power would be needed for full-sized manned vehicles. The principle is that droplets of a heavy element such a mercury are ionized, accelerated in an electric field, and neutralized by electron bombardment as they are beamed out of the engines. Because of the high-density propellant and the very high exhaust velocities attainable (tens of thousands of kph), ion-drives can provide very high specific impulses and very good mass ratios. Again because of the high-density reaction mass, propellant tanks are small and inconspicuous on ion-drive spacecraft: instead, solar-electric ion-drive ships are distinguished by wide 'wings' carrying massed solar cells. (NASA's SERT II ion-drive satellite carried the largest solar array flown in space up to 1970. [65]) Nuclear-electric ion-drive ships, too, would require large 'wings', but these would be radiator panels: owing to the multiple energy-conversion processes involved, the ion-drive is inefficient and 65-75% of the power plant output has to be radiated away as waste heat. [55] The radiator temperature should be as high as possible (red-hot at least), to minimize the weight of the panels and to reduce their area and vulnerability to meteoroids. At hyperbolic velocities, with areas of hundreds of square metres exposed to impacts, ion-drive ships may be confined within the region circumscribed by the Asteroid Belt—nor can they go far towards the Sun, since the ion-drive imposes large electrical charges on different parts of the ship and, as we now know, space is not empty but filled with the electrically conducting material of the Solar Wind.

The other disadvantage is that ion-drive thrusts are extremely low, giving accelerations of only thousandths of a *g* ('milligee thrusters'). Ion motors tested in space so far have been used for attitude control or to change the orbit of a satellite over a period of months. In the SERT II experiment the jet of the ion-drive was continuously directed towards the Earth, raising the spacecraft's orbital altitude by 47km in three months. [66] The spacecraft had two engines, used consecutively: the first failed after five months, the second after three, both due to short-circuits caused by electrical erosion. But damage caused by meteroids was only 1% of that expected [67] —anticipating the results of the Meteroid Technology Satellite already mentioned. In 1973 further tests were begun, but the spacecraft was no longer in the Sun-synchronous orbital plane into which it had been launched, and had to be spun up to increase the amount of sunlight gathered. Apparently the manoeuvre dislodged an eroded sliver from a molybdenum grid which was short-circuiting one of the thrusters. [114] Since then the thruster has been restarted many times and, in 1979-80, the spacecraft was due to be back in Sun-synchronous orbit where continuous thrust could again be generated. [119]

In early 1977 a variety of solar-sail designs (see Chapter 4) were being considered for a flyby of Halley's Comet and subsequent rendezvous with Comet Tempel 2. The total delta-v required was of the order of 23km per second, [115] and the only competing propulsion system was ion-drive, eventually selected because of its greater growth potential and the experience already gained. [116] The Marshall Space Flight Centre proposal involved launch by Shuttle and Interim Upper Stage in 1982. [117] In 1979, however, solar-electric propulsion was deleted from the following year's NASA budget. [118] Further initiatives may therefore rest with the USSR, Europe and Japan, all of whom are developing ion systems for possible use in space.

In deep space, low accelerations are no particular problem. Certainly, given two spacecraft with the same delta-v capability, one capable of high initial and final accelerations will reach its destination faster than one with continuous low acceleration; but the longer the journey the less the percentage difference, and the more massive the conventional rocket will have to be to match the other's performance. (For the same launch weight, 800 tonnes, an ion-drive Mars mission would be 100-200 days shorter than a NERVA mission. [68]) In the Earth-Moon system, however, there are problems: an ion-drive ship might be spiralling out from Earth for forty days before it reached escape velocity (an unmanned solar-electric Space Tug studied by NASA would take 35-50 days just to reach geosynchronous orbit [69]). The biggest difficulty is the prolonged exposure to radiation within the Van Allen belts. The crew might board from a Tug after the belts have been passed; [68] Ed Buckley suggested Deep Space Boosters equivalent to the Nuclear Shuttle. (Some more exotic methods will be considered in the next chapter.)

Using ion-drive, only half the launch mass of the NERVA ship would have been required for the same 1980 Mars mission. For a 370-day Mercury mission, the mass would be a quarter that of an all-nuclear ship; for a 1400-2000 day Jupiter mission, one-seventh. Given a suitable light-weight power plant, mission times could be reduced to 200-400 days for Mars, 400-900 days for Jupiter, 1200-1900 days even for Uranus. (Missions to planets beyond Jupiter may be shortened by Jupiter flyby, like the Pioneer and Voyager ones, but ion-drive ships may not be able to approach Jupiter because the dust concentration around the planet is 300 times that in interplanetary space.[70] On long-duration missions the ion-drive may be out-performed by the radioisojet[56], directly heating reaction mass (ammonia would be particularly suitable) with radioactive isotopes to generate milligee accelerations. The system is more efficient and less vulnerable than ion-drive, and would withstand Jupiter flyby without difficulty.

Apart from ion-drive and the nuclear pulse rocket (see below), all nuclear propulsion systems have the same basic principle, found at its simplest in the radioisojet: energy released in the form of heat during nuclear fission or fusion is transferred to gaseous reaction mass, which then becomes the exhaust of the rocket. The NERVA system was a 'solid-core' reactor, in which the gas (hydrogen) came into direct contact with the fissionable material. In the gaseous core reactor, which gives the same thrust-to-weight relationship but twice the specific impulse, the fission process occurs in a fluid material and the reaction mass can't contact it without sweeping it away. The likely solution is a 'light bulb' system, in which the gaseous nuclear fuel would be contained in a vortex at the centre of a transparent-walled reactor cavity. At the periphery of the vortex, the fuel temperature would be 5750-28,000 K, so it would be isolated from the chamber wall by a transparent coolant (helium or neon) injected tangentially to maintain the vortex. The coolant and chamber wall would transfer the heat to the reaction mass (hydrogen), earlier circulated as coolant through the graphite moderator/refrigerator enclosing the reactor cavity. Heated to 80% of the fuel temperature, the hydrogen would now become high-energy rocket exhaust.[58] A Marshall study featured a 35-tonne gas-core vehicle which could deliver 500 tonnes to geosynchronous orbit.[120]

The gaseous-core reactor motor calls for major advances in nuclear technology, and even in 1969 it seemed that its rôle would be for Earth-Moon transport rather than for interplanetary missions, on which it would be out-performed by the other nuclear drives.[71] Furthermore, at the higher attainable values of specific impulse, the system acquires one of the nuclear-electric disadvantages: high-temperature radiators are needed to disperse surplus heat. [58] The *2001* spaceship *Discovery* would have required such radiators, but they were omitted to save the audience being confused by a deep-spacecraft with wings. [72] (It's worth noting also that the *Discovery*'s mass-ratio wasn't good enough for return to Earth from Jupiter, without refuelling: the astronauts were to be placed in suspended animation for 5-10 years, until they could be rescued. [47])

Given the high specific impulse of gas-core reactor engines, the mass ratio of a given ship determines its delta-v capability. For brief-acceleration transfer, two-way missions impose Table 3's requirements. Missions requiring a delta-v of up to 100kps lie within the scope of the gas-core nuclear engine, taking it up to optimum potential performance. Even so, round-trip missions to the outer planets might take as much as twenty years. Ehricke suggested that to train for and complete such a mission might represent a full career, taking forty years out of a late-20th-century life expectation of more than eighty years;[73] but obviously we want to improve on this if we can.

Table 3: Brief-Acceleration Transfers

Mercury Missions	Mars Missions	Jupiter Missions	Total Delta-v Capability
8-10 months	6-10 months	900-1000 days	40km/sec
5-7 months	3-6 months	500-550 days	80km/sec
2-3 months	2-4 months	1 year	120km/sec

Both nuclear fusion rockets and nuclear pulse rockets would energize their exhausts by the fusion of light elements—the process used by the Sun and by the hydrogen bomb—instead of the 'conventional' fission of heavy elements. Fusion reactions occur at solar-core temperatures, millions of Kelvins, and the plasma in which they occur can't be allowed to touch any part of the power plant. In theory it can be contained by magnetic fields, and superconductivity in supercooled electro-magnet windings allows the currents required; but at the moment magnetic fields of the required intensity can't be kept sufficiently stable to permit fusion reactions. However, the plasma generated in a rocket engine is *required* to escape, and perhaps fusion can be attained in a deliberately weakened magnetic 'bottle' which will release and focus the plasma as a high-energy jet. [73] Fusing deuterium (heavy hydrogen) and helium-3 to yield helium-4 and protons gives the best energy output, relative to ignition temperature. Deuterium alone can be used, but yields less energy.

Considering the very high temperatures involved, it's surprising that fusion engines of this type take us back to continuous *low*-acceleration transfers. The specific impulse is hundreds of times that of gas-core reactors but, as with the ion-drive, its actual thrust is miniscule. In fact, a thrust augmentor has to feed extra hydrogen into the jet to achieve even the milligee accelerations of electric propulsion. Nonetheless, the augmented jet can out-perform the ion-drive on interplanetary missions,[55] although large radiating surfaces would again be required.

At first envisaged, the nuclear pulse rocket was at the opposite pole of sophistication. The USAF study (Project Orion) involved propelling a space vehicle by detonating hydrogen bombs behind it—an updated version of a proposal made by Hermann Ganswindt in 1981 involving dynamite charges.[74] In Orion the heat was to be absorbed by an ablative shield or reradiated by a huge hemisphere of copper. The force of the explosion would be transferred from the pusher plate to the ship along shock-absorbers up to 75m long, spreading the energy of the explosions, 3-30 seconds apart, so that the forepart was accelerated at an even 1*g*, with the back end alternately jammed up against it and thrust away.[75] The vessel would go pulsing out into the Solar System like a Jack-in-the Box, or more accurately like a maddened Slinky—'not a pretty sight', Archie Roy remarked.

Carrying such large numbers of fusion bombs, and delivering them fast enough through the heat shield to the midpoint of the pusher plate caused obvious difficulties. Nevertheless, Project Orion had great potential, especially for big spaceships: with pusher plates 30-50m across, up to ten times the specific impulse of fusion drive might be obtained.[55] Ideally, the plasma produced by the explosions should be magnetically contained and focussed as exhaust; such a 'nuclear magneto-dynamic pulse rocket' would be the next step forward.[71]

By 1963, however, the programme had been halted by the Test Ban Treaty. The 'Rainbow Bomb' test, in which an artificial layer was added to the Van Allen belts and several artificial satellites were silenced, had already caused much protest. Even if the political barriers could be overcome, all nuclear pulse experiments would have to be carried out beyond the Van Allen belts, if not beyond the Earth's magnetosphere. Ehricke proposed igniting them at the apogees of highly elliptical orbits, beyond the orbit of the Moon. [71]

By 1970 a new concept was combining the distinctive features of nuclear pulse and controlled fusion engines. It was suggested that frozen pellets of mixed deuterium and tritium could be compressed and detonated by multiple laser beams, with the time between detonations reduced to one second. [73] In January 1973, the British Interplanetary Society initiated 'Project Daedalus', a deliberately ambitious study of the problems involved in sending space probes to the nearer stars, [76] emphasizing nuclear pulse rockets as the only interstellar system likely to be available within the century. As of April 1974, the Daedalus proposal was termed 'nuclear pulse rocket with external ignition' and involved mixed, frozen spheres of deuterium and helium-3, injected into a cusp-shaped magnetic field at a rate of 250 per second. At the field centre the pellets would be struck by four electron beams: the outer layers would vaporize and the cores would be compressed to

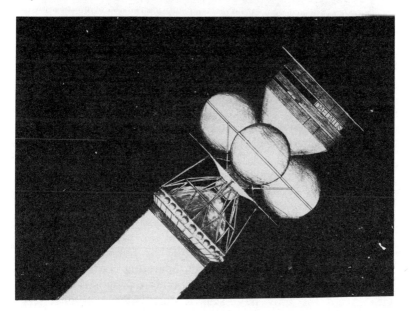

Fig. 5   Daedalus second stage under drive
(drawing by Gavin Roberts)

fusion temperatures. Bursting open with the eruption of plasma at its core, the magnetic field would be trapped between the plasma and a surrounding shell of molybdenum, thereby forming the containing and focussing field required for a fully developed nuclear magnetodynamic pulse rocket.

In the final version of the project, published in 1978, [121] the spacecraft had become a two-stage vehicle with a mass of 53,120 tonnes at launch and a payload of 450 tonnes. 50,000 tonnes of the launch mass consisted of fuel, 30,000 tonnes of it helium-3, and the boost phase would last for 3.81 years at an acceleration rising through $0.1g$ as fuel was consumed. At second-stage cut-off the probe would be travelling at 12.2% of the speed of light and would reach Barnard's Star, the reference mission target, in fifty years.

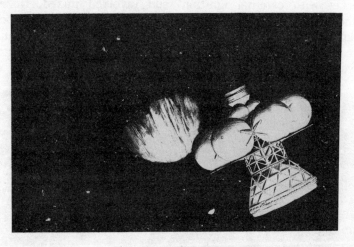

Fig. 6　The complete Daedalus probe in Jupiter orbit
(drawing by Gavin Roberts)

Helium-3, unfortunately, is very rare in nature, and to synthesize so much (on the Moon for preference) would require a fusion reactor, generating as much power as is currently used on the entire Earth, operating continuously for twenty years. The Daedalus team therefore proposed to collect He-3 from the only large-scale natural source immediately available, the atmosphere of Jupiter.

But, if Daedalus technology becomes available for the Solar System, then we are, in rocket engineers' terms, *fat*. Constant high-acceleration transfers bring spectacular mission times.

With an Earth-orbit launch mass of 2000 tonnes (equivalent to the Mars NERVA), a 1960s-type nuclear pulse rocket could have reached Pluto in 2.4 years, at $0.01g$ (Hohmann missions would require 45 years each way). Even that performance was deliberately inefficient, because the pusher plate was limited to 10m diameter to be compatible with a Saturn V launch. A 14.3m-diameter plate would have doubled the area on which the blast impinged, and 20.1m would have quadrupled it, [80] bringing down the launch mass considerably. Moreover, the Daedalus engine is much more efficient. For CHAT missions, with deceleration to arrival at the target planet, Dr Ehricke gives the figures shown in Table 4.

Table 4: Continuous Acceleration Transfers

Target	Constant Acceleration	Maximum Velocity	Transit Time
Mercury	$0.01g$	73km/sec	17.1 days
	$0.1g$	230km/sec	5.4 days
Venus	$0.01g$	44km/sec	10.3 days
	$0.1g$	140km/sec	3.2 days
Mars	$0.01g$	63km/sec	14.9 days
	$0.1g$	200km/sec	4.8 days
Jupiter	$0.01g$	590km/sec	1860 days
	$0.1g$	1860km/sec	40 days

A fully fuelled Daedalus probe could be transferred from orbit around the Earth to orbit around Mars in five days for the expenditure of 116.4 tonnes of He-3 and 77.6 tonnes of deuterium. Even more remarkably, a space colony of 500,000 tonnes, supporting 10,000 people, could be moved over the same distance, for the same fuel expenditure, in only a fortnight. For the same fuel expenditure as the probe, but allowing for braking, a similar colony could be moved to Alpha Centauri in 400 years or Barnard's Star in 600 years. [122]

Deuterium-deuterium pellet fusion has already been achieved in the USA, with converging laser beams. More energetic deuterium-tritium pulsed fusion, possibly involving feed rates as high as 500 per second, [77] may be more suitable for power systems on Earth than for propulsion: tritium decays to He-3 with a half-life of only twelve years. [78] Deuterium-tritium pellets would be easier to manufacture and store over a short term than the proposed D-He-3 ones, with the helium in liquid form at 2.5 K (about $-270°C$) in a solid lattice of frozen deuterium; but, in storage for any duration, outgassing from deuterium-tritium pellets would be a serious problem, especially since the pellets (whatever their composition) have to be sheathed in aluminium to be electromagnetically propelled into the combustion chamber.

The Daedalus team discarded deuterium-tritium fusion because twenty tonnes of extra shielding would be needed to stop the high neutron flux it generates. On the interstellar mission that would be a very high penalty, especially when the propulsion was also less energetic. In the inner Solar System, however, given the scarcity of helium-3 (current cost $27,000/kg)! [121], the less energetic system may initially be preferred. Deep-space boosters would still be necessary within the Earth's magnetosphere but, once the ship swung far enough out, we could let her go. 'Within the Solar System,' said Gerry Webb, a member of the design team, 'Daedalus is pure Flash Gordon in its potential.'

The technology for full strategic exploration and development could therefore be available within the 20th century. Even if big ships and structures have to move around slowly at first, pulsed nuclear fusion allows fast hyperbolic personnel transfers, removing most fears of galactic radiation damage and any residual dangers of weightlessness. And, as we shall see later, once the Jupiter system has been industrialized, its He-3 resources will allow us to do anything we like.

IV

All Done by Electricity

It may, of course, be purely a personal idiosnycracy, but I find it difficult to view with equanimity the prospect of careering moonwards atop a lighted powder magazine, however admirable the method of control.

P. E. Cleator, *Into Space*, 1953 [1]

Oh, let's not get maudlin about Newton's Third Law!
—Sandy Glover, Then President of ASTRA, 1965

There are already two techniques of altering the velocity of a spacecraft without using rockets. The first is 'gravitational slingshot', in which planetary flybys accelerate or decelerate it or change its orbital plane. Pioneer-10 was accelerated by its Jupiter encounter to more than the Solar System's escape velocity, and Mariner-10 was redirected from Venus to Mercury, where the first flyby altered the orbit to allow two more encounters. Voyagers-1 and -2 were similarly redirected from Jupiter to Saturn. The first spacecraft to use a gravitational field for an orbital-plane change was Luna-3 (1959), [2] and Pioneer-11 in passing Jupiter achieved an out-of-the-ecliptic trajectory to Saturn. Similar 'celestial billiards' are planned for the Galileo Jupiter orbiter. Slingshot manoeuvres (even if they involve long flight-time, as with Galileo) provide velocity changes which cannot be achieved by rockets within the present state of the art.

The other effect is the 'solar sail', which is large and light enough to experience significant thrust from the radiation pressure of sunlight. The effect can be demonstrated with lightweight vanes in an evacuated jar, and was used with the solar panels of Mariner-10 to conserve attitude-control gas. Again the application involves no expenditure of reaction mass by the spacecraft.

We can, therefore, ask whether rockets ultimately can be dispensed with. Archie Roy thought such proposals would later be labelled 'quaint', like 19th-century concepts of flying machines. But there are legitimate fears about the effect of rocket launches on Earth's upper atmosphere, and, around the larger airless bodies such as the Moon and Mercury, rockets could generate enough of a temporary atmosphere to inconvenience science and industry. Whatever the case, care must be exercised with high-energy exhausts near planetary bodies.

Kardashev defined a Type-2 civilization as one which controls the resources of a planetary system. We can take 'resources' to mean, not just the matter and energy directly available, but also the latent energy to be extracted from the gravitational and magnetic fields of the Sun and planets, and the potential uses of nulls and lows in those fields, such as the Lagrange points (see Chapter 6). Similarly, absence of matter can be an asset, as in the industrial uses of high vacuum, or in close orbit or grazing trajectories unfettered by atmospheric drag; and absence of matter *and* energy can be highly valuable, as when a spacecraft radiates surplus heat into vacuum from its shadowed side. Even local disruption of those 'negative resources' could be fatal—e.g., if a high-energy exhaust neutralized the electrostatic shielding of another spacecraft during a flare storm. If 'control', in the Kardashev sense, implies the possibility of restraint and, where appropriate, conservation, a Kardashev-2 civilization might decide not merely to limit the use of rockets as a policy but to forbid expenditure of reaction mass as a matter of principle. As an exercise, ASTRA set itself the task of studying the elimination of the use of rockets from a developed and industrialized Solar System.

Since the Moon has no atmosphere, a payload can be travelling at the full lunar escape velocity (8300kph) when it leaves the launcher, thus putting vacuum to use. In *The Exploration of Space* (1950) Arthur C. Clarke proposed an electromagnetic launcher (EML), sometimes caused the 'lunartron',[3] which can be solar-powered, at least during the long lunar 'day'. The system has one major limitation—it can't place payload into orbit around the Moon, because to make orbit around a body starting from the surface requires *two* impulses, one vertical and the other tangential to the surface. In his classic formulation of orbital dynamics, Isaac Newton conveniently eliminated the former by placing his imaginary orbital velocity cannon on an equally imaginary mountain top at the desired orbital altitude. The effect can't be achieved by an inclined track: if the path of the payload, projected back, intersects the lunar surface, then, as sure as eggs, the forward-projected path will do the same.

Clarke proposed launch into highly elliptical paths, for rendezvous using very little fuel; or launch away from the Moon altogether. At an acceleration of 100*g*, a track 3.2km long would launch payloads tangentially at lunar escape velocity. Clarke saw no immediate application for manned spacecraft: accelerations tolerable by human beings would need a track about 160km long. [3] The lunartron reappeared in the British Interplanetary Society project, 'The Colonisation of the Moon';[4],[5] and in *The Next Ten Thousand Years* Adrian Berry re-emphasized the 160km length needed for manned EML launches. [6]

Well, even Homer nods. In *The Exploration of Space* the bearable limits of acceleration were taken to be 3-4*g*, sustained for not more than a minute during climb from the Earth's surface; thereafter insertion into orbit and further manoeuvres could be relatively gentle. This was years before rocket-sled experiments and use of centrifuges in space medicine: with modern pressure suits and form-fitting couches, 20*g* accelerations can be withstood. A 160km lunartron assumes only 1.7*g*; at 20*g* the track would need to be only 14.4km long and the acceleration sustained for only twelve seconds. Using water or some other high-density fluid to distribute stress evenly over the body, even higher accelerations can be tolerated.

So manned EML launches from the Moon may indeed be feasible. With regard to unmanned launches, modern technology has been applied: for payloads above 100kg, accelerating to lunar escape velocity, 150*g* launches along a track a kilometre long seem feasible with solar- or nuclear-electric power.[4] So payloads, and almost certainly manned ships as well, can be returned to Earth from the lunar surface using no reaction mass except that required for midcourse corrections. For delivery to Earth-orbiting stations, a retrofire will be required, unless other means can be found to exchange electrical for kinetic energy—see below.

The extensive 'footprint' of landing sites available to Wave-riders, from any given orbital track, marks them out for un-manned delivery of industrial, scientific and medical supplies from orbital factories—clearly superior to the 'space-going box car' (little more than a gigantic Apollo capsule) usually postulated.[5] The weight penalty of the wing is offset by eliminating the heat shield, drag brakes and parachutes—not to mention land and transport savings, since the craft could use normal airports instead of drop zones. In deliveries from the Moon, with Waverider's entry performance, midcourse corrections shouldn't be necessary. The stainless steel hull should go like a bat out of hell from an electromagnetic launcher, but it might be preferable to keep the hull demagnetized and have the electromagnet pulse act on a core vehicle—like the original rocket launcher, but passive. Such a "bus" could, moreover, carry the fuel cells, attitude control and communications hardware for the coast to Earth, making the entry vehicle still simpler. Furthermore, since Waveriders are *stackable*, multiple launches would be possible using a single core vehicle. One can imagine a flight of Waveriders scattering at the top of the atmosphere like peaceable MIRV's* for a wide range of destinations.

It is *always* cheaper (once the transport system has been set up) to supply materials to Earth orbit from the Moon than from Earth's surface, unless the cargo carrier returns to the Moon. Since the Moon's surface is relatively rich in iron, it would be economic to use Waveriders for delivery to orbiting factories, since they could be re-used to take the finished products on down to Earth—to ordinary runways, in any latitude, from any factory orbit. Whether or not the present Moon Treaty becomes international law, the developing nations must have a stake in lunar exploitation as of right; Waverider deliveries could encourage them to leapfrog the ground-based industrial revolution altogether and establish their industries alongside those of the aerospace nations, in orbit. Since the world cannot continue its present rate of industrial growth (nor even rise to the present energy consumption of the USA) without major environmental effects,[8] that development should be most actively encouraged.

Returning from Earth, Waveriders could again be stacked on a core vehicle, especially if coming up empty. But, with the lunar steel industry producing the cargo shells in quantity, it would not be economic to return any but the more sophisticated manned ones to space. For Waverider cargo traffic, the

---

*MIRV: Multiple Independent Re-entry Vehicle; hitherto applied only to nuclear warheads.

overall movement in the Earth-Moon system would be down the gravity well—even if it began with low-energy 'sideways' movements to the Lagrange points (see Chapter 6). Many cargo Waveriders arriving on Earth would themselves be cut up or melted for their high-grade steel.

But a more interesting destiny is possible. Ian Downie suggested that, after touchdown, Waveriders might be fitted with a standard plug-in module to ride along mag-lift railway tracks. Although the British Government declined, in the early 1970s, to continue Professor Eric Laithwaite's work on mag-lift trains, research elsewhere makes them at least a contender for relatively low-speed railway systems.[9] The Waverider's handling characteristics at low speed should make it compatible with the railway system, and its computer could easily be programmed to follow a track instead of gliding in free flight. With unmanned Waveriders coming down all over the world, at giveaway prices, they could become the standard units for overland transport, 'flying along the railway lines'—the self-propelled, self-guiding containers of the 21st century.

To build large settlements and powersats in space, Gerard O'Neill calls for a large-scale launching of raw materials from the lunar surface.[10] An EML variant, the mass driver, would accelerate aluminium 'buckets' carrying moonrock in fibreglass bags.[11] At the end of the track an opposing electromagnetic force stops the bucket, while the payload flies on to rendezvous with a 'catcher' at the Lagrange-2 (L2) position, where it maintains a fixed relationship to the Earth and Moon and therefore, because of the Moon's trapped rotation, to the lunar surface (see Chapter 6).

The mass driver is a specific design for 100g launch of unrefined ore. Guidance requirements are extreme, but simplified by having what is in effect a stationary target. There's a point on the lunar Nearside from which mass-driver payloads would arrive at L2 with near-zero dispersion; a lunartron, appreciably longer but built in parallel to share power facilities, could send more sophisticated or even manned spacecraft to the same destination. A launch tangential to the lunar surface, at just over lunar escape velocity, takes the payload out to L2 in a gentle retrograde curve (fig. 7). Launch at higher velocity would allow the payload to drop Earthwards —to rendezvous with a space station, or to enter the atmosphere. Higher velocity could be attained by stepping up the acceleration or by using a longer track, so an obvious design challenge arises: a track for lunartron *or* mass driver launches at the accelerations and terminal velocities required.

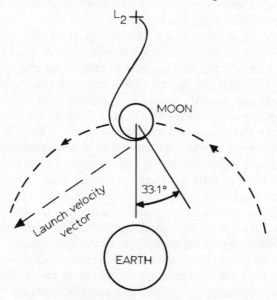

TRANSFER ORBIT - MOON TO L₂

Fig. 7 Transfer orbit from the Moon
to the second Lagrange point (L2)

In space, EML's limitation is that the rearward reaction would alter its orbit; it would also tend to lose attitude control in close-Earth orbit, aligning itself with the Earth's magnetic field. [12] But the mass driver's opposingly polarized bucket-braking field can be used to cancel out the transverse forces acting on the launch section. The stresses on the boom would be considerable, but it would in any case need to be stoutly built. The longest booms deployed in space to date are those of the Moon-orbiting Radio Astronomy Explorer, 228m long, and they had to be gravitationally stabilized (straight up and down in the Moon's gravitational field); they were also painted silver outside and black inside, and perforated with tiny holes, to reduce thermal stress flexing. [13]

A working mass driver has been built by MIT Students, with accelerations of 33g over a track length of 2.4m, [14] and O'Neill has called for funds to test a model in orbit. [15] In the longer term, he suggests, the reaction force could be used for propulsion, expelling aluminium pellets formed by grinding up Shuttle external tanks: every tank mass could take a full Shuttle payload to synchronous orbit. With a track length of 1100m and 1000g acceleration, the thrust would be equivalent to the Space Shuttle Main Engine. [16] In later applications, firing rock, mass drivers could move large structures or cargoes between Lagrange points or asteroids.

The mass-driver engine expels reaction mass and is therefore, strictly speaking, a form of rocket. However, electrical energy is used instead of thermal energy to accelerate the 'exhaust', and it's environmentally neutral. The high velocity of the expelled slugs takes them into trajectories where they pose little future hazard to navigation. [17]

Another potential application would tie in most effectively with the strategic approach. With strong protests about burial of nuclear wastes on Earth, there is growing interest in disposal in space. Michael McCollum's analysis favours disposal in the Earth-Moon system, [18] but that doesn't rule out future problems: the attraction of space techniques should be *permanent* disposal. I suggested that disposal into the Sun or into interstellar space could be achieved using Jupiter slingshot, [19] but the guidance requirements and narrow launch windows make that difficult.

Space disposal can never compete economically with burial if an expendable upper stage has to be taken up by the Shuttle each time, drastically cutting the useful payload. A recoverable Tug probably couldn't compete unless it was refuelled with liquid oxygen from the Moon. [7] But, with a mass driver in orbit, capable of accelerating payloads to solar escape velocity, the economics would look much better. Waste would be vitrified, as for burial, and the metal canisters opened at one end for use as 'buckets'. The empty canisters would then be returned to drop zones on Earth, and their retrograde launch would correct the launcher orbit, which has to be raised again after each outward launch. Prof. O'Neill has confirmed that an orbiting mass driver could launch standard 1.4 tonne vitrified blocks with the 8.7kps delta-v required. Frequent recurring flights favour building a complex like the ASTRA Starseed, described in Chapter 6, and would be much more practicable with the recurring launch windows of an equatorial spaceport.

Sandy Glover suggested that rotary motion might be used

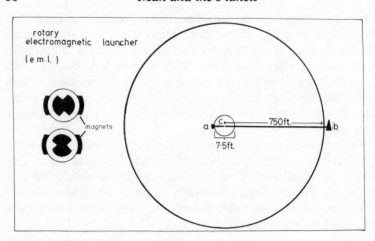

Fig. 8 Rotary Electromagnetic Launcher (EML) and boom.

instead to build up payload velocity, and after some heated ASTRA meetings I evolved the concept shown in figs. 8 and 9. A prototype compatible with the Shuttle cargo bay might have a circular track 4.6m in diameter, with a Radio Astronomy Explorer-type boom extending to 228m, and a ballast mass at A (projecting slightly beyond the track) 10 times that of the payload at B. When the system is spun up by a linear motor to 2.2 revs/sec (120.75kph on the track), the outer end of the boom is travelling at 3.22kps which, added to the orbital velocity of 8kps, gives escape velocity at the right moment of release. 'The most efficient way to go anywhere in the Universe is to go off at a tangent.'

At the moment of release at B, clamps C and E are simultaneously released so that the boom now rotates about D. The effect, if distance AD is computed correctly, is that the backlash travelling down the boom from B is met and cancelled by an equivalent one travelling up it from D. The pivot, D, is then moved inward along the spar FG, which is revolving with the linear motor. Bringing the counterweight nearer the centre speeds up the rotation of the whole system. Now, however, the clamp C is closed again, and the motor is slowed by braking against the gyro, until the boom can be clamped to it again at E; and then the whole system is braked to rest, with all its rotational energy transferred into the gyro—from which it will be recovered for the next launch.

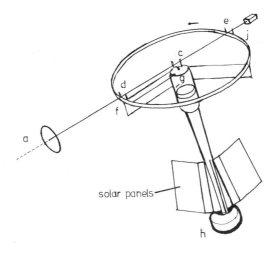

Fig. 9 The central unit of the Rotary EML of fig. 8

The advantage is that all functions which would otherwise use reaction mass are now maintained by solar-electric power including the cancelling out of the reaction to the payload's departure, which would otherwise lower the orbit. Attitude control can be maintained in gravity-gradient mode, keeping the boom tangential to the orbital path, if four gyros are mounted as shown. The big disadvantage is the very high *g*-pull at the end of the boom: for a delta-*v* of 0.805kps, giving a transfer to synchronous orbit, the *g*-pull before launch would be 290*g*—and, for escape velocity, 4600*g*! Since the pull is proportional to the square of the angular velocity, it goes up sharply with increased delta-*v*, and boom lengths of kilometres are required to offset it. The system could be used only for inert payloads like lunar ore or nuclear waste, even if we had the technology.

For the record, the rotary EML is *just* within the state of the art. Single-crystal sapphire fibre, formed by laser technology, has a tensile strength of about 110 tonnes per square centimetre.[20]   In round figures, a 39cm^2 cable could support 1 tonne at 4000*g*. So anyone prepared to manufacture 228m of 39cm^2 single crystal sapphire fibre could produce a launcher compatible with the Shuttle cargo bay, capable of sending as much payload as need be to escape velocity, one tonne at a time. When today's fabulous materials are routinely produced in orbiting factories, the rotary EML may have a future in Earth orbit. But launches from lunar orbit would be much easier.*

All delta-v's in the Earth-Moon system are minor, however, compared to that first 8kps to get into close-Earth orbit. 'Once you're in Earth orbit,' said Robert A. Heinlein, 'you're half way to anywhere.'[21] It would be good to phase out rocket motors for lift, because of the effects on the upper atmosphere.[22] If the ozone-forming processes in the ionosophere were interrupted for hours, a whole continent could be subjected to enough ultraviolet radiation to destroy all life in the open. (Skylab's launch vehicle seriously disturbed the ionosphere.) Such fears may be exaggerated, but it would be nice to remove them entirely—if energy, manufactured goods, raw materials and quite possibly food from space will be needed for the continued development of civilization, surface-to-space transport had better not threaten the environment.

A design for a magnetohydrodynamic lift vehicle was evolved in 1972 by Dr Richard Rosa, although its power supply and superconducting field coils were beyond present technology.[23] Air sucked in at the top of the craft, ionized within it by an electric arc, was expelled by the magnetic field generated by the coils. It would be 'not impossible but nevertheless highly difficult' to get such a ship into orbit from within the atmosphere—any free-fall path starting within the atmosphere must enter it again, unless it's an escape trajectory. An orbit might be circularized by interaction of the coil with the Earth's magnetic field, but that will take much more power than aerodynamic lift or the involuntary attitude control mentioned above.[12] A rocket for the final boost phase wouldn't pollute the atmosphere because it would fire at the apex of the trajectory, at the desired orbital altitude.

A system first suggested by Arthur Kantrowitz was developed by Pirri and Weiss of Avco Everett Laboratories, who have flown test models successfully. They propose multiple banks of lasers, pulsed 250 times a second, feeding 3000MW of energy into a 1m mirror and powering an air-breathing ramjet which could lift 1000kg at 30g acceleration for 30 seconds.[21] Again, the lift phase in the atmosphere is all right, but orbit circularization is tricky. Once the ship is out of the atmosphere, the thrust-chamber lining ablates in the beam and forms a rocket exhaust; but we still need a final impulse parallel to the Earth's surface. Variants which do not use air but which are still low in pollution include the use of water as reaction mass,[24] and hydrogen energized by a relativistic electron beam.[25] To produce the beam energy, Pirri and Weiss suggest using rocket motors to power MHD generators; in later development, their proposal or Rosa's might apply microwave power beamed down from orbiting stations.

At this point one of ASTRA's junior members, confused by the change of topic, asked whether a spacecraft could propel itself along a laser beam by linear accelerator effect. Robert Shaw at once rose to the occasion and proposed a 'laser bootstrap', whereby a *very* intense laser beam generated a shaft of ionization all the way to the top of the atmosphere and a suitably large Waverider or annular ship pulled itself up into space by linear accelerator action! *New Scientist* readers might think this worthy of Ariadne's photoperambulating friend Daedalus, but the joke points out the weakness of laser beam launches from Earth: the further the payload separates from the launcher the more beam energy is absorbed by the atmoshere, and the losses are greater if the vehicle goes anywhere but straight up.

Roger Arnold and Donald Kingsbury have a dramatic proposal to snatch into orbit payloads launched vertically from Earth.[26] In reaching close-Earth orbit, they point out, 11/12 of the delta-v required is orbital velocity and only 1/12 is used in gaining orbital altitude. (Thus laser systems offer economies in launches to higher orbits; e.g., synchronous or lunar.[24]) Could a spaceport in a close-Earth orbit capture payloads launched to orbital altitude ahead of it? From the station's viewpoint, the incoming payload is arriving at 8kps and can be brought to rest electromagnetically, transforming the kinetic energy into electrical. The station maintains stable orbit by returning the carriers to Earth—i.e., accelerating them away from itself. At 5g deceleration for the incoming payload, the spaceport would have to be 600km long; but, if the vehicle reached orbital altitude with half orbital velocity, at the peak of its trajectory, it could be 'caught' at 5g by a station 150km long. The vehicles could use ramjet thrust before engaging rockets, so the laser system has an obvious potential tie-in, despite the disadvantages of inclined launch.

But a laser on the spaceport could replace electromagnetic capture altogether, eliminating the reaction which lowers the orbit. 'Buzz' Aldrin's master's degree thesis provided techniques for rendezvous without the aid of ground computers, [27] with a special case where a Gemini pilot could catch a target ahead of him and in a higher orbit by a series of burns which kept the target 'stationary' with respect to the star background as seen from the spacecraft window. [28] By the same token, if a descending vehicle keeps its motor aligned with a propulsive laser beam from the spaceport, rendezvous should follow.

Without lasers, and with payloads arriving at half orbital velocity, Arnold and Kingsbury's station can handle a fleet of 10,000 vehicles, each about as massive as a cruise missile, arriving at the rate of one per second from a ring of equatorial launch sites. [26] Increasing the mass of the vehicles, or decelerating them faster to shorten the spaceport, increases the spaceport mass needed to handle the forces involved and increases the power levels of the operation. The empty vehicles have to be relaunched at twice incoming velocity (i.e., they come to rest over the Earth and drop vertically), and that requires extra power—8000MW at capacity, much more than can practicably be generated by solar arrays. [29] Their 150km station could support arrays to generate 370MW, 2.8% of its needs at capacity and 12.3% of a Pirri-Weiss laser's consumption. But solar cells could be more effectively laid out if they weren't spread along the very long spaceport, and with a powersat beam from synchronous orbit, continuously in sunlight, spaceport energy needs would be halved. Laser propulsion still seems preferable to the electromagnetic track—although we're still cheating in terms of our opening premise, since the ablating thrust chamber is technically a rocket. But it is a solar-powered system in which the spacecraft is passive.

The position changes, however, when we import material from the Moon. The incoming payload reaches the Earth-orbiting station with more than orbital velocity and, if captured magnetically, would raise the station's orbit as well as generating power. Arriving lunar material could therefore power cargo lifts from Earth and delivery of large payloads to the surface. The full energy potential of mass brought from the lunar surface to Earth is 59 megajoules per kilogram, or 25,000 times that of the water going through the Hoover dam. 'There is so much energy that moon power alone could support a space transportation system vast enough to stagger a 20th-century mind.' [29] As Sir Robert Ball said in 1892 (*In Starry Realms*), in the context of the hydroelectric use of Niagara, 'Had the Atlantic Ocean been seen pouring down from the moon it would not have done more than realise the expectations of volume and of altitude ...'

Over interplanetary distances, 'photon sails' could drive ships by light pressure alone. Using sunlight, manned ships would require very large reflecting areas for useful thrust, but lasers which can raise targets to solar temperatures at close range can provide bigger thrusts than sunlight. Systems of such power won't be permitted in Earth orbit, or even on the Nearside of the Moon, just in case a beam should happen to stalk uncontrolled across the face of the planet. But sites on the lunar Farside and on other planetary moons might beam ships out into space and slow them down on their return. Booster stations at the 'equilateral' points of the planetary orbits could give extra boost and guidance to well aimed passing traffic.

Positively charged sails could derive thrust from the Solar Wind by electrostatic repulsion; but there would be a risk of being dismasted by flare storms, or Solar-Wind turbulence. Robbie Chalmers suggested a parachute-shaped sail whose reflected energy was trapped and utilized by a power plant at the centre of curvature; then the sail-charging system could be independent of the ship's internal power. Cargo carriers might ride the outer envelope of a flare storm, but couldn't be manned unless flown from inside 'storm cellars'—magnetic or electron-cloud shielding would upset the particle flow impinging on the sail. The China clipper races of the Solar System will be sailed by remote control!

For Earth-Moon spacecraft exchanges, the only remaining use of rockets is for deceleration into orbit or down to a lunar landing. Permissibility of lasers depends here on the transit times required: minimum-energy transfers of the Apollo type require 3.059kps delta-v to enter or leave Earth orbit, and 2.254kps for direct landing on the Moon (less for braking into lunar orbit), so laser systems for those operations could be less powerful than the Earth-surface and lunar Farside launchers. (If the full power of an Earth-surface launcher were duplicated in close-Earth orbit, it could send a payload to the Moon in eight hours, but it would take a lot of stopping!) There would have to be safety cut-outs should the launch beam swing towards Earth, and lunar approach would have to be plotted *not* to pass in front of the Earth at a crucial moment. The alternative would be mag-lift landing or docking, with the bonus of providing power to lunar colonies. Even a 100-tonne ship, decelerated to rest on the lunar surface from circular orbit velocity, would generate enough power to satisfy the present demand of New York City. [29]

In *2001: A Space Odyssey* the heat-radiating panels were left off the *Discovery* in case they were mistaken for wings. In Gavin Roberts's painting of an SIOS spaceship over Mars (Plate 4), the propulsion section is out of the picture so as to leave the options open. Likewise, a flat surface on the forepart of the ship for an EML launcher has not been shown. We did contemplate showing the SIOS apparently orbiting Mars, with wings and a propeller—perhaps with, on the facing page, a deep-space payload apparently parachuting onto the Moon— but what follows will be weird enough. The Arnold/Kingsbury spaceport, with its continuous interchange of incoming and outgoing craft, can be considered as a free-flying version of a class of designs which aim to do away with rockets by manipulating the potential or kinetic energy of orbiting structures.

The first such proposal is known as the anchored geosynchronous satellite, the orbital tower, the space elevator or, most graphically, the 'bootstrap' or 'beanstalk'. The earliest known version was advanced by the Soviet engineer Y. N. Artsutanov in 1960, and involved the extrusion of a cable upwards and downwards from a satellite in synchronous orbit. When the lower end reached the equator below the satellite it would be anchored, and a counterweight added at the tip. Cargoes could then move up and down. [30] Discussing the idea at Glasgow University in 1964, A. E. Roy suggested that the counterweight could be a large disc in synchronous orbit, from which a solid structure could be built downwards as a tapering cone. The disc might be a framework to which more ballast could be added as construction went on: it would have to move outwards, so that the outward pull of mass beyond synchronous orbit countered the weight of the material below. In 1975 Pearson suggested a tapered upper section instead: a payload released from its tip would gain a delta-*v* of 10.93kps, enough for freeflight transfer to Mercury or Saturn. [31] Sandy Glover and I had calculated after Roy's lecture that a 5*g* acceleration up the single-cone tower would provide a further 58kps; continuing the acceleration to the tip of the double-taper tower, 150,000km out, would give a release velocity which would be very high indeed. Pearson suggested the tower for nuclear waste disposal: the payload at aphelion (furthest point from the Sun), beyond Saturn, will have a very low velocity, so a small retrofire than would cancel it altogether, allowing the waste to fall into the Sun. But with even 0.15*g* acceleration up his tower, direct launch into the Sun or out of the Solar System would be easy.

Energy to lift cargoes up the tower could be provided by electromagnetic braking of loads coming down. Other authors have taken that to be the most important feature and, since the structure is in dynamic tension, have chosen to consider it as an elevator. In his novel *The Web Between the Worlds* Charles Sheffield has it built in space as a cable: the tip is guided into a huge pit and weighed down with millions of tons of rock, at the same moment that the counterweight is attached at the top. [32] Arthur C. Clarke has expressed horror at this suggestion, which he terms 'harpooning the Earth': the danger is, of course, that if the counterweight fails to connect the cable will fall, wrapping itself at least once round the equator with a tremendous release of energy.

Clarke's own novel, *The Fountains of Paradise*, more conventionally manufactures the cable in synchronous orbit, with the tip eventually questing down through the atmosphere. [33] He, too, thinks of the beanstalk as a cable, primarily because to keep down the mass the diameter of the Earth-surface end should be very small. For existing materials, such as steel or Kevlar (five times stronger), the structure would have to be (respectively) 10^{50} or 10^{10} times wider in the middle than at the ends. Pearson and Moravec [30] believe single-crystal graphite whiskers, so far made only in the laboratory in minute quantities, could provide a 'taper factor' as low as 10, but Sheffield calculates that a still better strength-to-weight ratio is needed, with a 'support length' (distance over which the material can support its own weight, under Earth gravity) of 4940km. Graphite whiskers reach only 1050km. [34]

Interestingly enough, my understanding is that such a

material *does* exist in nature. After Roy's lecture I toyed with
ideas for it in fiction. I asked David Adams for help in the
research, and according to his sources the strongest known
cable is spiders' web, with a support length of 17,700km. I
haven't Sheffield's ability to calculate stresses up to synchronous orbit, with "*g*" falling off with the square of distance from
Earth's centre, but if spiders' web could support itself for
nearly half the distance under a full 1*g* then obviously it could
stretch the whole way in reality. The cobwebs linking Earth
and Moon in Brian Aldiss's *Hothouse*, [35] a beautiful image of
the last days of Earth, may not be as fanciful as they seem.

Spiders' web is obviously not the answer to the beanstalk
problem, bizarre though its strength may be. But it recalled the
embryonic field of bioengineering, where engineers duplicate
the ways in which living organisms solve problems. The DNA
molecule, which carries the hereditary code, would stretch to
several metres in length if it could be straightened out. So I
boldly invented, in a short story called *The Line up to Orbit*, a
future discipline of 'macromolecular engineering', whose prac-
titioners built a gigantic analogue of a DNA molecule in
synchronous orbit. It was nearly a kilometre in length, but at
full stretch it reached to the Earth's surface: one had only to
decelerate the payload on the end and it would draw the cable
down, ready to lift the next load back. If, instead, the molecule
began to contract with no mass on the end of it, the strands of
the double helix would separate; and the repair units, moving
rapidly along their linear tracks, could produce two molecules
where only one had been before ...

A lunar or Martian beanstalk could use existing materials. [30]
For the lunar tower Pearson suggests graphite/epoxy mixtures,
boron/epoxy, Kevlar 49, or boron/aluminium—perhaps most
promising, since aluminium is plentiful on the Moon and
carbon compounds are absent. Because of the Earth's pull the
centre of mass would not be in 'selenostationary' orbit but at
either L1 or L2, in line with the centres of Earth and Moon.
Either tower would be much longer than its terrestrial
counterpart—300,000km for L1, 550,000km for L2—but could
be shortened using stronger materials and larger counter-
weights. One possible application would be to tether a large
station in halo orbit around L2, keeping it in view of Earth
without using reaction mass for station-keeping. [36]

The L1 beanstalk is unlikely to be competitive with the

lunartron and the mass driver, but the L2 tower is a strong contender—see Chapter 6. Because of the Moon's slow rotation, there's no free velocity gift on release, but continuous acceleration up the tower would give very high launch velocities. And lunar beanstalks may be needed if (see Chapter 5) we decide to give the Moon an atmosphere.

For Mars a beanstalk would have obvious advantages, since the atmosphere is dense enough to rule out EML operations and surface gravity is high enough to make rockets costly: graphite whiskers would be strong enough for the Martian tower. But Clarke has drawn attention to a more dramatic possibility still. Deimos, the outer moon of Mars, is in an equatorial orbit which is nearly synchronous—seen from the surface, Deimos takes three days to drift across the sky from east to west. If it were tethered, it would precess like Pearson's L2 halo tower; the mass required for the tower itself would be reduced by two-thirds; and that massive counterweight would allow colossal payloads to be shipped out. Mars could after all become, in James Blish's phrase, 'the Pittsburgh of the Solar System'. [37]

Mercury and Venus have no natural satellites, and rotate very slowly. In either case, a beanstalk would have to be about a million kilometres in length. [34] Mercury's rotation could be speeded up but, if that's the plan, one might continue the acceleration until beanstalks become superfluous (see Chapter 9). There is, however, a system which could be used without orboforming (page 253-5) and that is the Non-Synchronous Rolling Space Elevator, known to its intimates as the 'skyhook'.

For this last idea on a remarkable list we're indebted to John McCarthy and Hans Moravec. [30] To stay within the strengths of known materials we build the cable in relatively low orbit while spinning it end over end to keep it in tension. A graphite whisker cable able to lift 1000 tonnes would be about 8000km long, like a transatlantic telephone cable, but much thinner and less massive. It would orbit the Earth with a period of two hours, turning like a rimless wheel, with the ends of the spokes coming alternately close to the ground every twenty minutes. Due to the huge size, from the ground the cusps of the tips' approach and departure seem almost vertical, with the tip coming momentarily to rest at its closest to the Earth. For safety, and to minimize energy losses due to air resistance, Moravec suggests closest approach should be no lower than 50km—within reach of ramjets. Although relatively gentle (peak acceleration 1.4g), each pickup subtracts energy from the system and should be compensated for by a fast capture at the top of the cycle, so, like the Arnold/Kingsbury station, this system requires two-way throughput if it's used at all. The rising payload unavoidably goes through the most intense part of the inner Van Allen belt, but is in the relatively clear zone between the belts when it's released, at well above escape velocity for that altitude. For any particular insertion into transfer orbit, major savings can be made by assigning half the delta-v to the skyhook and half to the vehicle: the effective mass of the skyhook *and* the rocket are both then the square root of what they'd be alone, and the strength required for the skyhook is reduced by half.

Not being tied to the Moon's slow rotation, nor limited to two points for picking up and setting down, skyhooks have much to offer to lunar settlements. The same applies to Mercury and Venus, especially Venus, where 50km altitude can be reached by aircraft or even balloon and may indeed be the standard operating altitude (see Chapter 8). The saving there is big because, in that dense atmosphhere, rocket lift from the surface takes 2-4 times the fuel for an equivalent lift from Earth! But on Mars the Deimos tower, although initially more costly, would inevitably outclass the skyhook in time.

Moravec goes on to propose free-space skyhooks spanning the Solar System: one in the orbit of Mercury (but well clear of the planet), another midway between the orbits of Mercury and Venus, one each in the orbits of Venus, Earth and Mars, the Asteroids, Jupiter and Uranus, each with a direct rotation (like most of the planets, anticlockwise as seen from above the north pole). Seen from the orbit of the Earth a spacecraft approaching on minimum-energy (Hohmann) transfer orbit from Venus is in retrograde (clockwise) motion, since it's travelling at less than circular orbital velocity; so it can be collected by the down-Sun arm of the skyhook and released up-Sun into Hohmann transfer to the orbit of Mars.

By the time it left the Uranus skyhook, the ship would have more than Solar System escape velocity—but it would take decades to get there from the orbit of Mercury. It seems unlikely that a traffic of relatively small, slow-moving ships would justify ringing the planetary orbits with skyhooks to be used in this way. If rockets are not to be used, photon-sail transfers are more likely on the interplanetary journeys. For cargo transfers, the mass driver will serve more easily for the airless worlds, and Waveriders will meet the atmosphere entry requirements. But it's interesting that, without violating any principle of physics, an air-breathing vehicle could be lifted from the atmosphere of the Earth and set down anywhere else in the Solar System, with no further expenditure of mass or electrical energy by the vehicle or any system acting on it. Perhaps there are still better solutions to come.

Whichever methods might be adopted, we can move personnel and equipment around the Solar System without using rockets. But to enforce such a policy would require a clampdown on further development. To alter the orbits of space colonies, or of asteroids for industrialization, the mass-driver engine might seem the obvious choice; but a mass-driver equivalent in performance to an LH_2/LO_2 rocket would expend 19.5 million tonnes of reaction mass in bringing even a 1000 × 500m 'Earth-grazing' asteroid into capture orbit around the Earth.[38] That's so obviously wasteful, compared to the performance of Daedalus engines, that the choice will be clear. At least for the big jobs, 'conventional' nuclear pulse rockets will still be dominant.

V

The Development of the Moon

A spokesman for the Soviet Academy of Sciences said today that
they would be happy to cooperate with America in reaching the
Moon, provided that concrete steps could be taken.

—News item, relayed by Sandy Glover, *c*1965

Although a few scientists still disagree, it's now generally
accepted that the Moon was never part of the Earth. Moon
rocks are wholly lacking in compounds of carbon, nitrogen and
hydrogen, except for surface deposits from the Solar Wind; and
from the absence of such 'volatiles' it seems that lunar material
formed much nearer the Sun than did Earth's. The big mystery
is how the Moon came to be here and what happened to the
heavy nickel-iron core it might be expected to have. Mercury,
only half as large again as the Moon, has a dense metallic core,
apparently solidified, and a significant magnetic field—yet the
Moon has neither: many surface rocks show 'residual magnetism', but that may be a result of meteoric impacts.

The Moon is rich in other heavy elements; its surface has
radioactive ores more concentrated than any on Earth. Internal
heating generates a small semiliquid core, at whose boundary
'moonquakes' are caused by tidal action when nearest and
furthest from the Earth. The core is displaced slightly towards
the Earth, for reasons not yet fully understood, and the crust is
extraordinarily rigid; it has to be, to support the mascons,
high-density regions which perturb the orbits of spacecraft
overhead. When struck by a meteorite or crashing spacecraft,
the Moon 'rings like a bell'.

It had been hoped that primordial Solar System material, 4.6
billion years old, would be found, but only tiny chips in rocks
of mixed composition proved to be so old. Around 4 billion
years ago, over a period of roughly 200 million years, the lunar

crust was melted by a saturating bombardment of meteorites; the cratering dates from the end of that process. We've learned since that the bombardment affected the Solar System from Mercury to the moons of Saturn at least; it may have marked the belated formation of Uranus and Neptune from cometary material. On the active surface of the Earth the signs have been erased, but satellite photographs are revealing the underlying traces.

After the bombardment, the Moon's captured relationship with the Earth made itself felt. About a billion years later basaltic lava welled up in the big impact basins to create the dark *maria* ('seas') around the region where the Nearside bulges towards the Earth. There are some *maria* on the Farside, but they're few and small, and evidently the lava rose with less force. Just *how* the Earth was involved, we don't know.

The 'highland' rock is anorthosite, with more aluminium and less magnesium, iron and titanium than the *mare* basalts. There's generally more titanium in moonrock than in any known rocks on Earth. Below the regolith ('broken rock') which covers the entire Moon, the mountains are solid rock and the mountains and rilles are stratified. The most common elements are silicon, oxygen, aluminium and titanium—ideal for large structures in space or for construction on the Moon itself. But the lack of carbon, nitrogen and hydrogen compounds (particularly water) is a severe handicap. All those elements, essential to life, will have to come from outside, initially from Earth.

For a return to the Moon, the transport system has to be created anew. With a lunar tug, the Soviet Lenin booster would allow creation of a semipermanent lunar base. [1] A joint programme to which the US contributed the winged shuttles might be welcomed, since the Soviets are generally behind the US in spacecraft technology. Of course, the US *could* reinstate Saturn V production, given sufficient motivation; but only something extraordinary would make it worth bringing back a booster based on 1960s technology. If the motivation emerges for a return to the Moon, we'd hope for a significant step forward, a heavy lift booster or a mixed-mode shuttle.

If the USSR does send men to the Moon, they won't be content merely to duplicate the American achievement—even for the sake of continuing the scientific effort, which is no more

popular or better understood than any other scientific effort
laid before the public for approval.* Politically, Robert Shaw
suggested, a lunar base is better than isolated landings or even
a lunar space station: it has a useful sound to it. The first
imperatives for extraterrestrial colonies, Andrew Nimmo
declared, are energy, materials and food—the areas in which
Earth's resources alone will prove insufficient. The next steps
are: large-scale industrial operations which can be performed
only in space; processing lunar materials on the surface, in
orbit or in Earth orbit; human settlements off Earth as
long-term survival insurance; and the opportunity for diversity,
for exploration of different social systems which may have
survival value for the future.

Those last will carry little weight with leaders who regard
the existing system as perfect in all but the most minor details.
(Who will be the lunar George Washington or Karl Marx?)
Manned space projects are undertaken for the least important
existing reasons, although the doers are often aware of their
greater importance; so the motivation for the return to the
Moon will be resource development. The present us leadership
is so unimaginative that the USSR's motivation is likely to prove
crucial: once the Soviets undertake it the us is likely to come
back into the field. The alternative is to sell the subject to the
us public all over again.

Ideally, a multinational effort should arise, whatever nation
may first chart the lunar resources and propose to apply them.
The Moon, like Antarctica, is international territory, and
development should be for mankind as a whole. The aerospace
nations, although the only ones who can reach the Moon,
would be regarded as holding its resources in trust and would
have to distribute them to all—so they might as well work
together.

Shaw insisted that, instead, they'd defy the world, separately
or together, and refuse to land any payload from space outside
their own national boundaries: 'Do you imagine that the us and
Russia will cut their own throats just out of trivial moralistic or
idealistic generosity to the Third World?' *How* would the
aerospace nations commit suicide if they honoured the present
UN agreement? Were they to defy it, indeed, and become

*Finding life in space, and particularly Contact, might break down the
barrier of indifference.

progressively more prosperous while the rest of the world ran short, terrorism and sabotage within their own boundaries would soon begin—up to and including nuclear weapons, eventually with all-out attacks on the space centres if still the bounty from space were not shared out. The situation could arise only if both the US and USSR became rabid isolationists, without necessarily excluding each other! But any other view, Shaw maintained, 'assumes people will be nice to one another —but they won't'. His own picture, however, assumes 'people will be nasty' despite the fact it's against their own interests and even threatens their survival. Survival is the key point, said Bob Cochrane: when resources are running out, nations *have* to cooperate to survive.

Since that argument took place, however, a much stronger Soviet-inspired treaty has been presented at the UN. It might have been written to attack the L5 Society (see Chapter 6), some of whose early publications discussed the resources of the Moon as if they were entirely American: anyone else who wanted a share was welcome to go up and lay claim to it. The new treaty specifically forbids anyone to claim any of it. 'Neither the surface nor the subsurface of the moon, nor any part thereof or natural resources in place, shall become property of any State, international inter-governmental or non-governmental organization, national organization or non-governmental entity or any natural person. The placement of personnel, space vehicles, equipment facilities, stations and installations on or below the surface of the moon, including structures connected with their surface or subsurface, shall not create a right of ownership over the surface or subsurface of the moon or any areas thereof ...' (Article XI 3). Clause 7 of the same Article provides for an 'equitable sharing by all States Parties in the benefits derived from their resources, whereby the interests and needs of the developing countries as well as the efforts of those countries which have contributed either directly or indirectly to the exploration of the moon shall be given due consideration.'

Very similar principles emerged from the ASTRA discussions, as a prediction that the developing world would settle for nothing less. Even the provisions regarding ownership aren't the disaster some have made out: INTELSAT manages in synchronous orbit without owning it or the ground below, and industrialists' policies generally might be enlightened by agreement that the resources they dealt with were held in trust. But the supplementary provisions of Articles V, VI, XIV and XV, taken together, mean that all results of lunar research shall be made known within 30 days; all missions shall be announced in detail in advance; all natural resources discovered shall be announced; all activities on the Moon or around it shall be the international responsibility of the States Parties whose citizens are concerned; any State Party shall have open access to all other States' lunar installations for inspection; any State Party objecting to any other State Party's activities shall first consult with that State, while any other State Party wishing to do so may attend; and if the consultations don't lead to a mutually acceptable settlement 'any State Party may seek the assistance of the Secretary-General without seeking the consent of any other State Party concerned ...' (Article XV, 3). In theory, the USSR could stop lunar exploitation by any other nation or international body, any time it was sure of a majority vote in the UN, simply by alleging that the other party is treating lunar resources as 'property'–great opportunities for harassment, and for cancellation of projects in political trade-offs.

The current state of Soviet plans may be gleaned from Article XVIII, whereby the Treaty shall be reviewed in ten years' time or at the request of one third of the States Parties after five years. The current state of US plans may be gleaned from the fact that initially President Carter was prepared to sign the Treaty. Under pressure, however, the matter was referred to a committee who were told not to hurry their report. In the meantime, there should be a constructive Western initiative: a programme, not a treaty, recognizing the rights of the USSR and the Third World to participate and positively encouraging them to do so, without surrendering control. Such an initiative could and should come from Europe.

A strategic return to the Moon (in Ehricke's terminology,[2] acquisition for mankind) could begin in the late 1980s with a space station in lunar polar orbit, following resource surveys by unmanned vehicles, and setting down research teams at sites of interest, with inflatable 'Moon houses' or converted fuel tanks [3,4] 'space stations on legs'. Much of their study programme would be concerned with self-support—power, air, water, fuel and food production. Systems for manufacturing water or free oxygen on the Moon were outlined after the

Surveyor landings[5] and patented by NASA after experiments on Apollo samples[6]; using lunar oxidant would increase a chemical rocket payload by 60%, and Moon soil is particularly suitable for growing plants.

Is a lunar space station necessary? While its primary operations could be carried on by specialized unmanned satellites (optical, microwave and gamma-ray surveys; traffic control, especially for cargo launches and for Farside missions; communications, especially over Farside), the Skylab experience shows how much more can be achieved on a multipurpose space station. For rocket flights between Earth and Moon, the highest payload-to-overall-weight ratios (or lowest fuel expenditures) are achieved by breaking up the journey, using specialized spacecraft or modules for each stage,[5] so there'll be extensive use of rendezvous; personnel, cargo, and often whole spacecraft will have to wait in lunar orbit, creating a need for a space station with docking facilities, accommodation (with, for preference, artificial gravity), radiation shielding, fuelling and maintenance facilities, etc. For surface exploration and for rescues (in space or on the surface), it'll often be easier to start from orbit than from the ground.

Landers will continue to carry wheeled vehicles: earlier studies included Rovers which could explore unmanned both before and after manned use, and carry inflatable 'Molabs' (Mobile Laboratories/Shelters) on surface trips lasting for weeks—one such was to land and gather samples in Alphonsus before a crew arrived to set up a temporary base; after they left, it was to climb out of the crater (an 1800m ascent) and travel unmanned to craters Sabine and Ritter.[7] Rocket-powered Lunar Flyers included an attractive variant which could make emergency rendezvous with a spacecraft in low orbit; but dust damage to Surveyor-3 during the Apollo-12 landing, 182m away, suggests that takeoff and touchdown might be a danger to personnel and equipment nearby. Proposed lunar 'pogos' range from a rocket-propelled individual version to Herman Oberth's gyroscopically controlled 'Moon car', capable of jumping 125m upwards or 99m horizontally and of circumnavigating the Moon in less than a lunar day.[8]

No programme of this scope (a thorough mineralogical survey of an area as large as Africa) would be undertaken without reason to believe there were valuable deposits. In an 'alternative scenario' for lunar development, Shaw maintained

that virtually no lunar materials would be worth sending back
because of the cost of transport. Negative predictions are
always dangerous, and this one seems desperately vulnerable to
technological advance. Merely by introducing reusable spacecraft for each stage, costs are drastically cut; use of lunar
oxygen in chemical rockets, or of lunar mercury or cadmium in
ion-drive carriers, would give costs comparable with air
transport on Earth—especially since the price of aviation fuel
is rising steeply. With lunartron launch of Waveriders, direct
delivery to any point on the Earth's surface becomes very
nearly free. Development costs are the only barrier.

Shaw suggested that the resources of the oceans are far
richer and more accessible; but fatalities among North Sea
divers are all too common, and he himself pointed out the
problems of colonizing the sea-bed (see later). A far surer point
is that civilization will become increasingly dependent on
processes and products possible only in zero-g and/or high
vacuum, and industrial growth must be taken off Earth's
surface: thermal pollution would make that necessary, even if
all other forms of waste could be recycled. The same applies to
a suggestion from George Byng, that with broadcast power
from orbit we could go deep into the Earth for materials and
not need the Moon: the environment can't stand industrial
expansion continuing at the present rate.

With equivalent transport systems, it's always cheaper to
send payload from the Moon to a factory orbiting Earth at
1600-3200km (or higher) than to supply it from Earth's
surface. Delivery even to 480km Earth orbit is cheaper, if the
vehicle returns empty; a one-way trip is *always* cheaper than
the corresponding launch from Earth.[5] Even with a laser-
launch from Earth (discussed in Chapter 5), the energy has to
be paid for, so it'll be used only to supply materials which are
scarce on the Moon; the lunartron gets its energy free.

Gavin Roberts asked if the lunar-resources survey was likely
to be financed by big international companies (almost certainly
not, if the Moon Treaty took effect). As with all such
investigations there'll be a large initial investment with years to
wait for a return but, as Earth resources become less accessible,
lunar exploration will be discussed in the boardrooms, especially if the companies are setting up orbital factories.
McDonnell-Douglas and Johnson & Johnson already have an
agreement with NASA to produce vaccines in orbit.[58] Oil

companies might invest in space research because the oil won't last forever and we need to graduate from fossil fuels if we are to protect the environment. Their initial interest would be in orbiting solar power stations, but associated industries should be attractive. Nations can preserve their environments by siting developing industries in space, but such investment would be at government level.

The most likely situation is a multinational consortium like INTELSAT, which places contracts with aerospace nations for communications satellites, leases channels, etc., and has more than one hundred member nations, including virtually all of the 'developing world'. Although INTELSAT pays launch costs, it doesn't pay for development of launch vehicles. A similar body to manage lunar resources would promote uses of technology and lunar-resource data built up by government space agencies —unless it's attempted too late so that when the Moon's potential has been evaluated, Earth no longer has the economic resources to develop it.

In allocating the output from the Moon, simple arithmetic (population, land area, GNP, etc.) isn't relevant. Obviously the materials must go where they'll be used but, if they go to the industrial nations, a share of the products must go to the developing world—on a basis of need, not percentage invest- ment. The advantage of orbital manufacturing with Waverider delivery should be clear. However, the developing world shouldn't accept permanent dependence but insist on develop- ing its own industries (off-Earth for preference) and a standard of living equal to that of the 'developed world'. *Then* arithmeti- cal division of lunar resources will be acceptable.

Shaw's 'alternative scenario' had no significant input of resources for many years, while the Third World's gains meantime were all at the expense of their former masters. The superpowers would protect themselves with economic weapons based on high technology, including space industry: the Moon would provide only essential products which couldn't be manufactured on Earth. To whatever extent a lunar colony became a social/political entity, it would be as 'the Switzerland of the Solar System', when both Earth and Moon were supplied from the Asteroid Belt (see Chapter 10). The service nations (typically European), unable to maintain technological levels equivalent of those of the superpowers, would give up the effort, while their standard of living dropped because of the economic gains of the Third World. Their functions would be as clearing-houses for information and as sources of highly sophisticated but minor skills, for subcontract work, research and export.

Apart from the limited space technology supposed, the politics seem unrealistic. The 'service nations' have too much to lose to let the superpowers develop their space monopoly. Shaw considered that they'd be glad to drop out and enjoy the high-technology return from others' efforts: an 'upstairs, downstairs' view of international relations in which everyone knows his place and stays there. British governments have shown such an attitude in the past (a cabinet minister once remarked, 'If ever the Americans refused us a launch, if we were prepared to pay for it, then we probably ought not to have requested it anyway'[9]), but taken a very different view in other areas, particularly computers and nuclear reactors. It might be cheaper to buy from the US than conduct our own research, which costs us relatively more because the US has a larger economic base, but such decisions aren't purely economic. The development of Ariane by ESA shows a determination to remain independent. The 'service nations' would be middlemen to be cut out wherever possible, and nations forced towards such a position will band together to fight it. The plain fact is that spaceflight is not *that* expensive: Portugal found £1 million per day for its colonial war in Africa. But the whole question can be avoided by forming a multinational lunar agency, for universal benefit, with UN supervision.

Stine has pointed out that minerals from the Asteroid Belt are more accessible (once the Belt itself is reached), and the long transit time (about 18 months) for a minimum-energy transfer to Earth doesn't matter once the flow's set up and deliveries are continuous at this end.[10] However, delta-v is considerably higher than for Moon-to-Earth launch, and solar power is weaker. In energy terms, exploitation will be more expensive: minimum outward delta-v is 8kps as against 3kps to reach the Moon, and 18 months' transfer is too long for strategic manned flight. High-energy transfers will be needed. Moreover it takes 8kps to get *back* from the asteroids, but only 2½kps from the Moon. Study and development would need far more duplication of effort because personnel and equipment can't be exchanged between asteroids (see Chapter 10). They'll become our major source of raw materials eventually (we hope), but meantime the Moon will be Earth's main source of supply.

Initially, processing on the Moon will be kept to a minimum, raw materials being delivered to Earth-orbiting and surface factories instead. If rocket transport is used, there may be factories orbiting the Moon, to maximize fuel economies, but with EMLs we want as few flight stages as possible. Solar-powered EMLs (even with rocket braking into Earth orbit) will always be cheaper than all-rocket systems. An EML payload needs a second impulse to be placed in circumlunar orbit; the direction change could be achieved by swinging the payload around Earth and back, but then retrofire is needed to cancel the initial extra speed.

Mineral riches, and therefore permanent bases, may be concentrated on the edges of the *maria*, along rilles, and around volcanic domes—also, perhaps, in crater peaks and walls, where material from deep within the Moon is exposed. Sites will tend to be grouped along the Moon's tectonic grids, whose orientation may determine the plane of Moon-to-Earth transfer flights, and hence the orbital inclinations of the space factories. Launch windows from the Earth to particular lunar targets will then depend on the time of the month, while the Moon can launch to Earth any time. Shaw therefore suggested 'space-trains' of stackable Waveriders returned to the Moon together, coming back separately with cargo.

As regards nickel, one of the metals becoming scarce on Earth, impact craters would be prime sites. Most of the world's nickel comes from a meteorite crater at Sabrina in Canada. At an ASTRA lecture Dr David Antia of Glasgow University felt there was no need to go to the Moon for nickel yet; but mentioned a foundry in Leicestershire which found it cheaper to process high-grade ore from Australia than low-grade ore from just down the road. Much depends on the quality of the lunar resources. One would look for lineations in the surface: features resembling terrestrial 'sea-floor cracking', such as the Alpine Valley north-east of Mare Imbrium, would seem to indicate rich metal deposits about 3km below. Differentiated ore deposits could be expected in lava intrusions, especially below the *maria*; they could be found by magnetic surveys and might lie within a few hundred metres of the surface. We took these as the basis for colony planning.

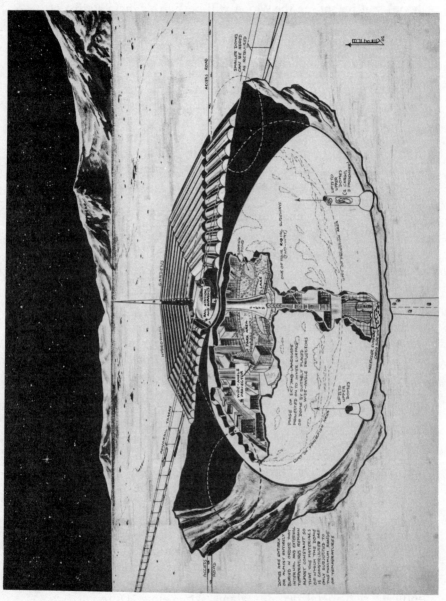

Fig. 10

The 1950s image of a lunar colony was of large domes with pressurized tunnels below. [11] Arthur C. Clarke's novel *Earthlight* had an entire city under the Moon, in a huge pressurized dome [12], drawn by Ed Buckley in 1962 (fig. 10). Clouds and sky could be projected on it realistically, although a dome that size might have its own weather. Surface domes housed airlock entrances to the city, the inter-city monorail terminal, and big vehicle locks: they were surrounded by hydroponic gardens, producing food and oxygen for the colony. But the danger from meteorites was greatly exaggerated, and a chance hit would probably smash a subsurface dome, since the Moon's crust resonates for hours after impacts: the dome would be subject to a tremendous upthrust from the air inside, while in lunar gravity the covering rock and dust would take a long time to settle and never provide as much bracing as on Earth. If the dome fractured, air could make its way explosively to the surface.

There's no need to go underground to stabilize temperatures. Even a few centimetres of lunar dust provide excellent insulation—the astronauts had to keep cleaning it off the heat-radiating power plant of the Rover. Big machines to seal caverns or build large surface domes (like the moonbase in *2001*) must be either built on site or brought from Earth. It would be easier, Buckley suggested, to lay out 'streets' of cylindrical modules on mattresses, on the surface. But for radiation protection we have to go underground—5m down, to escape the most energetic cosmic rays. A moonbase painted for the *National Geographic Magazine* had buried cylindrical and spherical units [13] —so large that they'd have to be built *in situ*.

If we're going underground anyway, for mining purposes, the colony can be planned around exploitation over decades or centuries: a large central shaft with galleries radiating from it, and intermediate tunnels for habitation. The shaft would be open to vacuum, but formed as a closed cavern: Ehricke has calculated that a one-kiloton nuclear device exploded in moonrock will liberate 10^7kg of oxygen in forming a cavern 40m across. [14] For a cavern perhaps five times as wide and ten times as deep we'll need a much bigger charge (probably in the megaton range), [15] and we don't want to lose all that oxygen. It could be pumped out and liquefied for future use.

Since there's plenty of oxygen in moonrock, ironically the

reason for conserving this quantity isn't that it would be lost but that most of it would stick around. Dr Richard Vondrack calculates that a lunar oxygen atmosphere of total mass 10^8 kg would form an ionosphere and take several hundred years to dissipate. [14] The oxygen release from our cavity would be 10^9_i-10^{10} kg and would impede industrial and research operations without being dense enough to be useful.

Underground explosion creates a cavity in a very small fraction of a second, trapping most of the radioactivity in molten rock which slumps to the bottom. Partial collapse from the walls and roof can then be expected: if the explosion is in a bed of valuable ore, a 'chimney' of broken rock can afterwards be mined out very easily, without releasing the radioactivity at the bottom of the shaft. [15] This creates the cylindrical cavity we want, after oxygen has been tapped from the high-pressure, hemispherical reservoir at the top. Safety factors would determine whether the radial mine galleries and habitation tunnels would be created before or after the shaft top was opened. When operational, the shaft and galleries would be automated, and in normal working people wouldn't go into the big chasms at all. In processing, oxygen would be extracted and stored as a matter of course: Jean Sendy suggested that iron ore, etc., will be 'oxygen ore' on the Moon, but it seems relatively easy to derive oxygen from ordinary moonrock either in chemical reactors or with growing plants.

The real problem is the need to supply carbon, nitrogen and hydrogen from Earth. Water, for example, would be easy if we had a source of hydrogen. In *New Worlds for Old* Nimmo suggested that hydrogen deposits from the Solar Wind on lunar grains might be the answer. In a million tonnes of lunar soil, it turns out, there are 40 tonnes of solar hydrogen (which would make enough water for an Olympic swimming pool), 100 tonnes of nitrogen, and 200 tonnes of carbon[47] —not enough to be very much help. A superconducting ion scoop with a field radius of 10,000km could collect 227 tonnes of solar hydrogen per year, making 2270 tonnes of water. [48] Unfortunately, only three such scoops could operate from a body the size of the Moon without interference between collecting fields, but the contribution is significant—especially if we can trap the carbon and nitrogen as well. It might be possible to orbit scoops around the Sun, coming back once a year to unload; another solution is importation from Earth-grazing asteroids, and later the main Belt, the giant planets and their satellites.

Agriculture won't be simple, despite the good growing properties of lunar soil, the remarkable plant development which may occur in low gravity, and the intense sunlight. Few plants could reach maturity in 14 days, even with continuous sunlight, unless their growth were speeded up a great deal. Continuous month-long sunlight exists only on the Mountains of Eternal Day, near the crater Shackleton at the lunar north pole. Interestingly enough, if ever there's been any significant release of water vapour on the Moon, some of it could be frozen in permamently shadowed craters and valleys near the poles.[16] Apparently all such volatile compounds were driven off during the Moon's formation, but in unusual circumstances a comet or carbonaceous chondrite (see page 192) might strike the Moon gently enough to release water vapour. The most the 'cold traps' could hold would cover the Moon to a depth of 1m, and the odds are against there being any—even if there were, farms on the mountain summits could scarcely feed whole colonics.

However, northern plants adjust happily to 14 days or more of light and of darkness. Lunar plants would face continuous sub-Arctic summers and winters, without any springs or autumns. From Soviet experiments, plants can be kept alive during lunar night by dropping the temperature and slowing their metabolism. Wheat recovers its growth rate in a spurt when light is restored, maturing in the same time as control plants on a normal cycle.[49]

J. W. E. H. Sholto Douglas suggested growing fungi in caverns, and on the surface during the two-week night (fungi *could* mature in that time).[17] Robert Shaw took the idea further: if higher plants can be adapted to a 14-day growth cycle then, after they have been harvested, fungi can work on the debris and soil during the night. Below ground, sunlight could be piped in during the day along optical fibres. Normal plants will have to be sheltered for half the lunar day, and artificially lit and heated during half the darkness, in 24-hour cycles. That point leads us to power sources on the Moon.

The inexhaustible, high-energy flow of solar energy through the Earth-Moon system can operate orbiting factories, EMLs and powersats (see Chapter 6). But orbiting installations are never out of sunlight for more than hours, and can be placed so that they never enter shadow at all. A lunar base must either use nuclear power (wasteful, since needed only half the time) or shut down all systems which can't be run on fuel cells. If hydrogen for *them* has to be shipped from Earth, the limitation will be still more serious.

Marcus O'Day suggested in 1958 that silicon dioxide (quartz) should be melted by parabolic mirrors during the day and tapped for heat at night.[18] Unfortunately, quartz is one common terrestrial material apparently absent from the Moon.[19] (But O'Day had a useful suggestion for the mirrors at night: focussed on the hydroponic farms, they could supply enough concentrated Earthlight to maintain photosynthesis. No good on Farside, of course.) It remains to be seen whether any existing moonrock can be used instead of quartz. Robert Shaw improved on the enormous volumes suggested by O'Day, calculated to remain liquid despite 14 days of heat drain: instead, the material could solidify in smaller tanks, teflon-lined to prevent sticking, and at sunrise these could be raised like ice lollies into the foci of the mirrors on the surface, a more effective process than heating the material from the top with reflected beams.

Oscar Schwiglhofer suggested orbiting mirrors, as Oberth had proposed years before for the Earth.[5] A similar suggestion, probably less effective, was an inclined ring around the Moon in a Sun-synchronous orbit. Since it's only in Earthlight and eclipses that the Moon gets any colours apart from grey or golden tan, and only at night that the stars can be seen, it seems a pity to make permanent the daytime lighting which Neil Armstrong compared to a floodlit baseball park.[20] Orbiting units could be powersats with microwave links, but 1km mirrors, reflecting sunlight to surface power stations, would be more effective.[50] With luck, the affected area can be restricted.

Still another idea, from Patrick Moore and Anthony Michaelis, involves liquid nitrogen turbines on the surface; four stations would be required to maintain constant power in a Moon-wide grid.[21] However, tungsten would have to be found for superconducting power lines, in permanent shadow and insulated from the lunar surface. The initial cost of viaducts girdling the Moon would be very high, and nitrogen is scarce there; but if ammonia (NH_3) were shipped from Earth as a convenient way of transporting hydrogen, the nitrogen supply would be assured.

Unless plentiful rocket fuel comes to light, the scarcity of hydrogen will make intercity travel on the surface preferable except in emergencies. The Moon provides a bumpy ride for wheeled vehicles; Oberth's Moon-car, on its telescopic leg, offers one alternative to building roads. In the low gravity, machines might float on electric arc jets, like the 'Moon bus' in *2001*; but if they were literally ground-effect machines, incapable of free flight, they might have difficulty descending, say, the 1800m into Alphonsus. Gavin Roberts suggested mag-lift floating trains, an attractive notion since the aluminium tracks wouldn't tarnish, and should be visible from Earth at appropriate angles of illumination; but it seems a waste of potential exports. Like Shaw's proposal, to bulldoze dust tracks and glaze them with laser beams from low orbit, it's labour-intensive and at best might be usable only in the *maria*, not in the really rough terrain between. The most efficient and versatile system still seems the monorail of the 1950s proposals —especially since the low lunar gravity makes long spans between pylons possible.

A conventional tracked railway would be practicable only across the *maria*, uses more labour and materials, and takes less advantage of lunar conditions. But the discussion led Ed Buckley to an interesting notion: his proposed living units were roughly the size of railway carriages. There might be a network of lunar railways or monorails, and a nomadic civilization going round with the sunlight, perhaps trading with the cities or cannibalizing them if they're left as ghost towns when the mining boom ends (far in the future).

There might then be no cities, only open-cast mines abandoned at the onset of night; but, since mines, smelters, lunartrons and railways cannot move, ways will be sought to keep them working during the darkness; and these fixed sites would provide shelter during solar flares. The nomads would be glad about that, because otherwise they'd have to stay close to the sunrise/sunset line. They might do so anyway, for temperature control, but with no cities they'd have no choice: at the onset of a flare storm they'd have to run for the terminator, and far beyond it into the night.

Transport within cities raises intriguing possibilities. In an underground dome, human beings could fly with feathered wings and make classical mythology come true. Eventually there may be manmade caverns deep enough to allow this freely. Meanwhile, Roberts suggested floor strips for mag-lift vehicles—more economical than moving pavements. Ramps and stairs can be steeper and flimsier than on Earth (like the Lunar Module ladder) but elevator design remains unchanged, because inertial effects in acceleration and deceleration are independent of gravity. (Similarly, vibratory and rotary mechanical designs are unchanged, although load-bearing structures can be much lighter. Convective flow of air and rate of flow of liquids *are* affected, so heating, power, water, sewage and ventilation systems all have to be tailored to lunar conditions.) [22]

Shaw suggested bicycles in the cities: the exercise would keep up the inhabitants' muscle tone. (In 1962, before the difficulty of working in spacesuits was known, Buckley proposed a lunar 'electrocycle'—essentially a tandem towing a trailer, with solar cells to conserve spacesuit batteries—for man-powered transport on the *surface*!) Traction would be lower but inertia unchanged, so wide tyres would be needed, and even then turning might pose a skidding problem. Tony Thomson suggested banked tracks; Robbie Chalmers suggested the layout of the city should be basically a double saucer, with tracks leading downhill from periphery to centre, lifts in the centre, and downhill tracks from the top floor of the centre to the periphery. The notion seems sound, except that for the sake of exercise the luckless inhabitants might have to cycle *uphill* each way.

Because of the resonance of the lunar crust, all blasting for future operations may have to be done before the first tunnels are sealed and pressurized. If further excavation can be done only with drills, lasers, etc., that limits further expansion of the complex, although the living area will expand as worked-out galleries are converted. Finally, the central shaft might be covered and pressurized, although one remains unhappy about a large air-filled volume close to the surface. More likely, the city would be evacuated during further blasting and become the antechamber to a huge cavern below, big enough for Earth-surface conditions—apart from the gravity. Big spaces are needed for 'natural' walking or running on the Moon, 60% faster than on Earth. [7] Oscar Schwiglhofer characterized sub-surface development on this scale as 'half-terraforming'.

If permafrost is found anywhere on the Moon, it'll be possible to thaw out cities without using explosives. Caverns could be created just by tunnelling and then allowing the ice to sublime in vacuum, but there's no chance of that—every drop of water will be conserved. (If water is found at an early stage life-support costs for lunar bases can be cut by 90% or more. [5]) But the subsurface ice predicted by Firsoff [23] — 'a sunny pleasure-dome with caves of ice', perhaps even liquid water in caverns measureless to Man or in a sunless sea—now seems very unlikely. There are radial channels around some craters, notably Copernicus, which might suggest water liberated by the impact, but now it seems clear that they're lava channels. There was an interesting suggestion that material encroaching on the dark floor of the Farside crater Tsiolkovsky might be a glacier protected by dust from sublimation. Detailed studies from Apollo-15 in orbit didn't support the notion; [24] and an apparent release of water somewhere on the Moon, perhaps by volcanic action, was more probably water dumped from the Apollo-14 CSM and eventually detected by the Suprathermal Ion Detector on the surface. [25]

A traditional suggestion, erecting domes over craters, is dangerous: large craters are shallow relative to their breadth, so a relatively large roof would need to be pressurized for the living volume generated. Crater walls are not very stable (many show tracks of rolling boulders), and a landslide or crustal slump could cause a major outburst of air. Cliff or hillside dwellings would be preferable, and will be used if suitable caves are available below observatories and other research outposts.

Buckley suggested cities might be built in volcanic domes like the Marius Hills, [13] following the cracks leading into them (if safe). Large numbers of natural, branching tunnels might be expected, perhaps leading far underground. He envisaged covering the natural dome with solar power units, all tracking the Sun across the sky. Peak power would be at noon, when most reflectors were at maximum exposure. (Plate 1 - cf. fig. 10.) Since volcanic regions may be rich in minerals these may be the first radiation-shielded permanent settlements.

Lunar agriculture and industry will be far more automated than their terrestrial counterparts: although a reusable transport system will make it relatively cheap to send personnel to the Moon, it would take too long to establish labour-intensive lunar activities if a building programme and a flow of imports were needed to house and support the workforce. One would no more take that approach to lunar industry than begin a modern construction project with a war to capture slaves. The first wave of people on the Moon (apart from researchers) will be decision-takers, trouble-shooters and maintenance experts, with an international makeup even if based on US/USSR exploration.

However, Andrew Nimmo predicted that within 10-20 years anybody who wants to go to the Moon will be able to do so—in Arthur C. Clarke's view, for about the cost of a transatlantic journey today. Lunar tourism will bring service industries —one can't imagine a slot-machine taking the place of the barman in the Lunar Hilton! The effect will be a general rise in the standard of living—once a channel opens for goods that are not strictly for survival or production, it'll immediately be used to ease the spartan existence of the lunar producers. With extended tours of duty and families being brought up from Earth, the colony will evolve from a mining camp towards a township. (In Heinlein's *'It's Great to Be Back!'* a married couple leave the Moon, only to sign up again because life on Earth isn't the idyll they 'remembered'. [26])

There could be emigrants seeking a longer or fuller life in lunar gravity: heart cases, accident victims, handicapped groups ... It might be thought unrealistic to expect room for compassion in a resource-development programme but, if medical research facilities have not already been set up on the Moon, we need wait only until some powerful figure, or some scientist thought invaluable, has only six months to live under Earth gravity. Invalids can be taken to the Moon in water acceleration shields, and if manned lunar-- tron launches are going on the technique may already be routine.

Once the lunar hospital exists and handicapped people can lead useful lives on the Moon, skilled personnel in that category may be recruited for permanent emigration. Unless life on the Moon is unbearable, few refusals can be expected; indeed, groups like the thalidomide children, scanned for scientific and technical talent, might insist on emigration for *all* their members who wished it. Some people will go to the Moon because they're told to, for financial reasons or to further their careers, planning to return to Earth; but some, perhaps quite a high proportion, will go for survival or to escape dependence on others. They'll be committed to permanent lunar development, and their children will be the first extraterrestrial generation.

If bones and muscles become permanently adapted to $\frac{1}{6}g$, trying to stand in Earth gravity would lead to multiple injuries, and prolonged exposure—even lying prone—could cause heart failure or internal damage. We don't know how long a tour would have to be to make return to Earth impossible (two years, perhaps), but children born on the Moon may be committed to life there unless removed to Earth at once. Pat McNally, ASTRA's medical expert, pointed out that, in children born limbless or crippled early in life, body weight grows to compensate for the missing members. Women might return to Earth to have children, to keep their options open, especially if the normal tour of duty is less than nine months (J. N. Leonard has drawn a parallel with the conquest of the land by the first amphibians, returning to the sea to reproduce [27]). But Margaret Schwiglhofer argued that pregnant women wouldn't want to travel, and pregnancy and delivery would be easier under $\frac{1}{6}g$. Parents who can't return to Earth, and who accept the permanence of the lunar colony, may choose not to send their children away; history may view the claiming of the Moon (and therefore the Galaxy, in Asimov's view—see below) as a crusade of the handicapped, a final gesture before tissue regeneration and transplant surgery make all injuries and defects repairable.

Not all ASTRA members accepted the idea. Even if transport costs fall dramatically, only the best might be permitted to go. But what about the best brains? What government would have refused Einstein ten more years? And, to be blunt, one feels that a Brezhnev with six months to live would get to the Moon whatever the practicalities. As with the flow of goods, once the channel is opened the volume of traffic will force expansion. But, even if only the perfectly healthy were allowed to go, there would still be accidents. Men and women, average age probably mid-30s, would find themselves still able to work on the Moon but condemned to inactivity if returned to Earth. If ordered to leave they might well refuse, and their colleagues might refuse to force them. In such circumstances a committed lunar generation would soon be born; Nimmo's suggested slogan, 'Copulate to Populate', might be taken up in all seriousness.

Buckley and Nimmo suggested jointly that among people who could lead more productive lives on the Moon would be older men and women, who on Earth would be fated to become administrators to make room for new talent. On the Moon, life expectancy and working lives may be prolonged—only the very rich will be able to use the Moon purely for retirement. Any group expecting to end their days on the Moon will work to make the settlement permanent, although children of the younger colonists will inherit it.

McNally asked whether such evolution mightn't be frustrated by military control. But NASA isn't military, and nor are Antarctic and seabed explorations, although military personnel are involved in all three. Nor is INTELSAT, which probably parallels the lunar project more closely. Space-management techniques have to be more advanced than military ones, because the areas of application are far wider. Perhaps, McNally suggested, the military will be on the Moon as an arm of Earth government? It seems unlikely, when the project is so far outside their proper area: the British Army doesn't run the National Coal Board, although it's a nationalized industry. There might be a military presence 'to protect vital national interests', just in case any of the *other* nations should stage a takeover, but let's hope for no such nonsense.

Science-fiction ideas on the evolution of lunar society have been fairly slender so far. In *Earthlight* Clarke suggested that a telegraphic lunar dialect might evolve as an alternative to the universal standard English of interplanetary communication. [12] In *The Moon is a Harsh Mistress*, 11 years later, Heinlein added a large leavening of Russian and other languages, [29] far more than any minority has interpolated into everyday speech in the USA. Such leavening will depend on the numbers and *interna*tionalism of immigrants to the Moon. Groups who maintain independent traditions and speech will have little influence on the language—few Indian or Pakistani words have infiltrated English in the UK.

In *The Gods Themselves* Asimov envisaged the evolution of lunar sports as dangerous as skiing or bobsleighs on Earth, taking advantage of the $\frac{1}{6}g$,[30] and in 'The Menace from Earth' Heinlein portrayed muscle-powered flight in lunar caverns. [31] Asimov also foresaw penalties: despite the temptations of near-nudity in the sublunar tunnels, sex between visitors and Moon-born was dangerous if not impossible because of the relative strength and lack of coordination on one side, and lighter bones and muscles on the other—although which partner would be injured wasn't entirely obvious. In *A Spectre Is Haunting Texas* Fritz Leiber took the contrast further, with a 2.6m tall inhabitant of a lunar space station visiting Earth in a powered exoskeleton.[32]

Asimov's 'Waterclap' drew parallels between lunar cities and seabed colonies[33] —which can be taken quite a bit further (see below). These glimpses of emerging lunar society, however, don't give a full picture even if lumped together. They're minor spinoffs from lunar conditions rather than social insights. The most detailed lunar society—in *The Moon Is a Harsh Mistress*—is a highly artificial one built around a penal colony. Its major institutions (group marriage and 'tanstaafl'—there ain't no such thing as a free lunch) reflect a 2:1 immigrant ratio of the sexes and a simple philosophy of 'pay or starve'—or, more likely, be 'eliminated' without a pressure suit. (But Alexei Panshin points out that women are protected and half the male immigrants die of mistakes or 'elimination'; even without that, three generations should even up the numbers.[34])

The lesser features—impromptu courts, death penalties with or without trial, and female supremacy (which has no corrupting effect, oddly enough)—all stem from the penal function of the colony and cannot be envisaged except as the compromises of a group self-selected by exploitation of all forms of social order. Still less rationally, the Moon is stripped of essentials, through exporting food to Earth for no economic return. Breakdown and cannibalism are foreseen, the colonists revolt and bombard Earth into submission with EML-launched rocks. Leiber, Clarke and so many others have described lunar revolutions or independence movements that schism has come to seem almost inevitable.

The comforts and stresses of life will be the factors affecting social attitudes. With men and women on the Moon from the outset, the colony will never be as basic as an all-male mining camp—although even those can produce operatic societies, theatre groups and art classes. Luxuries will be scarce until tourism begins, but the spirit of making-do will have a binding effect. It was suggested that life in the tunnels would be as constricting as in tower blocks, but that needn't be true. Rock dwellings in the Australian opal fields can be very civilized indeed, and don't suffer from the real curses of high flats: noise, vandalism, wind turbulence, lack of recreational and communal space, the old and very young imprisoned by the journey to the ground ... The skills required, and still more the educational qualifications, will make the group less disparate than the Australian and American pioneers; although, since all groups can receive TV from their own cultures, no minority need feel cut off. Oscar Schwiglhofer's prediction, that colony groups would be close-knit from an early stage even beyond the requirements of survival, seems reasonable.

What would be their relationship to Earth administration? More specifically, at what stage do people begin to think of themselves collectively as 'the Moon', no longer adequately represented by their national governments on Earth? Obviously not while they all intend to return, nor—as Bob Cochrane pointed out—while all can be called back by economic factors on Earth. But within a few years there will be a fixed population, some with physical handicaps eased on the Moon. When children are born, or even when a sufficient number of adults are committed, some factions are bound to want more autonomy. Robert Shaw suggested that children on the Moon would be a precious resource, with the emotional import Clarke described in 'Out of the Cradle,'[35] and wouldn't be permitted to leave: in becoming committed to the Moon they'd ensure the continuation of the colony, where the administration might otherwise decide it couldn't be maintaned for the sake of cripples who'd receive the best of treatment on Earth. The symbolic value of 'Moon-children' is so potent that Shaw thought they might be forbidden by bureaucratic fiat: the first pregnancy would be a top-secret act of revolution. The revolution would certainly take place; as Ernest Taves showed in a set of stories, trying to prevent it virtually guarantees it.[36]

More probably, Schwiglhofer said, medical research would lead to planned pregnancies. They'd be virtually certain in the Russian bases even if others chickened out. Shaw suggested that the same experiments could be simultated in Earth orbit with no risk of permanent 'Moonchildren' as a *fait accompli*. Duplicating lunar conditions in Earth orbit seem unlikely, however, if a moonbase already exists for other reasons; indeed, for a space station big enough for such medical flexibility, the materials would probably have to come from the Moon.

Plate 1   Mixed-mode Single-Stage-to-Orbit Space Shuttle. The liquid oxygen/kerosene outer engines (see page 146) are used only for the first part of the ascent. Some such Heavy Lift vehicle will be needed for 'strategic' missions to the Moon and beyond. (*Buckley, based on diagrams by Robert Salkeld.*)

Plate 2   Lunar colony in the Marius Hills. These rock domes, apparently volcanic, may provide shelter from solar and galactic radiation for a colony without its having to go underground (see pages 89 and 95); compare the 1950s concept illustrated in fig. 10 (page 88). Because of the sharp curvature of the lunar surface, a very high radio mast—made feasible by the low lunar gravity—is needed for communications in the surrounding work area. Lunar communications over greater distances would have to be *via* a relay at the Earth/Moon L1 point (see page 112). (*Buckley, based on a Lunar Orbiter photograph.*)

Plate 3 'The Inheritance' (*Buckley, 1962.*) The relative sizes of the planets symbolized their supposed importance in the future. Today, the asteroids would be in the foreground; Jupiter would be as large as the Earth and related directly to the starfield at upper left; Mercury and Saturn would be next in prominence; while Mars and Venus, as remote, long-term possibilities, would be very small.

Plate 4   SIOS over Middle Spot. This is one of the smaller variants of the Standard Interplanetary Operations Spacecraft (see page 132), with simulated gravity in living quarters sited on rotating booms. Before being identified as one of the three great volcanoes on Mars's Tharsis Ridge, Pavonis Mons, in the background, was during the 1971 dust storm dubbed 'Middle Spot'. (*Roberts, based on Mariner-9 photographs.*)

Inevitably the lunar group (especially the permanent settlers) will want more say than a postal vote in Earth elections. Nimmo suggested, as we saw, that lunar militants might adopt the slogan 'Copulate to Populate', to which Roberts added: 'No Copulation Without Representation.' With foresight, such confrontations can be avoided by transferring most of the colony's administration to the Moon within (say) ten years. Initially, no doubt, there will be a Director; as night follows day that leads to demand for an elected council with representation on the board of the corporation developing lunar resources. If that body has any sense, it'll prepare for the day and welcome it when it arrives.

Chris Boyce remarked that the colony group's size would be a key factor. We're imagining a large group in several embryo cities, composed of highly motivated people who go to get things done. Population could grow rapidly, since each city may be tunnelled out to maximum size before habitats are installed; each may come into being *as a city* as soon as recreational facilities are established. Permanent settlement is cheaper than continual rotation to Earth of several hundred men and women; with a dozen bases, lunar population could reach thousands in a very short time.

As a political and social unit, the Moon will probably be highly democratic—people of the calibre required may insist on frequent referenda, with votes computerized and weighted for competence on the issues (an idea Nimmo suggests as an aid to Earth's survival) because of the high degree of specialized knowledge available. There would have to be absolute authority in some areas, primarily during emergencies—e.g., redistributing commodities to settlements in trouble. While such decisions *should* be unanimously accepted, such authority raises the question of enforcement. Economic sanctions could be applied against recalcitrant cities by diverting incoming rockets and cutting power (life-support would have backups for the lunar night, but industry would depend on the solar energy grid). The interdependability of the cities is so obvious, given the Moon's slow rotation, that probably such sanctions need never be used. Police action by armed forces should be avoided—such forces could establish a dictatorship by threatening to cave-in the cities, with near-surface blasts or even from a distance with rockets and mortars.

Internal police should for preference be voluntary and

dedicated, not chosen by lot, for instance. We must avoid the situation John Macvey imagined elsewhere, where all divergence is antisocial and carries an automatic death penalty,[37] and Heinlein's other extreme of survival of the strongest, with duels and kangaroo courts to maintain an elementary level of order. Either form seems characteristic of a penal colony, whereas the sort of people we imagine on the Moon would draw up a constitution automatically when a governing body was formed.

A constitution guarantees the rights of the individual, and a judicial structure is needed—without the bizarre sanction of 'elimination'. Final appeal would be to the International Court, which now becomes the Interplanetary Court and ultimately will have to meet on the Moon, because lunar protagonists can't go to Earth—nor can colonists from Mars, Mercury, and the moons of the giant planets, although all can go to the Moon. Where the judiciary takes up residence, the legislature may follow: Buckley's 1962 lecutre to ASTRA ended with the symbolic 'Federation of Solar Worlds' on the Moon (Plate 3), with the size of the planetary discs in the sky indicating their supposed influence in government.

Asteroids or low-gravity space stations might be represented by three-dimensional holographic projections from diplomatic suites on L1 or L2 satellites: would-be assassins should be suitably confused by not all the visible delegates being physically present! If they *have* to attend, water-filled tanks would be needed (as they may in any case be for seabed dwellers), or powered exoskeletons with partial pressure suits to protect vital organs. For the Solar System conferences, pens that write underwater may be essential.

Tony Thomson wondered if robot police might suffice for the Moon's highly responsible population. Certainly initial policing will be conservationist, safety-oriented, and computerised: recorded voice warnings, etc., will have to be supplemented as people become careless. Unfortunately, as Harry Harrison showed at the beginning of *The Stainless Steel Rat*, there's no moral compunction about destroying a robot policeman, and outwitting one becomes a challenge.

Crime on the Moon will largely depend on the medium of exchange. Almost anything in short supply *can* be used—Shaw suggested printed circuits, by analogy with the 'germanium standard' in Blish's *Earthman Come Home*,[38] but that's vulnerable in a place where electronic components are manufactured. Alcohol might be used, although there's the problem of evaporating assets! Could there be inflation on the Moon, Robbie Chalmers asked? (Deflation is to be avoided.) The most likely system was outlined by Cordwainer Smith in *The Planet Buyer*: FOE money (free on earth) and SAD money (sealed and delivered), depending on whether one's buying a commodity sent from Earth or making purchases (e.g., stocks and shares) on the other planet.[39] Although the Moon isn't likely to impose fantastic import duties to preserve its pioneer life-style, interplanetary economy would be based on luxury goods, because necessities would be manufactured on the spot or supplied from Earth in return for services.

Theft (of luxuries) would arise next after waste. Crimes of passion will occur and assault and murder must appear eventually. The astronauts have remarked, however, that the Moon is a low-tension environment because of the gravity, and it'll make assault difficult and not very effective—the only murders may be premeditated, and require high technical competence. 'A jury of his peers' takes on a new meaning.

Roberts asked whether the colony might itself require a penal colony ('Sinus Botanicus'?). More probably there would be work sentences, as in Scandinavia, or social work impositions, as in Germany and elsewhere: there wouldn't be a penal colony as such, but persistent offenders would be exiled back to Earth. (Bishop Godwin in the 17th century wrote of the Moon's inhabitants: 'And because it is an inviolable decree amongst them, never to put any one to death, perceiving by the stature, and some other notes they have, who are likely to be of a wicked or imperfect disposition, they send them away (I know not by what means) into the Earth ... And their ordinary vent for them is a certain hill in the North of *America*, whose people I can easily believe to be wholly descended of them ...'[40])

Some minor but interesting notions emerged in discussion. Roberts suggested rotating 'centrifuge hotels', 100m or more across, figured for $1g$ pull on the inner surface, to be used by anyone on extended stay but intending to return to Earth. It was agreed that they'd have fresh butter with every meal!

Trees and parks should be provided. It was suggested that later generations might not like or want them, but they're intended to counter just that—to stop the colonists becoming isolated from other forms of life, denying their own organic nature like Asimov's Outworlders in *The Naked Sun*. [41] When animals are introduced, conditions may lead to huge 'Moon-calves' for protein export—'Wells was right!'

Anthony Lawton [42], Charles Muir and John Braithwaite independently suggested spinning a liquid on a turntable so that its surface takes up the parabolic figure of a telescope mirror. (Braithwaite suggested using mercury, so the mirror would be *permanently* liquid. 'Lend us a Saturn V and we'll send a 200-inch mirror to the Moon in a bottle.') With no atmospheric interference, a 36cm-aperture lunar telescope can equal the performance of the largest on Earth. [43] The only telescope on the Moon so far, in the shadow of the Apollo-16 LM, exploited the other lunar advantage: access to wavelengths such as the ultraviolet which don't reach the Earth's surface. Lunar telescopes can be much lighter because of the lower gravity and also because tracking speeds (to follow objects across the sky) are much lower. The same applies to radiotelescopes, and lunar craters could become giant reflectors, like the Arecibo valley on Earth; however, the relatively close horizon imposes a diameter limit of 6.4-8.0 km. [44]

An aluminized 100m Mylar mirror concentrates 11MW of energy in vacuum at this distance from the Sun. [45] As described independently by Lawton and Muir, parabolic mirrors could be cast by spinning discs of epoxy resin and silvering them once set. Various writers propose to create spherical mirrors by inflating a balloon, silvering the interior and cutting the sphere in half: Oscar Schwiglhofer devised a 'power ball', half silver, half transparent, for a variety of applications. Low gravity, solar energy and vacuum will generate many processes which couldn't be used on Earth.

Development of the Moon is part of a general expansion of our existing civilization, to allow better management of Earth's resources. Our society has to expand to maintain its stability, so that infringement on individual lives doesn't cause breakdowns in the social order. 'We're staving off the day,' Nimmo agreed, 'but all we can do is keep staving it off until the Universe runs down.' The first function of a lunar colony would be to provide hope. Everyone has a right to as many children as they want, he said: with low mortality and high resource consumption it's responsible not to want a large family, but the freedom to choose is worth preserving. The importance of the lunar colony is that it provides an alternative to crowded Earth, particularly for the pioneering spirits. Living on Earth with a Moon colony in existence, or without one, is the difference between living in a coffin with no lid or having the lid nailed down.

The Earth-Moon relationship, like East-West trade at present, will consist largely of materials and technology exchanges. Money transactions will be relatively minor because there's not much question of revenue from the Moon—revenue is generated by lunar materials, once they're supplied to users. In a system not based primarily on cash transactions, intangibles like expansion of human knowledge and experience will affect decision-taking much more than at present.

Close contact can be expected between lunar colonies and seabed cities, when they exist, although that may take longer because permanent cities may imply lasting adaptation, as on the Moon. It's possible to breathe water (mice and other mammals have done it) but mechanical assistance is needed because water's denser than air. Chemical factors, especially pH, have to be carefully adjusted; the salinity of blood still matches the seas of 600 million years ago, when life crawled on to the land. Artificial gills have been tested but couldn't be used below 10m because of oxygen narcosis. Nimmo thought that the sea won't be colonized unless the conditioning process is safe and easily reversible.

Early seabed settlers are therefore likely to be routinely rotated back up to the land, and so take longer to develop a group identity. Groups committed to the Moon and the sea, however, will be able to visit each other's environment more readily than either could visit the land surface of the Earth. Lunar visitors, unaffected by Earth's gravity while immersed in water, could make the flight in water-filled spacecraft, although the return lift would have to be in protective suits. Lower levels of lunar cities might be water-filled to save oceanic visitors the inconvenience of surgery. Interemigration can be foreseen, since both groups would be used to enclosed cities.

Earth-surface humanity shouldn't become estranged from the cultures of the Moon and the deeps. If the polar caps were melted—e.g., by lunar dust scattered on them to absorb sunlight—much of the present land surface would go under water. Indeed, Shaw suggested this might be a desirable policy, creating new fisheries, new farmlands, and allowing more efficient use of land resources—think of those millions of square kilometres of unproductive concrete disappearing under the ooze. If the land is ruined—e.g., by pesticides or artificial fertilizer residues—eventually we may dome the cities and flood the farmlands to purify them. There would be plenty of artificial reefs afterwards for fish farms. Perhaps nothing else will stop the spread of the Sahara, or the unforeseen consequences of environmental damage in Vietnam and Brazil. It ties in with O'Neill's idea that, with most of the human race living and working in space (see Chapter 6), Earth's population would fall naturally, allowing the planet to recover 'from the near deathblow it received from the industrial revolution'. [46] Perhaps, however, before setting out to cleanse the Earth on such a scale, we should try something smaller—like making the Moon habitable.

THE MOON (to the Earth):

> *'The snow upon my lifeless mountains*
> *Is loosened into living foundations,*
> *My solid oceans flow, and sing, and shine:*
> *A spirit from my heart bursts forth,*
> *It clothes with unexpected birth*
> *My cold bare bosom: Oh! it must be thine*
> *On mine on mine!*
> *Gazing on thee I feel, I know*
> *Green stalks burst forth, and bright flowers grow*
> *And living shapes upon my bosom move:*
> *Music is in the sea and air,*
> *Winged clouds soar here and there,*
> *Dark with the rain new buds are dreaming of:*
> *'Tis love, all love!'*
> —Shelley, 'Prometheus Unbound'

Of the four categories of planetary engineering defined by Oscar Schwiglhofer, mutaforming, half-terraforming (already-mentioned) and terraforming proper could be used on the Moon. There's no 'orboforming' case for changing the orbit and, since the Moon has no magnetic field, its rotation could be changed only by a major impact;[51] drastic if the Moon is already inhabited.

Pat McNally considered that mutaforming in the 'pantropy' sense of James Blish [52] —literally 'changing everything', new biological models of Man—lay far in the future, beyond the main scope of our discussions. Even then, adaptation to the hard vacuum of the Moon, with no protection from solar or galactic radiation, would be one of the most difficult challenges. But lesser mutaforming begins as bone structures, blood counts, etc., adapt to $\frac{1}{6}g$—perhaps irreversibly. The next generation could be said to be mutaformed, although only in acquired characteristics.

Another direction mutaforming can take is towards Man-machine interaction, adaptation by surgical implants, etc. We're already within reach of the 'space leotard', a second skin which interfaces between natural skin and vacuum. [53] Very hot objects in sunlight, and very cold ones in shadow, could be handled with further skins, perhaps surgically applied. With an implant to break down carbon dioxide, a cyborg (cybernetic organism) could survive on the Moon with only a face mask, leotard and air bottle. Full adaptation would require further implants to take over the remaining body functions, at least in part, and some way of extracting oxygen from rock. The more significant the military presence on the Moon, the more likely such experiments will be—and once started they'd be likely to continue.

Many of us felt the temptation should be resisted, particularly with 'volunteers' like military personnel, convicted criminals or the unemployed. For the colony to be healthy, members should be born there or commit themselves to it: a cyborg would be committed physically, like it or not, and there's no surgery for homesickness. A cyborg's children would undergo almost continuous operations, or else be separated from the parent(s) until adulthood; the effect on family life would make apartheid look merciful, and the authorities can scarcely use excuses like 'we have to keep them on the Moon because otherwise they'd keep running off'. Pressurized domes in cyborg colonies are no answer: the child would still be raised by normal adults and find its parent(s) terrifyingly different.

Changing or redirecting the cyborgs' emotions would distance them from humanity, already a danger. In Clarke's 'A Meeting with Medusa' [28] his character sees himself as a transition between puny organic Man and the all-electronic beings who'll supersede him. Larry Niven's cyborg in 'Becalmed in Hell' [54] and Anne McCaffrey's in 'The Ship Who Sang' [55] remain totally human although transplanted into the 'bodies' of *spaceships*, but there's a great deal of doubt about the survival of personality in such cases. The easiest way to adapt a human to the Moon might be to remove the brain and wire it up to the controls and sensors of a lunar rover, but are we 'ghosts in the machine' who can flit from one machine to another without loss of identity? Personality is largely keyed to available means of expression—consider the dreadful implications of Ellison's 'I Have No Mouth and I Must Scream'. [56] Anne McCaffrey unconsciously perceives the danger: although her 'brain ships' are sent into desperate situations, it never occurs to anyone (and therefore not the author, presumably) to give them weapons. Think of brain-ship Helga as a musical Dalek and the point becomes clear: the 'Dr Who' Daleks, with their repetitious dialogue, lack of creativity and hatred of purely oganic beings, are more convincing 'shell-people' than a spaceship who falls in love with her pilot and sings Grand Opera.

Clarke's and Niven's cyborgs were accident victims, while McCaffrey's were so deformed that they could survive only with continuous intensive care. But if society *needs* cyborgs, will accident victims receive cures? Will tissue-regeneration research be halted? Chris Boyce (see Chapter 13) looks forward to mind-machine blends switching between organic and mechanical bodies at will, but the key words are 'at will'—with no strings attached, as it were. The fear is of an intermediate Burke-and-Hare case; or criminals, bankrupts and the infirm being offered a 'choice' between the cyborg state and Something Worse; or a military-type draft with the usual bias towards the young, the lower-income groups and the minorities. In those cases disaffection in the cyborg ranks could make the US Army in Vietnam look like a Sunday-school outing—and, if cyborgs are essential to interplanetary society, pity help that society once the cyborgs have secret food-farms and fuel-cell manufactories.

It's always fatal to adapt oneself to one's surroundings. The thing to do is to alter your surroundings to suit *you*.
                              Arthur C. Clarke, *The Sands of Mars* [57]

The candidate worlds for terraforming are the Moon, Mars, Venus, Jupiter and Saturn (with moons as a possible bonus). Uranus and Neptune may be needed in their present form as deuterium/helium-3 reservoirs and giant-planet laboratories. Surface area determines the worth of the operation: Singer suggests that, if the Moon were sufficiently compressed by nuclear explosions, its gravity well would become deep enough to hold an Earth-type atmosphere ('Miniforming'). [21] But the surface area would be less than that of any Earth continent, so it's unlikely to be worth doing.

For practical terraforming, Bob Cochrane suggested that there would be a limiting mass in relation to density and distance from the Sun. For example, Mars at its present density and distance couldn't hold an Earth-type atmosphere but could hold a carbon-dioxide atmosphere giving Earth-normal surface pressure. Free oxygen and some nitrogen would escape into space, but perhaps not too fast to be replaced. The Moon, $\frac{1}{80}$ the mass of Earth, at its present density would lose up to 1000kg/sec of oxygen from an atmosphere, [14] implying 210,000kg of rock to be processed per hour to make good the loss of oxygen alone—not impossible, but a massive process to keep going century after century, wasting resources. It's probably not worth giving the Moon breathable air unless, as Ted White suggested in a short story, a high-altitude membrane could be thrown around the whole Moon to contain the atmosphere, periodically sprayed to plug meteoroid punctures. [59] Jim Campbell said a 'rock membrane'—i.e., half-terraforming—would be preferable.

If the Moon *were* terraformed, the process would be beautiful in time-lapse photography. First the lunar outlines softening into new perspectives under the thickening atmosphere, then the first true mists and clouds around mountains which still projected high into the sharpness of vacuum. Then the aircraft, seeding life in long lines of vapour across a barren land as big as South America; the greens and browns tinting the lunar features as first algae, then lichens, took hold. The rains, cutting the first stream beds which would become rivers, bringing down the first deposits of soil into the valleys; the triumphant advance of grass up the crater slopes, through passes and rilles into the plains beyond; lastly the trees, bursting like bombs out of the soil and rising to incredible heights and breadths of foliage in lunar gravity, settling into stillness with maturity and casting slow-moving shadows for kilometres across the sunlit land. Autumn comes every 14 days, unless the trees are evergreens. The Moon's seas would be rocky, since many of the 'highland' areas fall below *mare* level; huge coral reefs would grow on the craters to form atolls, heat-reservoirs to which life would flock at night to escape the frosts.

Sea breezes at nightfall and land winds at sunrise might be more intense than on Earth: temperature changes would be greater but relatively gradual, with the Sun taking more than an hour to rise and set. During the night, sea breezes would steady once the input of warmth from the sea matched the heat loss into space. During the day there might be no circular storms because Coriolis forces were inadequate: fronts bearing rain and hail would be gentle compared with Earth's. But Jim Campbell suggested there would be constant winds blowing across the terminator into night—he thought they'd be very violent, but that may not be true. Orbiting mirrors can heat up the nightside a good deal. The atmosphere might take on a Venus-type pattern, rotating faster than the Moon itself—if it went round in four days like the Venus clouds, wind-speed would be 97kph, although presumably lower at ground level.

The real danger could be the great Moonstorms which might build up over the raised plains of the *maria*, as Martian dust-storms do over high, bright plateaux. They could form in the middle of the day, generated by the Earth just as the Moon affects rainfall in the early part of the month. Fed with solar energy continuously for seven Earth days, they could reach epic proportions by nightfall—unless, of course, we had weather control to contain them. With growing meteorological insight, comparing weather systems on Earth, Mars, Venus and the giants, such control may be possible.

The Moon may prove too small for practicable terraforming, but it gives a notion of what might be done elsewhere.

VI

Space Colonies and Space Ships

For in the fevered world which we have inherited (and how Evans hated it!) no monument of stone, however ancient, beautiful or revered, is safe; all, equally, are at the mercy of 'a boy in a bomber'. But perhaps even after the holocaust of an atomic war there may survive, in some remote place, the great volumes of Evans's 'Palace of Minos'. And if that should happen, our surviving descendants can, if they wish, know as much about the prehistoric civilization of the Aegean as we do, though not one stone of the Palace itself should remain.
—Leonard Cottrell, *The Bull of Minos*, 1955[1]

'In that case,' said Ivanov, 'it would be a good thing if instead of sitting and waiting for the possible catastrophe mankind migrated to other worlds, even in these deserts of space, which at least contain all the materials man needs to set himself up here.'
Konstantin Tsiolkovsky, *Beyond the Planet Earth*, 1920[2]

At Princeton University seminars in 1969, Professor Gerard O'Neill asked: 'Is a planetary surface the right place for an expanding technological civilization?' The conclusion was: no. The proposals weren't altogether new: Tsiolkovsky, who first formulated the principles of astronautics, foresaw almost immediate space habitats once means were found to get above the atmosphere;[2] J. D. Bernal put forward similar ideas in 1929;[3] and in the 1950s Stine and Remick designed an orbiting 'space city'[4] while L. R. Shepherd suggested hollowed-out asteroids.[5] In 1964 Cole and Cox proposed cylindrical asteroid habitats, big enough for Earth-surface conditions inside (see Chapter 10); Arthur C. Clarke's *Rendezvous with Rama*, set inside such a cylinder,[6] was already in print before O'Neill found a publisher in 1974.[7]

O'Neill's thesis was that habitats were the key to Solar System industrialization, and that construction could begin almost immediately. Like Tsiolkovsky, who postulated thousands of settlements each supporting a thousand people in synchronous orbit,* O'Neill argued that by the 2050s half the human race might be living and working in space.

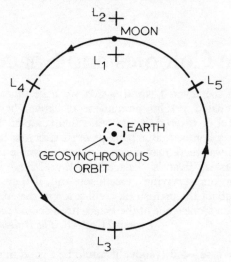

EARTH - MOON LIBRATION POINTS

Fig. 11   The Earth/Moon Lagrange points
and geosynchronous orbit

O'Neill's scenario involves the five 'Lagrange points' where an orbiting body can hold a fixed geometrical position relative to the Earth and Moon (fig. 11). L1, directly between the Earth and Moon, will almost certainly be used for over-the-horizon communications on the lunar Nearside. L2 relay would obviously be used by Farside bases and has line-of-sight links to geosynchronous satellites at their maximum elongation from the Earth-Moon line.[8] A 'Hummingbird' satellite in forced orbit around L2, using ion-drive or electric-arc thrusters, could keep the Earth in view over the rim of the Moon.[9] A 'Lissajou' satellite, in elliptical orbit around L2, could communicate with

*There's a campaign to call geosynchronous orbit 'Clarke orbit', because in 1945 he was first to suggest its use for communications satellites, but it seems Tsiolkovsky was ahead at least as regards the significance of the 24-hour period.

Earth and L1 but would be occulted by the Moon every three months, unless in 'Halo orbit' with deliberate perturbations of the orbital plane ('phase jumps'): [10] this technique is used to keep International Sun-Earth Explorer-3 in orbit around the Sun-Earth L1 point. In theory, existing materials could tether a satellite swinging around the Earth-Moon L1 or L2 as the counterweight of a lunar beanstalk (as discussed in Chapter 4).

L3, directly opposite the Moon, is the least stable position. L4 and L5, the most stable, are respectively 60° ahead of and behind the Moon in its orbit, making permanent equilateral triangles with the Earth and Moon. They're likely points for interplanetary communications stations, with an L3 counterpart, because they're very seldom occulted and are well clear of radio noise from Earth. They take less energy to reach than synchronous orbit, and solar sails are adequate for station-keeping. [8] Equilateral probes have been suggested to sample dust clouds, possibly containing primal Solar System material, observed by Kordylevski in 1961; and permanent satellites there could be valuable because at least one would be outside the Earth's magnetic 'tail' during any solar event. [8] There are mysterious Long-Delayed Radio Echoes (LDEs) [11], first reported in the 1920s and now shown statistically to emanate from the Equilaterals.*

For physics the Equilaterals' importance is that they're 'lows' in the Earth-Moon system's gravitational fields. Research may include redetermining the gravitational constant, investigating gravity waves, and studying the effects of gravity and magnetic fields on the biorhythms of living organisms. Artificial comets to study Solar-Wind processes are also

---

*In *Man and the Stars* I investigated Professor R. N. Bracewell's suggestion that LDEs might represent a spaceprobe from another civilization trying to attract attention. James Strong suggested [13] that such a probe might be in one of the Moon Equilaterals. The 'echoes' were much too loud to be natural reflections, the conventional explanation for more than forty years, and dates and times showed a strong correlation with movements of the Equilateral points, especially meridian transits. Working with all known cases of LDE up to 1970, George Sassoon found odds of thousands to one against coincidence. [12] Until then it had been taken for granted that LDEs were atmospheric. Lawton and Newton suggest that they're generated in 'Trojan ionospheres', but such stable charged clouds are unlikely and the spaceprobe hypothesis is still in contention, although the 'translations' I put forward proved invalid. [14]

mentioned. [8]

With oxygen, silicon, aluminium and titanium prevalent, O'Neill believes space stations and powersats could be created from lunar soil. An excavation 750m square, 4m deep, would provide material for a space habitat supporting 10,000 people; over six years, it could be collected by a single bulldozer, [9] launched by mass driver to L2, and shipped to L5 using mass-driver engines. 'Island One', the first habitat at L5, would build the Solar Electric Power Satellites advocated by Dr Peter Glaser. Mass-driver engines would move the powersats into synchronous orbit and each would beam down 5000MW to ground-based rectennae feeding energy into national grids. More recent designs promise 10,000MW. [15] A typical power-sat, 12km long and about 45km² in area, would be in shadow for only 72 minutes per day, near midnight at the ground station when power demand was past its peak.[16] Any move-ment of the power beam would shift a reflected laser beam through twice the deflection angle and immediately operate a cut-off. The edge of the rectenna would be a restricted area, and at the centre the beam would be mutagenic (that is, could cause mutations in living organisms), [17] but the surrounding environment remains clean. At an ASTRA space applications seminar, however, Dr. A. K. Jefferies of the Post Office argued that powersat beams would generate massive communications interference; that is a question yet to be resolved.

O'Neill's original habitats were twin cylinders 1km long and 200m in diameter, counter-rotating to cancel out the gyrosco-pic effects of their spin as the cylinders turned to keep their long axes pointing to the Sun. The inner surfaces would have three strips of 'land', each with an overhead window the length of the cylinder and an inclined mirror outside to reflect the Sun. As the mirror angle varied, the Sun would 'rise' and 'set'. At 3rpm spin, simulated gravity would be 1*g*. The interior would be landscaped and planted.

However, a cylindrical colony needs more radiation shield-ing mass than do other designs. [18] The 'Bernal Sphere' would have been 460m across, rotating at 1.97rpm, with axial air-cooling and agricultural life-support rings between the mirrors and radiators. Shielding mass was much less, but structural and internal atmosphere mass were still high. A compromise design, 'Sunflower', had a cylinder 460m across, perimeter 1.5km, surrounded by an agricultural ring. [19] But

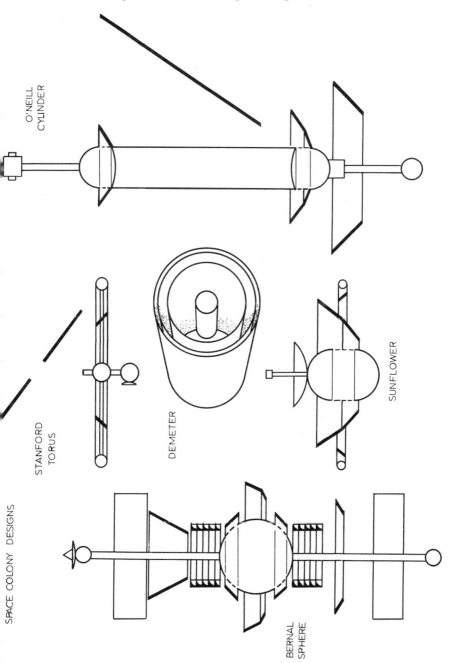

Fig. 12 A selection of space-habitat designs

medical research suggested the rotation rates were too high and a 1975 Summer Study at Stanford and Ames took 1rpm as the safe maximum.

1g at 1rpm needs a design nearly 2km across, ruling out cylinders and spheres for a practicable Island One. With the agricultural ring enlarged so that people lived in it, the 'Stanford Torus' was a gigantic version of the space station promoted by von Braun in the 1950s.[20] The colony rotates at 87m/sec within 10 million tonnes of stationary rock shielding, much more than colony-with-powersat construction produces as slag. Powersat building begins at L5 13 years after the start of the programme; work on the colony and commercial production of powersats begin in the 15th year.[21] By the time the colony is completed, in year 23, powersats are supplying 45-50% of US power needs, taking over completely in only two more years;[18] benefits to the US would be still greater if the programme were international.

Another method of shielding would help greatly. Magnetic shielding could give solar-flare protection but accumulated cosmic-ray dosage becomes a major hazard after a few years. For children conceived and born in space, mounting nerve-tissue damage would be 'disastrous'.[19] A sufficiently intense magnetic field *could* divert cosmic radiation, but the massive equipment required would make a reasonable shield even when switched off![22]

A permanent plasma shield would involve a positive charge high enough to repel incoming nuclei, with a magnetic field to prevent free electrons from neutralizing the colony's potential (in more ways than one). In effect, the station becomes its own inner Van Allen Belt surrounded by a very energetic outer belt of orbiting electrons—interfering considerably with planned colony operations.

If the hub becomes a long tube ringed with superconducting coils, 1000 coulombs of electrons circulating within the 'electron well' give the habitat a positive charge of 15 billion volts.[22] Initially charged up by sending a high-energy electron beam into space, the 'plasma core shield' cuts out passive shielding, making the mass of the torus only 200,000 tonnes (structure and atmosphere). It makes it worth processing material on the Moon—or, to bypass the 14-day lunar dark-ness, at L2. Docking with the station is possible only within a Faraday cage, which fires off an electron beam to reach the same positive charge as the habitat. Since like charges repel, the caged spacecraft is then winched in to save reaction mass. [18] Since the colony as a whole is electrically neutral, however, it can be discharged in an emergency by releasing ionized gas, so taking out the positive charge and allowing the electrons to flood from the tube well, restoring the electric balance in milliseconds with a most impressive auroral display.

D. J. Sheppard pointed out that even Island One colonies were typically 10,000 times more massive than airliners and 10-100 times more massive than the largest metal structures ever built, namely steel ships and bridges. [24] An MIT habitat study preferred tensile steel to aluminium, because it is less liable to catastrophic failure under pressurization. The largest mobile structure to date is the Ninian Central oil platform (prestressed concrete, 500,000 tonnes), while reinforced concrete dams can weigh more than 20 million tonnes. The rock-to-metal ratio for shielded habitats was more than 9:1, similar to prestressed concrete braced with steel, which would give a total mass about the same as the aluminium/rock torus, and using much less metal than the steel one.

Compressive concrete can withstand considerable damage without failing, because cracks don't tend to propagate. Many of the network of internal cables can snap before the structure as a whole is threatened; and, even if the fabric were stressed to the point of leakage, they'd have sufficient elasticity to prevent sudden rupture. Weak spots show immediately after manufacture, when the material is under maximum load, whereas 'the best that can be done for a metal hull is to test a few samples and pray that uniaxial proof tests mean something for triaxially stressed plating'. Fused rock concrete is inert where 'corrosion would be more of a problem with a steel skin, and one can imagine an ecological hazard due to the continuous painting of the inside skin ... the surface layer is not essential for structural strength. Compare this with the problems that occur when bits are welded on to high-strength steelwork. One can even imagine an enthusiastic do-it-yourself colonist drilling right through the thin metal skin while trying to fix up a shelf.' [24]

The concrete hull offers radiation protection from the outset, whereas unshielded metal would be dangerous because of secondary particle showers generated by impacting cosmic rays. The windows, always a weak point in a pressurized structure, could be integral with the hull and thick enough not to need separate radiation screens. Seventy times more glass might be needed but 'it would be a fine thing to build a transparent, smooth-skinned Space Colony instead of the blind, slag-covered alternative ... We can think in terms of a thousand-year colony, like a cathedral in the sky. With a metal hull one could only hope for a hundred-year life. After all, steel has not been invented long enough to tell us how it behaves past its first century ...

'Would you prefer to live in a concrete colony or a metal one? Does the type of structure make any difference to the occupants? The answer is obviously "yes"—just compare a church with an oil tank of the same size. Metal is cold, slippery, noisy, vibrating, and generally insecure and unsympathetic. Rock is solid, acoustically splendid and reassuringly familiar ... This robustness allows more freedom to the architect to design the inside surface of the structure, perhaps emulating the soaring fan vaults of mediaeval stone architecture. On an individual scale, the strength of a concrete colony would be great enough to cope with local decoration and carvings. Psychologically there is a lot to be said in favour of a rock-solid floor 1.6 metres thick. Combine this with the ambience of a vast airy cathedral, and it will be agreed that prestressed concrete is the most favoured material architecturally.'[24]

Soviet research on applications of basalt, the principal material of the lunar *maria*, has produced sound-absorbent, fireproof asbestos-type fibre, as malleable and 'one-and-a-half times as light' as aluminium and with the structural strength of steel,[25] which can be refined to a fabric thread as lustrous as silk. There will be more about these techniques in Chapters 10 and 11; but note that neither plasma core shielding (when in operation) nor the nonrotating mass-shield is suitable for habitats with Daedalus drive, even at Matloff's proposed $0.01g$ (Chapter 3).

Dr Frank D. Hess suggested similar techniques for a second-generation habitat called 'Demeter',[26] a cylinder 1.63km long with a 1km diameter (simulating $1g$ at 1.25rpm). The aluminium hull would be surrounded by opaque glass fibre cable spun from lunar basalt, in cross layers under tension to a depth of 2m. Design priority was the largest possible area for agriculture, rather than Earth-surface conditions; an internal cylinder of clear glass, made from lunar anorthosite, would reflect sunlight in from the end caps and reduce atmospheric mass. Height between the inner and outer cylinders would be 50m, room for a 15-storey building, and the inner cylinder would be a zero-*g* workshop, with high temperatures for manufacturing purposes available near the end-cap mirrors. Agricultural and manufacturing facilities, on the outside of O'Neill's design, would now be behind the radiation shielding, but wouldn't have as high a grade of industrial vacuum or direct radiation cooling.

In the ASTRA discussions Nimmo proposed large-scale food exports to Earth from lunar farms, but large pressurized areas on the lunar surface are dangerous. Demeter could support 10,000 people, even on more demanding estimates than O'Neill's,[27] and no doubt could be farmed by a much lower number. With continuing sunlight, crops could be raised faster than on Earth or Moon; they'd be much more expensive than, say, sea-farming, or similarly sized self-supporting communities on Earth[28] but, using Waveriders, could deliver crops easily to where they were urgently needed. The big weakness is again the mass of organic material, water and nitrogen to be found—even Demeter's limited internal volume needs 60,000 tonnes of nitrogen, although helium might replace some of it.[26] The Stanford torus requires 6000 tonnes of atmospheric nitrogen, 15,000 tonnes of supplies such as hydrogen to make water, and 6000 tonnes of biomass (excluding people).[29] Colonies aren't likely to be built until extraterrestrial volatiles are obtained—from the Earth-grazing asteroids, later the Main Belt, and later still the Jupiter system. Demeters could be built among the asteroids and put under drive: agricultural settlements, importing volatiles from the asteroids and exporting food to Earth, may orbit L4 and L5 in large numbers by the late 21st century.

O'Neill's plans for Earth and its people by the time this happens are still more ambitious. 'Island Two' cylinders, 1800m in diameter to meet the rotational criteria, could support 140,000 people in village communities separated by 'parks or forest areas', and each could produce *another* Island Two in just two years—enough new living area, within 18 years, to absorb the 4% p.a. population increase of a billion-people nation. If world population were by then 10 billion and rose at 200 million (4%) per annum, in 30 years enough Island Two colonies could be in production to absorb that increase.

Such traffic isn't inconceivable, O'Neill insists. Even the present Shuttle could carry about seventy passengers into orbit if fitted with LH_2/HO_2 boosters;[30] the Boeing Heavy Lifter could carry a great many more, and still more energetic fuels may become available.[31] A fleet of 200 shuttles, carrying 500 passengers each, would be much smaller than the current world fleet of over 4000 jet airliners.[7] If interorbital transports to L5 carry 6000 people each then 1100 of them will be needed, equivalent to Earth's current traffic of large ocean vessels. At 10 million tonnes total, they could in theory be built at L5 in just three years.

But, if the population were stabilized at 10 billion or less, and emigration were pursued actively, within 35 years more than half the human race would be living in space. World population would be well below its present level and much of the heavy industry would be removed, allowing the environment to recover. Meanwhile, advancing L5 technology would be generating Island Three, 32km long, 6.44km in diameter, supporting 10 million people in conditions still more Earthlike. 1.12 tonnes each of carbon, nitrogen and hydrogen per immigrant would be needed to establish biospheres and agriculture, and would have to come from the asteroids. If the interiors are allowed to look less Earthlike, Island Twos could be spheres with the population density of the Stanford torus and big mass savings,[18] while an Island Three could be a titanium sphere 20km in diameter, with a usable land area as large as a Swiss canton or an English shire. The polar caps would be 'high' enough above the equator for ships to fly in or out through permanent openings.

In theory, O'Neill colonies could answer Earth's population problems. If Island One were established by 1998, population decrease on-planet would begin in 2018[32]—a year after the start of emigration foreseen by Tsiolkovsky.[2] The early start attracts close scrutiny. Is embarking on space colonization a feasible enterprise in the 1980s? The programme requires: a lunar workforce of 200 to set up the mass driver; rotary catchers at L2 (see below), moving to L5 on mass-driver thrust; a 'construction shack' at L5 with transport for a workforce of 2000, and later for the biomass and the volatiles for the colony; transfer of completed powersats to synchronous orbit—all to be operated for 25 years, by which time powersat revenue makes operations 'Free on Earth' (page 103). First cost estimates were equivalent to Project Apollo.[33] O'Neill's 1976 estimate for Island One was $100 billion, with $80 billion for expansion to build powersats.[7] The Stanford torus estimate was $110 billion in 1975;[21] inflation to 1977 would add at least $20 billion.

The late A.V. Cleaver contrasted Moon-landing estimates in 1977 dollar equivalents. In 1939 Clarke supposed that a small lunar mission could be created and flown for the equivalent of 15 million dollars. In 1953, von Braun quoted $10 billion for 50 men in three ships; Cleaver himself estimated at least five times that. The minimal Apollo landing actually cost $25 billion, the equivalent of $45 billion in 1977, but near the lower end of NASA's 1961 estimate, $40-80 billion-equivalent. But Apollo was a relatively small forward step in space technology; O'Neill's programme has so many untried techniques that Cleaver thought the cost might lie between $450 and $4500 billion.[33]

The anguished debate about priorities, and the occasionally heated one about practicability,[34] assume that space colonies have to be built *before* powersats, and created like Apollo in one leap. But, when governments decide powersats are needed, they'll be wanted 'immediately if not sooner', and until that priority is met the growth potential of the system won't be tapped. In the 1960s the Pilkington Group's plans for a city in the North Sea aroused great interest but, when the time came to exploit the North Sea, the governments and companies involved built oil-rigs and paid people to work on them, however basic the conditions.

The Boeing approach is simply to assemble powersats in close-Earth orbit and move them out on ion-drive. The only problem is the need to roll up and shield the solar panels on the way through the Van Allen Belts:[34] for that reason, there's still interest in collecting solar energy with mirrors.[19] While it's more efficient to use lunar materials once transport systems are set up and the new technologies are established, the Boeing plan needs only large framework assembly in orbit. The Grumman Corporation has a machine for extruding prefabricated aluminium beams 1m in diameter, at about 1m (length) per minute,[35] and specialized tools are being developed for use with the Shuttle arm.[36] Free-flying assembly devices such as the Orbital Servicing System[37] and the 'Spider' teleoperator[38] are on the drawing board. The colony would need an immediate start to beat the Boeing target of having the first powersat in synchronous orbit by 1996. [39]

One strange assumption of the colony scenario is that building powersats will be an ongoing task. In the Stanford/Ames Summer Study, for example, a powersat lifetime is assumed to be thirty years, as for a power station on Earth. [18] While that figure may be valid for the mirror-powered high-energy turbine proposal, [19] it seems odd with solar-electric powersats. Originally, O'Neill assumed merely that powersats must pay for themselves over thirty years, continuing to operate with only minimal maintenance. [7] Solar cells do degrade in use, but Pioneer-6, launched in 1965, is still going strong and many long-lived examples could be given. The point of O'Neill's original question was that machines are hampered or attacked by gravity, friction, water and free oxygen. Space particularly favours systems like solar cells with no moving parts, and maintenance of a ring of equatorial powersats will consist of systematic refurbishing, like painting the Forth Bridge, rather than replacement of entire units taken out of service. That makes powersats themselves more attractive, but seriously damages the economic case for colonies.

Continuing economic growth might generate continuing demand for powersats, but we're up against environmental limits. At the present growth rate, waste heat released into the environment will within 85 years[7] raise the Earth's mean surface temperature by 1°C, enough for noticeable climatic changes. With 150 years at the same growth rate, our energy usage will equal 1% of total solar radiation received by the Earth, with still more drastic effects. [15] Despite the claim of one militant trade unionist, you don't 'only get waste heat when industry is run on capitalist lines'—the Second Law of Thermodynamics is no more ideological than the Law of Gravity.

Worse still, if all the world rose to the *present* energy consumption of the USA, overall global temperatures would rise by a staggering 10°C. [40] Few figures more sharply illustrate the difference in affluence between the developed nations and the developing world. Some prophets of doom see it as proof that industrial civilization can never be shared and therefore can't survive. But the remedy is obvious: at least 60% of US energy consumption is industrial. [41] Putting new industry in orbit as a matter of principle, phasing out Earth-surface technologies, stabilizing the planetary population, and with conservationist domestic energy policies, the environment can be preserved without condemning most of the world to eternal poverty. But, to avoid crisscrossing gigawatt beams in space, factories will have their own solar facilities rather than use powersats, unless their demand is enormous.

Boeing's Heavy Lifters would be more than adequate for Stine's 'Third Industrial Revolution'—iron and steam gave us the first, then electronics, then space.[42] But there are worries about *their* environmental effects: the powersat programme calls for ten launches a day, shifting ten times the daily cargo of a major international airport.[39] The extra cost of lunar, and later asteroidal, exploitation may therefore be worthwhile. Once transport links are established, space offers the twin lures which traditionally have drawn industry to new locales: labour is also a factor, but when energy and raw materials are in the balance *mobility* of labour tends to be what's needed.

Unfortunately, using the North Sea analogy, the Sea City is still not in the race to get the oil ashore. The idea of putting into space millions of tonnes of colony mass from the Moon, and tens of thousands of tonnes of life-support from Earth to build Island One, doesn't make sense to a world which needs powersats as soon as possible. If more than 10-20 Boeing powersats were to be built (50-100 would run the US[15]), assembly at a manned synchronous station would be economic,[39] and the same applies with lunar materials—orbiting 'rigs' are cheaper than the colony approach.[43]

The 1976 NASA Ames Summer Study produced the final blow to the original order of priorities. The new element was '2:1 resonance orbit', not shown in fig. 11 (page 112) because of its complexity in a nonrotating reference frame (fig. 13). Its major axis precesses rapidly around the Earth-Moon system, grazing L2 every two lunar months, while the closest to Earth is at synchronous orbit. Transfer delta-v from L2 to 2:1 resonance is only 9-31m/sec, as compared with 440m/sec transfer to L5,[44] while the deceleration into synchronous orbit is much less than the 1700m/sec to get there from L5.[18] Wastage of raw material is drastically cut: for every 500,000 tonnes of Moonrock delivered from L2 to L5, using mass-driver engines, 125,000 tonnes would have been expended in reaction mass *en route*.[21]

The colony cuts out rapid rotation of personnel, but that matters only if powersat building continues for a long time,

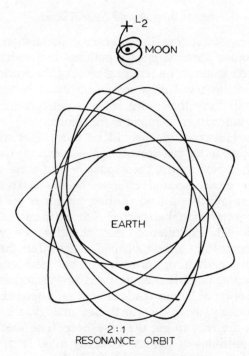

L_2

MOON

EARTH

2:1
RESONANCE ORBIT

Fig. 13 2:1 resonance orbit

even if the colony is in 2:1 resonance orbit, as Heppenheimer predicts. [19] The object is high-speed production, but L2 encounters to pick up raw material occur only once every two months, and the low-delta-v transfer takes 65 days; [44] to supply more frequently removes the low-delta-v advantage. Surely the answer is to build the powersats *at L2*, so that the lunar base can maintain continuous deliveries of raw material. Another result from the 1976 Summer Study was that a launch site at 33°.1E, near the craters Censorinus A and Maskelyne A, gives most accurate delivery to L2. [44] Arriving at 200m/sec, the payloads could be caught in a computer-controlled net within a triangular frame, or a rotating Kevlar cone with a cable grid across its mouth. Incoming bags of lunar soil burst on the grid and deposit the material on the inner surface of the cone, where it's held by the simulated gravity of the rotation. [45] Such 'passive catchers' were designed for transport to L5, by mass driver or rotary pellet launcher. [19] The active catcher, which delivers the bag intact to be a central collector, would be better for continuous processing at L2.

L2 isn't suitable for a colony, however—at least initially. All references to stations 'at' Lagrange points are shorthand: the installations apparently orbit the points, although the true situation is more complicated since the Lagrange points have no gravitational fields of their own. Orbits may be stable at about 145,000km from L4 or L5, with a period of a month;[19] even pessimistic calculations, treating the orbits as ellipses, suggest station-keeping delta-*vs* of only 30m/sec per year.[48] The less stable Halo orbit around L2, with the same period and a 10,000km radius from the Earth-Moon-L2 line, requires station-keeping with a monthly delta-*v* of 150m/sec. Holding a colony in that orbit would be like shuttling it between L2 and L5 every three months, expending at least a million tonnes of reaction mass per year.

The emphasis then falls on a purpose-built structure for powersat manufacture, stationed at L2. Such structures would in any case have been needed at L5: O'Neill had a 'construction shack' for a workforce of 2000; and, for the Stanford torus, building powersats at the same time, over 5000 workers were to be housed in 500-people shacks.[21] Gerald Driggers proposed to house them in two shacks of 2232 occupants, with processing in a sphere 91.5m across and modular living quarters on a hub and booms.[19]

Unless the shack is to be pressurized, a sphere is unnecessarily difficult to make, ship, assemble and maintain. O'Neill's shack was a 50m pressurized sphere (not spun), but as much processing as possible should be both in vacuum and in zero-*g*. A less ambitious proposal, making use of existing systems, is a 'Travelling Work Station' built of Shuttle external tanks.[14] I designed such a station independently at ASTRA, calling it Project Starseed because of its growth possibilities. So far Starseed hasn't been subjected to the structural evaluations of the colony studies, but it seems reasonable compared to the stresses of assembly and flight out of the atmosphere.

The first priority is a logical gathering place for Shuttle tanks in orbit. In the absence of an equatorial launch site, thus far, a target for repetitive missions is needed, and our proposal is a manned orbiting observatory, as a complement and successor to the space Telescope. The initial 'seed' might be a project for ESA: the first tank would be placed in orbit with the core module and left docked to it by the nose, and the first crew would be put aboard by the mission which added the fourth tank (fig. 14).

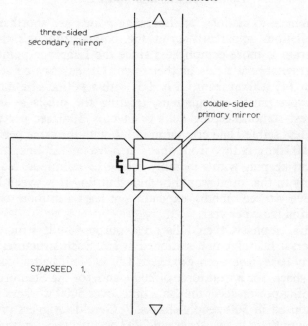

three-sided
secondary mirror

double-sided
primary mirror

STARSEED 1.

Fig. 14 Schematic layout of Starseed 1

John Braithwaite argued that a telescope in space should use every available surface to generate multiple or alternative operational modes. Thus the upper and lower surfaces of the main mirror would be worked with different optical figures, and the two secondary mirror units would be three-sided. Thus, in theory, the telescope could be used in twelve different modes. In operation the main mirror would spin with 'magnetic mountings' like the gyros of the rotary EML (page 66), allowing 'blink scanning' (electronic and optical, with screen displays in the control room) of a variety of sensors mounted on the mirror rim. Alerted or forewarned by the subdisplays (e.g., ultraviolet or X-ray warning of a solar flare), the observers could then switch the main system into the appropriate mode. The spinning mirror would operate as a gyro and help to maintain 'pointing accuracy'; and when braked to rest against the structure, it would spin it up for simulated gravity.

The Starseed now goes through expansion stages, 'outgrowths'. Outgrowth One begins by docking two more tanks to the core module, improving overall stability (fig. 15); on the same missions to exchange personnel and equipment, extra segments added to the core module, as shown, give work crews access to the other three tanks in the plane of rotation and generate a large volume for materials-processing experiments. Eight more tanks are than added in the 'vertical' plane (fig. 15), and will be permanently in zero-*g*. Already the Starseed has sufficient internal volume for commercial production of vaccines, silicon-chip wafers, ultrapure metals, optical fibres, perfect ball bearings, exotic alloys and other possibilities being pursued by the US, USSR, Europe and Japan. With each activity attempted and mastered, the volume of traffic will grow, and for every flight, as a condition of access to Starseed facilities, another tank should be added to the stockpile for Outgrowth Two.

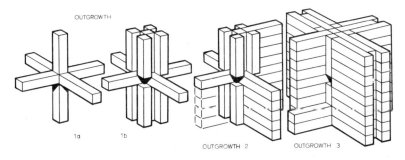

Fig. 15 Starseed (see fig. 14) with Outgrowths 1, 2 and 3

Forty tanks are added in Outgrowth Two (fig. 15), for expansion of the workforce and large-scale processing with techniques already mastered. By now the astronomers will have moved out in search of cleaner conditions, so the evacuated core of the Starseed is available for mass-driver experiments, with progressively longer booms added. If nuclear waste disposal by mass driver is possible, complete disposal of all UK wastes would need 20 Shuttle flights per year, or four Heavy Lifters using STS components, by the year 2000. Disposal of all the world's anticipated production of wastes by then would take 600 Shuttle flights or 120 Heavy Lifts per year. The HLV missions are particularly helpful because each adds two tanks, which can be docked either in pairs or symmetrically without stockpiling. A single year's world disposal would take Starseed through Outgrowth Three, which adds 104 tanks to the structure (fig. 15).

(Starseed is discussed here in terms of Shuttle tanks, but the Eurospace report called for Heavy Lift development, and there's strong European interest in space nuclear waste disposal. A European Starseed programme has the major advantage of equatorial launch from Kourou.)

Starseed now has 136 tanks with simulated gravity. If 100 of these were converted into 10 levels of living quarters 4m high, O'Neill's workforce of 2000 could be accommodated at two per level! A further outgrowth would be possible but it would be better to use next year's tanks for Starseed Two, keeping Starseed One manoeuvrable.

Another kind of waste disposal provides a sidelight on ecology in space. David Sneddon's methane digester for Glasgow Parks Department is dominated by a vertical tank which reminded us of a scaled-down Shuttle tank. Sneddon finds that $7.6m^3$ of plant waste produces 1600 litres per day of methane and carbon dioxide. Human waste would give still more and leave a residue which was 80% nitrogen, an excellent base for fertilizer. With average production of 75g dry waste per person per day [46], a single Shuttle tank could process the output of 2000 people. Methane is useful in space, being easier to store and transport than liquid hydrogen, [47] and capable of being burnt in lunar oxygen to give water, along with more carbon dioxide, which would be fed into the greenhouse tanks. Since carbon dioxide breathed out is also most usefully dealt with by plants, there'll be a lot of greenery inside Starseed —another respect in which it's better than the average oil-rig.

Starseed One will move out using a mass-driver engine, firing aluminium slugs from crushed-up tanks: it'll be required for station-keeping at L2, so it should be put to work now. Some tanks, fully insulated, will be serving their original function filled with LH_2/LO_2, but that's for lunar operations; and slugs for mass-driver thrust can be stored on the *outside* of the station. Initially Starseed will go into circumlunar orbit, to set up the surface base, maintaining links with a manned variant of Centaur, compatible with the Shuttle cargo bay, which can deliver 7200kg to lunar orbit, or take 2-3 people there and back. [49] Still smaller vehicles can shuttle to and from the surface. Whenever possible (i.e., when it can take the acceleration), payload will start down from the mass driver, using rockets only for final braking. Possibly Starseed could send down modified Shuttle tanks as 'penetrators', which would bury themselves in the regolith as radiation-proof living quarters (taking down the good china later). The technique is under study for planetary probes (see Chapter 7).

As soon as possible, Starseed will move on to Halo orbit around L2, leaving either a mirror or a small powersat at L1 to keep the mass driver/lunartron operational during lunar night. There's no case for staying in lunar orbit because station-keeping requirements are large, due to perturbations including those caused by the mascons (see page 78). [19] At L2, the first construction will be the mass catcher: the first rock bags to arrive won't be processed but packed around Starseed for shielding, now we're beyond the protection of Earth's magnetic field. Starseed's hollow core might allow plasma-core shielding, but that wouldn't be compatible with its most important potential use.

The crucial element in a lunar powersat scenario is rapidly processing large quantities of ore. The 1975 Summer Study includes complex processes for aluminium, titanium and glass, continuous and automated but chosen because they don't need gravity rather than to take *advantage* of zero-*g*. [18] In solar-cell production the key element is silicon produced to high purity. [19] A production layout for powersats from lunar materials was designed at MIT in 1978-9; [55] it seems compatible with the Starseed concept.

John Braithwaite proposed taking full advantage of vacuum and zero-*g*: again no attempt has yet been made to assess feasibility in practice. Incoming material, with an electrostatic charge to make it controllable, is fed into the focus of a mirror on top of Starseed, concentric with the open end of the central shaft, and heated into plasma, after which magnetic fields draw it down the shaft. It becomes a huge mass spectrometer separating the elements, including the Solar Wind deposits of carbon, nitrogen and hydrogen which are lost in other methods. Metal could be kept in plasma state for making seamless structures by 'vapour deposition', but for powersats the main process will be extrusion of rolled, hollow booms for assembly into frameworks for solar cells. Attitude-control systems, electronics, transmission antennae, etc., would be installed by teleoperators, remotely controlled from Starseed. Silicon, oxygen and iron would be produced in 'surplus' and cast as Sheppard's prestressed-steel/fused-rock hull material. That stockpile would grow too large to be kept in L2 Halo orbit:

surplus oxygen could be used for station-keeping, but it would be better to place the material in 2:1 resonance orbit, hopefully at two-month intervals, so that it was all in much the *same* orbit. With or without 'official' terrestrial approval, a teleoperator can set about assembling it.

If so much can be automated, even the building of Island One as a hobby, does Starseed need a workforce of 2000? If they're mostly redundant after continuous processing is established, then they could commission 'unmanned Starseeds'—clusters of cylinders, however many proved optimum, with hollow core and mirror—to work with Starseed One behind the mass catcher. But, for preference, manned Starseed assembly in close-Earth orbit should continue. Each year of global waste disposal would provide enough tanks to build and move a Starseed and the opportunity shouldn't be neglected, even if it's flown out by a skeleton crew and commissioned by surplus personnel from Starseed One. If a Starseed in full production can build a 70,000-tonne powersat in a month, and it takes a year to work up to full production, then each year each experienced Starseed produces twelve new powersats and each year's new one produces six. After nine years, the 496 powersats produced would be enough to meet the *upper* estimate of Earth's energy needs in the early 21st century. As powersats came on line, coal- and oil-fired stations and nuclear reactors could be phased out and, to end proliferation of nuclear weapons, threats of nuclear terrorism and the possibility of major accidents, shutting down reactors should be encouraged with discounts on Starseed energy and lunar materials. The same should apply to conventional power stations, for environmental reasons—this process might be under way in any case, since fossil 'fuels' are needed for petrochemical industries.

Phasing out reactors as powersats take over has no effect on Starseed building. Burial, or any form of disposal, is preceded by ten years in which nuclear waste is stored above ground, until its activity and therefore its temperature drop to a level at which it *can* be vitrified and disposed of. The case for burial thereafter is a good one, but space disposal is permanent with no chance of future problems, however remote.* The Starseed

*Waste could be stored within the Earth-Moon system in case we find a use for it, but total disposal is better: disposition to Lagrange points

scenario removes existing wastes and the need to make any more, and is completed before the annual amount of waste begins to drop. It can be run with existing Shuttle system elements (even HLVs aren't essential, although cheaper than 600 Shuttle flights annually); it can be started immediately and on a relatively small scale with the manned orbiting observatory; and it can be completed before the year 2000, with all the powersats built, all the reactors shut down, all the wastes to date disposed of, and nine operational Starseeds at L2. As a bonus, we can have 500 million tonnes of prefabricated habitat hull material 'parked' in 2:1 resonance orbit, enough for fifty Island Ones!

Five fully manned Starseeds could occupy Island One with no further personnel from Earth, although a 50% transfer quota would keep all nine units operational and encourage continuing emigration. But the Starseeds can't spare the biomass and atmospheric nitrogen to make more than a few segments of the Stanford torus habitable, without weakening their own survival capability. To put Island One fully into commission, we must turn to the nearest major source of volatiles—the Earth-grazing asteroids (see Chapter 10).

By the 21st century, Daedalus technology may be available. The low delta-vs for rendezvous with Earth-grazers could be reached with mass-driver power, but there's no need to waste usable rock and inch Starseeds about if Continuous Acceleration Transfers are available. With foresight, plans for the asteroid mission could now be ready to mature. As soon as Starseed One goes into Halo orbit, the possibility of Farside activities opens up: one is a fusion breeder reactor to make helium-3 for Daedalus. To produce the 30,000 tonnes for the interstellar probe would generate, not use, 1-15 times the current energy production of the Earth, and require 13km^2 of heat radiator surface at 1000 K even for the lower value.[51] But nothing like such quantities are needed to move even habitats between planets (page 57), much less Starseeds to Earth-grazing asteroids or Island One from 2:1 resonance orbit.

or the Moon compromises future activities there, and if we *do* find a use for the stuff—e.g., as reaction mass for a fission-powered interstellar medium probe[50]—we can easily make more, but *off* Earth. The Moon has richer fissionable ore than any on Earth, and there'll be other nuclear plants on the Moon in any case (see below).

Alas for the L5 scenario, L2 will be the empty Island One's destination. For when the carbon and other materials reach it the *first* priority won't be habitat biomass but the lunar beanstalk, which can be built with already known materials. With Island One tethered as a 10 million-tonne counterweight, the beanstalk mass is much reduced and the cargo it can handle much increased. The habitat becomes the import terminal for volatiles and the export terminal to the Solar System for helium-3, until the exploitation of Jupiter (discussed in Chapter 11). For industrialization of the main Asteroid Belt and thence the Jupiter system, its rôle will be vital. Over the next hundred years traffic expansion may postpone Island Three in favour of fifty Island Ones, all tethered in L2 Halo orbit at 1250km intervals. For tethered habitats, torus design will be preferred to cylinders (adopted elsewhere for mobility) because the overhead mirror can still adjust for changes in illumination during the lunar month. Farside exports *via* 2:1 resonance orbit will now come up the beanstalk; the mass catchers will be occupied with incoming payloads from the asteroids; and beside Farside Base, at the foot of the elevator, a mass driver/lunartron will be built for direct launches to L5. [18]

Island Threes at L4 and L5 can now absorb Earth's population increase, if the need still exists and enough people want to go. O'Neill suggests that, if population growth continues, life in Island Three may be *much* better than conditions on Earth. But, if the habitats aren't to build powersats, we have to ask what they are to do—otherwise, with their blue sky, vast living space and permanent sunshine, they could be traps: giant honeypots absorbing the human race, like the Dyson Sphere in Bob Shaw's *Orbitsville*. [52] One activity suggested by O'Neill, [32] earlier put forward by Gavin Roberts and discussed at ASTRA, would be shipbuilding for the next phase of the strategic approach. Because of the heavy L2 traffic and the station-keeping factor, the Moon may establish its docks at L5.

Roberts' SIOS (Standard Interplanetary Operations Space-craft), big enough for shielded cabins, could be the bridge between Starseeds and mobile cylindrical habitats, with a lifetime of 200 years from the 2030s, returning to L5 perhaps every 20 or 50 years to be refurbished and modified for the next mission. With a stock of manned and unmanned probes and landers, a SIOS would mount and direct an entire phase of planetary or asteroid development. Each might support a work force of several thousand, equivalent to several present-day Mission Controls, vehicle processing and launch facilities.

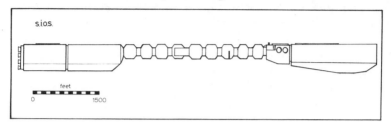

Fig. 16   Standard Interplanetary Operations Spacecraft (SIOS)

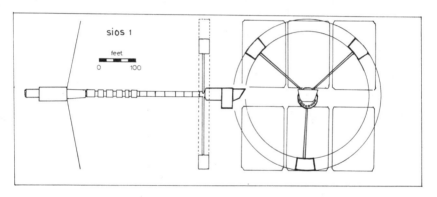

Fig. 17   SIOS 1

For logistics support from the Earth-Moon system and rotation of personnel, hyperbolic orbits will be needed. Ehricke suggested the designation HISV (Heliocentric Interorbital Space Vehicle) for ships in this transport rôle, [52] where Daedalus craft seem virtually certain. For freight transport, however, regular deliveries and high cost-effectiveness are more important than fast transfer; if caesium and mercury are readily available from the asteroids, unmanned vehicles may still use ion-drive. Since a SIOS moves about relatively little, but requires low-thrust engines for station-keeping over years in planetary or lunar orbit, it might have banked ion engines rather than a giant Daedalus motor (fig. 16).

The forepart would be clustered research modules interchangeable for different missions. To escape contamination and interference from spacecraft and from the power plant,

Robert Shaw suggested a free-flying lab module, docked nose-to-nose with the SIOS for powered manoeuvres but well clear of the ship when operational.

The smaller variant in Gavin Roberts's painting (Plate 4) has research modules enclosed in a thin, non-pressurized meteor bumper, also containing a 'hangar level' for servicing manned and unmanned spacecraft externally stored on the 'flight deck', from which an EML boom could be extended. Chris Boyce suggested a central crew sphere with three flat faces surrounding it, giving the ship a triangular appearance from the front: one face for winged spacecraft, one for plug-nozzles, and the third with research sensors shielded from the worst emissions of the other two. Inside, surrounding the crew sphere, would be a ring of acceptance bays in the points of the triangle. Shaw suggested more facets for specialized functions, but that would cut down the storage space.

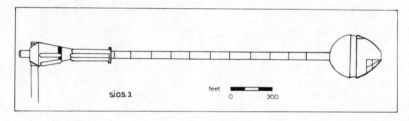

Fig. 18   SIOS 3

Bill Ramsay, Oscar Schwiglhofer and I took out the zero-*g* crew sphere and placed the living quarters on rotating booms (fig. 17). (Roberts originally proposed centrifuge cabins on cables, deployed for exercise periods.) Research modules would be on the axis, forward, using the 'flat top' as an EVA pallet, and between them and the centrifuge hub would be a half-ring of docking bays, designed to break away in an emergency. Spacecraft would dock parallel to the axis, approaching from the front. But, as Roberts pointed out, manoeuvring close to the ship's side is dangerous, and breakaway sections might collide with the centrifuge. In general, docking should be along the axis of the ship, the direction in which it is stressed (as in Apollo/LM and Skylab) rather than radial. Unbalanced sideways thrusts are always dangerous, and in an emergency—as with the jammed thruster on Gemini-8—axial docking allows the smaller ship to break away cleanly, where it might collide with the main structure after leaving a radial docking collar.

If the meteor bumper encloses the centrifuge (fig. 18), its diameter is 100m and there's no external vehicle storage, although the hangar can be open to space; the bumper may have to be nonmetallic, to prevent secondary particle showers from cosmic-ray impacts. Instead of rotating the centrifuge, now that docking and undocking are at the nose of the ship the entire SIOS could be spun-up; incoming spacecraft would dock by matching the rate of spin, and zero-*g* facilities would still be available along the ship's axis.

The only drawback is that the larger designs *have* to carry very large crews to realize their potential. The all-modular ship devised by Schwiglhofer, Ramsay and myself could operate with only two centrifuge modules, diametrically placed, or three as in the painting—or any number up to a complete ring accommodating thousands of people when required. Perhaps, however, the work load will keep SIOS continually at full stretch.

The rotation speed of centrifuge and ship is quite another question. Roberts wondered whether Lagrange habitats would compete among themselves, or with the Moon, for research and development contracts with Earth. The Moon is in a strong position because it supplies raw materials to both; but, if it didn't take the lead in the SIOS programme, one could imagine Earth and habitats cooperating to reach the asteroids and break the lunar monopoly. The lunar settlers should therefore follow the Starseeds with SIOSs to avoid being bypassed.

Isaac Asimov has suggested that the Solar System may belong naturally to the lunar colonists, because they'll be psychologically adjusted to closed environments. [54] For instance, if an ion-drive SIOS took ten years to get to Pluto a lunar crew wouldn't regard the journey as any disruption of normal life—if the rotation were set for $\frac{1}{6}g$. However, once a SIOS is on station for a work programme lasting years, must any Earthling taking part be permanently exiled, adjusted to lunar gravity? Alternatively, the ship has to provide 1*g* cabins, either rotating faster than the $\frac{1}{6}g$ ones (a complex and thus risky arrangement), or at a greater distance from the hub. It's unlikely that the ship would carry enough Earthlings to occupy an entire ring of such circumference, so these would be balanced cabins on pressurized spars.

The same practical problem, in regard to Lagrange colonies themselves, could have major political consequences. The huge torus of Island One, and its extra millions of tonnes of shielding, are products of the '1g at not more than 1rpm' requirement which rules out O'Neill's original cylindrical design. Many problems would be solved and structural masses much reduced [18] if the value of g was $\frac{1}{6}$. If it were, emigration from Earth would be permanent; if 1g, the habitats would be closed to later generations of lunar settlers.

One can envisage an Earth-Moon conflict over who owned the colonies and set the g value. On a capital investment basis, the Moon has a controlling interest in the second phase at L5, and tethering L2 settlements to the Moon confers authority if not ownership. Redesign for $\frac{1}{6}g$? Supposedly, since the new Moon Treaty forbids *all* ownership of resources on the Moon or in 'orbits around or other trajectories to or around it' (Article 1.2), Earth could veto lunar developments at L5, limiting the sites to pure research. Rather than that Gilbertian situation, there should be a joint Earth-Moon development agreement for L4 and L5, with habitats represented on the decision-taking board as they come into being—a Lagrange society evolves like the lunar one and leads to an Earth-Moon system federation. At least then the g value for a particular settlement or SIOS needn't become an issue for UDI!

Ed Buckley suggested that, as a compromise, $\frac{1}{3}g$ might be standard on all deep-space ships but, until there are colonists on Mars, that doesn't suit *anybody*. Any Earthman returning from a $\frac{1}{3}g$ environment experiences effective 3g until, and if, his body readjusts. Buckley suggested acclimatization on space stations, gradually increasing the rate of spin, but we don't know that would work. If it does, before the voyage a lunar astronaut would have to adjust to double his 'normal' gravity —enough to spoil his psychological adjustment to spaceships, one suspects, and certainly enough to be resented if the ship itself were a Moon-product.

Eventually, as Buckley pointed out, there are going to be *at least* three 'solar races', all human but with differences which show the triviality of today's race problems. Perhaps, since it's ridiculous to despise someone because of the gravity field he or she was born in, we may then agree that skin colour is equally irrelevant. The solar races will be (1) Earth people, (2) Mars people, and (3) the people of the Moon, Mercury, Pluto and the larger moons of Jupiter, Saturn and Neptune, all of which fall in the same size range. A standard value of *g* for interplanetary vessels would have to be the lowest relevant one, but Earthpeople will be the couriers of the Solar System because they can take continuous 1*g* transfers which would immobilize the other races.

Beyond SIOS, the next stage is cylindrical habitats with Daedalus engines, moving to sources of raw materials with specialized processing facilities. Roberts asked whether the Lagrange settlements might eventually move out in this way, but most likely they'd be flimsy, and too valuable where they were. The solar furnaces and specialized processing of the travelling habitats have been designed for this distance from the Sun and for the Equilaterals' gravity gradient. Their supporting factories will probably be disc-shaped, with permanent solar power on one side and heat-sink on the other, with thermocouples for emergency generators. (Solar screens will be an effective sanction, if any city's harming the rest.) Hollowed-out asteroids may produce a fourth solar race in time, adjusted to *very* low gravity; the inner regions of the spinning wheels will provide settlements for them.

But, with the SIOS programme over, and their specialities being duplicated by roving asteroids, will the Lagrange units still have a rôle? The Moon may no longer be exporting; probably by this time it needs all its output to maintain its own population. The Lagrange factories may still be able to supply industrial products to Earth, as long as the materials supply from the asteroids and the giant planets keeps up, since by now close-Earth and synchronous orbit will probably be saturated. Otherwise, their output will grow increasingly specialized and unique to their location. If they've been cutting down internal gravity, they'll be offering recreational facilities to all the solar races; even, for the asteroid dwellers, a holiday habitat with no spin. But there will still be demand for big, specialized interplanetary vessels, and the customers will go to the experts. L4 and L5 colonies may eventually become 'the Switzerland of the Solar System', in Robert Shaw's phrase; but in alliance with the Moon, unrivalled at building ships, they'll also be its Clydeside.

VII

The Exploration of Mars

To such advantage were they seen that it has been possible to construct a map of the Martian south circumpolar regions to a degree of detail such as has never been possible before, and which I have accordingly done. It will be seen from it how much farther advanced is our knowledge of the Martian south pole, and the regions about it, than is our knowledge of either of our own. It is also pleasing to remember that during this our polar expedition we were not frost-bitten for life, nor did we have to be rescued by a search party. We lived not unlike civilised beings during it all, and we actually brought back some of the information we went out to acquire.

—Percival Lowell, *Mars*, 1895 [1]

Lowell believed that Mars had a thin but breathable atmosphere, generated by the vegetation of the dark areas, and canals built by the civilization of a dying planet: '... in the Martian mind there would be one question perpetually paramount to all the local labor, women's suffrage, and Eastern questions put together—the water question. How to procure water enough to support life would be the great communal problem of the day.' [1]

The Mariner-4 spacecraft found surface atmospheric pressure was only 1% of Earth's, equivalent to our atmosphere 32km up—too thin to allow liquid water. Mariners-4, -6 and -7 photographed dry, cratered terrain, and even the polar caps seemed to be carbon-dioxide ice. But after the planet-wide dust storm of 1971 Mariner-9 found sinuous valleys like river beds in the Martian tropics, with chasms and faults everywhere as evidence for water ice, on and below the surface. The puzzle was how atmospheric pressure could ever have been high enough for water to exist in liquid form, and Carl Sagan and others advanced a 'Long Winter' model (see page 161) in which 90% of a carbon-dioxide atmosphere would currently be locked up in the northern polar cap. In 1976, however, the Viking Orbiters found temperatures over the pole were too high for carbon-dioxide ice at ground level, and the amount of water vapour implied that the cap was entirely water ice.

As the dust settled in early 1971 four dark spots, visible only as shadows in the storm, were revealed to be huge volcanic calderas—the greatest of them, Nix Olympica, being 25km high. The other three stood in a line on raised terrain, the Tharsis ridge, at the head of an equatorial chasm 120km wide and 4000km in length. Identified only with minor canals on Lowell's maps, the feature is now known as the Great Rift of Valles Marineris. Since no magnetic field had then been detected, Mars might be undifferentiated internally. But the Soviet Mars-2, -3, -5 and -6 all reported a weak planetary field, and the Viking Landers detected a possible magnetic field shockwave during descent. Mariner-9 tracking data indicated at least a partly formed core,[2] and the Viking-2 seisometer indicated a crust 15km thick;[3] Mars was 'lumpy' with mascons, particularly under the Tharsis ridge;[4] and Viking soil analyses showed 10-100 times more sulphur and five times less potassium than Earth's crust,[5] with 12-16% iron.[6] The seismometer results showed the interior of Mars to be uncannily quiet, even by comparison with the placid Moon. It was as if Mars had frozen halfway through Earth's process of formation, with the core only half formed and the Great Rift like the beginning of crustal spreading and continental drift.

The results of the Viking biology experiments didn't give a coherent picture. Soil samples were incubated in many combinations of lighting, heat, moisture and nutrients: oxygen and carbon dioxide were given off in quantity, along with some nitrogen,[7] in ways which resembled the action of life as we know it but weren't identical—some at least could be simulated with very dry, iron-rich soil.[8] In direct soil analysis, no organic compounds were detected.* It behaved like soil from the 'dry

*Acetone was found with one sample from under a rock, but the test chamber hadn't been used previously and might have been contaminated. Or then again ...

valleys' of the Antarctic, then believed sterile except where permafrost lay near enough to the surface for moisture to move upwards during the summer months.[9] But meantime it was discovered that apparently lifeless soil from the dry Antarctic valleys would show organic results if incubated for 200 days or more, far beyond the span of the Viking experiments;[10] and subsequently rocks from them were found to have rich and unsuspected microbial vegetation in 'microclimates' within porous rocks or fissures.[11] Even if the Viking reactions were abiological, they don't show that the soil was indeed lifeless; and the US National Academy of Science recommended against further searches for life by remote sample analysis.[12] But NASA estimates that eight years' development work will be needed for a Mars sample return, and it's unlikely before 1995 at the earliest.

However valuable a sample would be, it's a very poor substitute for a manned mission: NASA dropped the idea for the Moon and the USSR adopted it only after their manned lunar programme had collapsed; the Luna missions show the limitations all too clearly, with only three successes out of seven attempts, at least two of the failures due to landing blind in rough terrain. Both Vikings came down in boulder fields where they could easily have overturned; Viking-2 ended up with an 8° tilt because one foot was on a rock, although the selected target looked like a dune field from orbit. It may in fact be in a 'deflation hollow', from which the dune material has been removed by the wind,[13] or on the ejecta blanket from the nearby crater Mie. Sagan has suggested that *both* Vikings may be among recently exhumed rocks, not typical of the Martian surface.[14] Surface samples can be contaminated or blown away by the landing, and a core sample like those returned by the Luna probes is selected virtually at random. To improve the odds at least a little NASA proposed preliminary missions, either detailed surveys from close orbit or unmanned roving vehicles; but even if a rover remained operational it's doubtful whether an unmanned lander could home in on it with much precision.

The problem with Mars Rovers is primarily the timelag between the Earth and Mars owing to the finite speed of light. At close oppositions the delay can be as low as four minutes but, when Mars is far from the Earth and the Sun—as it was in the Viking missions, to minimize the solar storm threat—then the lag can be forty minutes or more. Even the Soviet

Lunokhod, which was tried only twice on the Moon, tied up a team of controllers for months as it inched over distances which the Apollo astronauts traversed at speed. The Mars Rover might have to travel up to 5km without supervision; [24] it would need to recognize and negotiate obstacles. Soviet designs feature a six-legged walking robot, with a laser 'eye' to stop it before obstacles and a 'brain' to compute an avoidance route or refer the problem to Earth. [15] 'Hands' to take samples require major developments even in US computer technology; [16] but how can a machine recognize 'targets of opportunity' like the Apollo-15 'Genesis rock' or the Apollo-17 orange soil?

The plain was covered with large, spherical boulders, and the robot was rolling straight towards one. Its builders were not worried; the machine's obstacle-detecting skirt would warn it before there was a danger of collision, and it would automatically turn off at a right angle. That was the theory; what happened was somewhat different.

Before the robot could reach it, the boulder moved. It heaved itself off the ground on a myriad stumpy legs, crawled slowly out of the track of the advancing explorer, and settled down again. As it plunged forward, unaware of the consternation it was causing on Earth and Mars, the robot disturbed two more of the boulders; then it was through them, and encountered no others until, ten hours later, it became trapped in a canyon and continued to radio back maddeningly repetitious views of bare rock until its batteries failed.

—Arthur C. Clarke, *The Lost Worlds of 2001*, 1972 [17]

One way around the direction problem is to dispense with it altogether. JPL proposed a 'sage-brush probe' to bowl about the surface in a balloon, wherever the winds may take it. [18] But the designers want to deflate and stop on command—by which time, as sure as eggs, it will be beyond the zone of interest! To be able to retrace the path, JPL has considered pilotless aircraft: a 20m wingspan and a 41-484kg payload could give a range of 4025km, [19] a third of the way round the planet. The thin air needs 47 times the lifting surface of a comparable wing on Earth, [20] not four times as was once thought; [21] but that doesn't affect Waveriders, merely raising the stalling speed.

The most obvious Waverider mission would be a sustained glide down the Great Rift, studying volcanic and water action, and photographing the walls to determine how the chasm was formed. Chryse overflight would add greatly to the surface observations by Viking, and possibly detect life if Viking landed in a barren patch. Close-ups of the cliffs around Nix Olympica, suggesting water action, and the 'laminated terrain' around the polar cap would be of great value; Ian Downie suggested a glide across the Nix Olympica caldera, followed by a spiral down the outer slope and the 2km cliffs at the base.

Since Mars' atmosphere is mostly carbon dioxide, with small components of argon and nitrogen, jet engines will be no use and only a rocket burn could prolong the flight. At 400kph landing would be very hard, but braking rockets would reduce instrument payload. It would be better to follow the Waverider with a conventional probe like Viking, to land at the most interesting point revealed in a 'quick-look' scan of the glide-path photos. If the Waverider carried thermite charges to sterilize it on impact, since the hull is stainless steel the weight penalty would be less than for other spacecraft.

On approach the lander could relay communications to Earth, reversing the rôles of the Viking Lander and Orbiter and reducing the power required for the Waverider transmissions—a considerable advantage, since solar cells would have to be jettisoned before entry. Fuel cells could be fed by jettisonable LH_2/LO_2 tanks and, since the upper surfaces are in vacuum during atmosphere entry, the tanks could be retained in the glide until the speed dropped and the airstream approached the upper surface. Since the plasma generated during entry is contained below the vehicle, antennae on the upper surface can maintain contact when other probes would be cut off.

Landers can be carried as 'deck cargo' on the upper surface without having to fit within an aeroshell (Plate 8). Nonweiler agreed that liberties could be taken with the shape during the entry phase—stopping short, perhaps, of an open cockpit ('Biggles on Mars'). Shaw suggested laminar flow from gas jets to protect 'deck cargo' to touchdown, but the technique would be least effective at low speeds, just when the streamlining of the upper surface becomes important. Gliding in for landing, all forms of resistance have to be eliminated: if too many aerodynamic liberties have been taken because they're permissible at high speeds, we could end up with something very difficult to control and to fly at low speeds. Cargo to land with the Waverider would be better stored inside the double pyramid of the wing section, which is 'relatively amiable' as long as it isn't *too* thick—otherwise there's not enough lift to give low landing speeds.

Penetration of the surface could yield valuable data, and that brings in a class of free-falling payload which could be delivered with precision from a Waverider.[22] The Barnes Wallis 'tallboys' and 'grand-slam' bombs of WWII reached depths of 60m before exploding,[23] and by the end of 1974 Sandia Laboratories had achieved penetrations of 120m with 450kg payloads, 46cm in diameter.[24] Terradynamics, 'flight through the Earth', resembles 'shooting a candle through a barn door': the vehicle flies in a shock-created void formed behind the nose, which alone is in contact with the ground, until enough energy has been lost for the sides to trap the vehicle's flanks as they close in—at which point the stop can be so sudden that the probe oscillates vertically. Even so, after recovery the payload's flank is found to be virtually undamaged. The Mars probes were intended to penetrate 1-15m, carrying seismometers, heat-flow sensors, and water-measurement and soil-analysis experiments. From a Waverider, penetrators could be placed with an accuracy unrivalled since 617 Squadron themselves![23]

One prime target is the north polar cap—more so than the smaller less developed southern one. On Earth the best 'near-term record' of the last 10,000-100,000 years comes from polar ice-core samples, and the icecaps are the best identifiable targets for such records on Mars.[24] Robert Staehle advocated a Viking/Pioneer-based system to return an ice core 50m long and 5mm in diameter[25],[26] to be searched for the climatic and volcanic history of Mars and for airborne organic materials such as pollen. Life could be carried around the planet within dust grains, protected from the solar ultraviolet radiation.[27] If the cores went deep enough they could be correlated with climatic changes on Earth for evidence of external causes, such as changes in the Sun or passage through interstellar clouds (see Chapter 1). Year-round coverage can be obtained by sampling both poles.[24] Penetrator missions would be an important adjunct to polar sampling, and Ian Downie pointed out that, even in Martian air, a Waverider landing might be possible on smooth ice. There seems little chance of a 1986-88 mission, most favourable for landing between summer melting and winter deposition; [25] but for a glider landing a spring arrival would be better.

Another crucial target, if confirmed, would be two 'oases' in Lacus Solis and Noachis Hellespontus, where atmosphere water vapour may be 10-15 times that elsewhere on Mars. [28] For half the year there could be a freeze/thaw cycle giving liquid water for a few hours each day; and if the water's brine (a possible sodium-chloride deposit has been found in an equatorial crater [29]) the cycle could continue all year round. [30] According to Lowell, Lacus Solis was the capital of Mars; however, JPL experts disagree with that interpretation of the water-vapour data.

The Mars situation is now like our knowledge of the Moon early in the Surveyor programme: we have extensive photographic coverage from space and partial analysis of two surface sites which may or may not be typical. We need more comprehensive exploration at surface and full analysis of materials, with deep cores much more valuable than surface samples. Further orbital studies should be of Apollo Scientific Instrument Module quality—implying return to Earth at least, if not on-the-spot human control. In surface exploration and sample return, the major problems are due to time-lag and could be greatly offset by human control, even from orbit.

Circumstantial evidence—nothing more—suggests that such a mission may be in the offing. Since 1976 there has been a series of mystery launches by Proton D or D-1 boosters, normally used for Salyut space stations, at the 51°.6 inclination normally reserved for manned flights. Cosmos-881-882 (15.12.'76); Cosmos-929 (17.17.'77—2.2.'78); Cosmos-997-998 (30.3.'78) and Cosmos-1100-1101 (23.5.'79) all had two telemetry channels, one normally used for Soyuz spacecraft and the other for Salyuts, with independent timing systems and independent antennae, big enough for one sometimes to obscure the other. [31] From visual observations the vehicle is as large as a Salyut, and fitted with solar panels. The three payloads that were announced to be paired returned to Earth over the USSR after only one or two orbits. [32] Cosmos-929 executed an elaborate series of manoeuvres, raising and lowering its orbit, with a total delta-v of at least 180m/sec by the time it was de-orbited and destroyed over the Pacific like a Salyut. [33]

During August 1977, however, VHF telemetry from Cosmos-929 ceased and a payload may have been returned to Earth. [31] The position is further complicated by Cosmos-1001 (1978-36A) and -1074 (1979-8A): both were launched by the A-2 Soyuz booster, used Soyuz telemetry channels, left units in orbit before they returned to Earth, [34] had orbital elements almost identical to those of Cosmos-929, and may have been the enlarged Soyuz-T.

Western and Soviet journals have linked the Proton launches to the Soviet shuttle, but that seems unlikely to use a Proton booster (see Chapter 2). Phillip Parker suggests [35] that they may be the promised 'heavy Salyut': and Cosmos-929 may have been a tug. A Proton failure on 4.8.'77 might have been an unpowered space-station module, to be collected by Cosmos-929 and later docked to Salyut-6. [36] If so, however, and if that's the explanation of the paired launches, then it seems the module is relatively small and uses Soyuz-type telemetry; so why a Proton booster?

The payload might have been a complete, unpowered Salyut, but so far they've had their own engines, and the Progress ferries have adequately demonstrated the capability of refuelling. If Cosmos-929 was a 'tanker' its capabilities are very large: assuming mass in the 12-16,000kg range of Proton payloads, the fuel expended was enough to take three complete Salyuts from its initial orbit to the highest one attained. [33]

Could the paired payloads correspond to the US Mars mission plan, with a space-station module as living quarters and ending with direct Earth atmosphere entry? There's still time to run a full three-year orbital simulation of a minimum-energy Mars mission, and then actually fly one for the 1986 close opposition. The delta-v demonstrated by Cosmos-929 was just under 10% of that required for minimum-energy return from Mars; [21] flight times may be 290 days each way, with a 450-day 'waiting time' at the planet before the return launch window; [37] but entry velocity into Earth's atmosphere comes down to 12.2kps, comparable with Apollo technology, [38] as opposed to NERVA proposals (see below). Lacking LH_2/LO_2 technology, a Soviet mission would presumably use hypergolic propellants like the von Braun/Ley *Exploration of Mars* [21] (hypergolic propellants ignite spontaneously on contact).

That mission involved placing 2000 tonnes in close-Earth orbit for a passenger ship and cargo vessel, to carry 12 men to

Mars and back. It would take 100 Protons to lift that mass; and the 1950s breakdown for the two ships now seems very optimistic. But the Soviets would be thinking of a much smaller crew and not, apparently, planning a manned landing. Unmanned rovers and sample probes can be controlled effectively from orbit, and considerable fuel savings become possible with elliptical parking orbits like those of the Vikings. As chemically fuelled missions are heavily penalized for fuel in the less favourable oppositions, 1986 may be the last chance this century to beat the West to another planetary body. It would be spectacular even without a manned landing.

Caution may in any case be justified. The Soviet record with Mars landers is rather daunting: one crash (Mars-2); one failure (Mars-3), during the 1971 dust storm, 110 seconds after landing; and a more mysterious failure (Mars-6) 20 seconds *before* touchdown. Imaginary manned missions have tended to fare little better; a 1954 painting by Fred Wolff [40] showed the first men on Mars crawling away from the wreck to die (a fate he had previously earmarked for lunar explorers [41]). A thin crust gives way under a landing leg of the *Figurao* in John Wyndham's *The Outward Urge*, killing one of the crew of three; another dies in a futile attempt to right the ship. [42] In the film *The Conquest of Space* the ascent stage nearly goes the same way during a 'Marsquake'; and melting permafrost does as much for the *Phoenix* in Arthur C. Clarke's 'Transit of Earth'. [43] But few disasters have been as comprehensive, convincing or gripping* as the expedition led by the *Discovery* in the BBC's radio saga *Journey into Space*:

> April 15th, 1972—Earth time: the Mars fleet, or what was left of it, was returning to its base on the Moon —nearly a year before its scheduled time. The expedition to Mars had started out with nine ships and twenty men, but only three ships and eight men had survived to make the return journey. Four men were dead, their bodies destined to drift around the solar system for ever or until, drawn to some planet by gravitational attraction, they go hurtling down towards its surface to be vaporised in the planet's atmosphere, like a meteor when it is captured by

*There must be a whole generation that turns pale at the mere *mention* of Whitaker.

the Earth. The remaining freighters, empty of human life, are for ever circling the planet in free orbit. Their crews are held prisoner on Mars with hundreds of other 'conditioned' captives of the Martians—Martians whom we never saw but from whose terrifying power we the survivors of the expedition escaped only by a miracle. [44]

Mariner-9 and the Vikings notwithstanding, it will do no harm to take a good look before we go down.

In Ehricke's terms, even the NERVA nuclear missions were 'marginal'. To stay within realistic limits for Saturn V payloads assembled in Earth orbit, 400-600 day missions dictated highly elliptical orbits around Mars, and direct atmosphere entry on return [45] at 16-20kps, depending on the mission year, compared with 11kps for the Apollo return from the Moon; the entry corridor to be hit would be about 3km in depth, although no doubt the required accuracy could be achieved with radar tracking. [46] Rocket deceleration into Earth orbit (without which there could be no quarantine) would increase initial mass by 40%. [39] Since all 400-600 day missions involved cutting across Earth's orbit on the return trajectory, in some years final entry velocity could be reduced by a close pass around Venus, although that would add 100-200 days to the mission: in the worst years, 620 days would be the total. [45] Launch windows for a Mars mission with a Venus swingby return would recur in a 6.4-year cycle, during which there would be opportunities for relatively low-energy launches, allowing 'stopovers' in orbit around both planets. Such missions would last 600-1000 days, again depending on the year of launch (because of the ellipticity of Mars's orbit). Initial mass would be greater than for a single-planet mission (although not much greater than for a typical Mars mission), but significantly less than the total mass required for separate missions to the two planets. [47]

The capabilities of NERVA were far too limited for Ehricke's 'strategic approach'. [48] Growth potentials were restricted to tighter orbits around Mars, longer stopovers or lower return velocities: even using the Nuclear Shuttle as a recoverable launcher from Earth orbit,* the NERVA system remained severely limited by the specific impulse available, and still

*Not discussed in references 45-7.

more by the need to push every last kilogram of ship mass up from Earth's surface using chemically fuelled, throwaway Saturn Vs. Better propulsion systems should be available towards the end of this century; and to the society we've envisaged, with its space factories and EML launch of raw materials from the Moon, the cost of interplanetary missions will be much less of a burden.

For 'strategic' missions, ion-drive, fusion drive or nuclear pulse (Daedalus) will be essential. Buckley's first-phase inter-planetary ships (*New Worlds for Old*, plates 14 and 17) have ion-drive with radiator fins shaped to keep the heat away from the propellant tanks. Planetary landers dock nose-to-nose into an airlock module giving access to all four wrapped-around command and living modules. The propellant tanks are also in a wrap-around configuration allowing the outer ones to be jettisoned: for longer missions they can be clustered in a grid pattern, possibly with the disposable ones paired (fig. 19). Behind the living quarters is a rotating boom in which the six crew members spend time in rotation, to remain acclimatized to gravity. The problems (loss of attention, disorientation) in adjusting to a centrifuge can be minimized by head and eye exercises and by making the transitions gradual.[49]

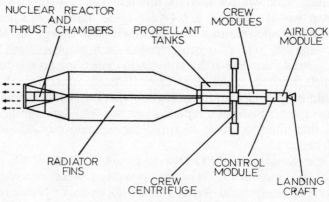

Fig. 19   Ion-drive ship

The 'traditional' Mars lander, painted by Chesley Bonestell for Ley and von Braun,[21] was a winged glider carrying a cargo cylinder and a rocket which was to be winched upright for launch back to orbit. The cargo cylinder held tractors and transparent bubble tents for the temporary base. Bonestell produced a much better variant, however, for the George Pal film *The Conquest of Space*, where the return rocket was on the back of the glider instead of in front of the cargo cylinder, where it would easily be damaged during landing (in the film, the glider fetches up against a rock). Nine years later, Bonestell updated the scenes for Richardson's *Mars*: an aeroshell lander instead of wings, with parachute and braking rocket. [50] The Martian atmosphere was still thought to be far denser than it is.

Buckley's concept is a three-module, single-stage-to-orbit plug-nozzle Multi-Environment Lander (MEL). The second module, the same diameter as the Command Module, holds extra fuel required only for Mars landings (fig. 20): for landing and takeoff from the Moon, Mercury, Pluto or the moons of the outer planets, the lower module's tanks would be adequate. Mars needs an extra module, not wrap-around tanks, because the mission begins with atmosphere entry. The craft carries two or three people and would be used on Mars as a personnel transport, with emergency lift capability to the orbiting exploration base (see below). The plug-nozzle is used instead of conventional rocket engines to minimize cabin height above the ground during touchdown and to make the vehicle squat and stable on the surface.

However, the vehicles used by the *first* expeditions will

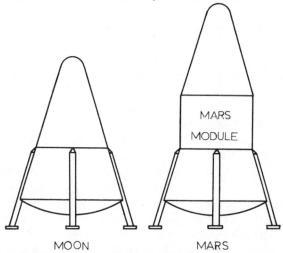

MOON   MARS

Fig. 20   The Multi-Environment Lander (MEL)

have to be more rugged and carry more cargo, prepared for dust storms with speeds up to 650kph—dust-drifts at the summit of Pavonis Mons in 1971 revealed winds blowing at half the local speed of sound. The storm mechanism is still mysterious in part, but much better understood than before Mariner-9. The biggest ones form like hurricanes on Earth, beginning with a bright core of suspended dust over one of the raised 'continents' in the southern hemisphere when Mars is nearest the Sun. Apparently the floating dust, first raised by 'dust-devils', absorbs solar heat in a positive feedback which builds up a storm in about two weeks, expands and covers the planet in five to six weeks, and takes 10 to 25 weeks to clear. [51] Planet-wide storms are rare, but lesser ones are often reported.

The particles are less than 0.004mm across, for the most part, and might easily have penetrated and silenced the USSR's Mars-3 (see page 146). Its fate isn't too mysterious: it landed at the height of the storm and not too far from Hellas, probably the least healthy spot on the planet at the time. But what about Mars-6? There was no storm then, but the spacecraft didn't even reach the ground before falling silent. The Viking Landers, moreover, set down without generating violent dust-devils. There's a Soviet suggestion that fine dust isn't spread all over the planet, but is concentrated in bowls like Hellas. [52] Maybe there isn't enough of it in most places to be dangerous. But a manned ship has one advantage a robot doesn't have: a pilot can choose bare rock for his touchdown.

Touchdown on rock would avoid a possible danger in the surface itself. If Mars has subsurface permafrost even a Viking, with a radioactive power source and an ambient temperature of 300 K, could melt the ground beneath it and sink from view. [53] But, since the 'plug' of a plug-nozzle is refrigerated with liquid hydrogen during atmosphere entry, its base can be kept below freezing after touchdown.

For an emergency windbreak, the first suggestion was a dome over struts springing from the sides of the ship, hinged at the nose. Braced to bedrock, double-skinned, and pressurized between the skins, it would deflect glancing blows from wind-borne fragments. The whole dome could be pressurized, but with bubble tents inside: positive interior pressure would make it easier to repair a breach from inside.

Perhaps we could deliberately hover on rocket thrust long enough to melt a shelter in the permafrost? ASTRA again discussed doming over a crater but, remembering the Apollo-11 experience, we don't want the first Mars lander *trying* to put down in one. John Kelk suggested blasting a suitable cavity out of solid rock with a shaped nuclear charge, but that involves taking off to land in it again, with radioactivity still at its height.

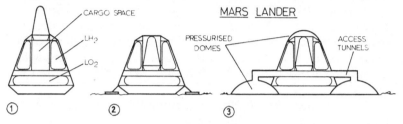

Fig. 21 A Mars lander as the nucleus for a surface base

In any case, the storms shift a lot of material around. Our ship would look silly in its capped hollow with a great sand dune over it like those deposited in Hellespontus in 1971. We want our ascent stage above ground, but fully protected against dust and flying rocks, and in no danger of being overturned. The first Mars lander should be a two-stage vehicle, with annular liquid oxygen tanks surrounding the descent stage cargo bay (fig. 21). When that has been unloaded, a balloon can be inflated in the cargo space; deflating, it would lower the ascent stage (which has $\frac{1}{3}$ of its Earth weight) into the protection of the bay. With the descent stage anchored to bedrock, the cargo doors would be flame deflectors for ascent stage ignition. It should be able to lift from inside the descent stage, so that if it has to launch during a storm it doesn't have to be exposed during the countdown.

Delicate instruments would be in the ascent-stage compartments for geological samples on the return. Equipment unloaded to the surface—drilling gear, explosives, 'Mars buggies', balloons, sounding rockets, etc.—should be organized and stored behind screens (curved aeroshell segments, if the ship has conventional rocket motors instead of a plug-nozzle). As sand accumulates behind them the wind will be deflected over the top; and, when the banks are cemented, a permanent shelter will have been created.

Living quarters won't be the traditional clear plastic bubbles but stressed geodesic structures, clustered against the ship to use the ascent stage as a storm cellar. Because Mars has no magnetic field to shield the surface, solar flares will send the crew to shelter just as rapidly as a coming dust storm. A 1968 Mars Surface Module design was an elliptical cylinder on legs, because it required least surface preparation and combined maximum storage space (above the ceiling and below the floor) with minimal surface contact and insulation problems. [54] However, the study assumed wind speeds of the order of 60kph; nowadays the advantages of the elliptic cylinder would be traded for a hemisphere or a hemispheric cylinder, with surface preparation time cheerfully allocated to make sure the wind couldn't get under it.

Three domes could be grouped around the ship: the one on the top, suggested by Bill Ramsay, would be first because it gives fastest access to the ascent stage (through the floor straight into the docking tunnel) in an emergency. It would be the control room for weather watch and radio contact with the roving vehicles. It might nevertheless be the least solid of the three, since it *has* to be shifted before takeoff; if time allowed before a storm, it might be struck and pulled down into the docking tunnel. For preference, all three domes would be dismantled before ascent-stage launch; in use, access tunnels and interior ladders to the ascent stage will have to be pressurized.

Cryogenic propellants have the advantage that you can breathe the oxygen, if you can get at it, or combine it with the hydrogen and drink the water. Although permafrost would ensure water supplies for the expedition and the eventual Mars base, it would conserve power if the plug refrigeration could be switched off and the LH_2/LO_2 residuals could be stored in the bottom tank as water: the rocket chambers around the rim of the plug might be adapted for the conversion or the fuel cells might draw on the main tanks until the residuals were used up. (One of the *nice* things about fuel cells is that their waste product is potable water.) Hubertus Strughold has suggested that the Mars base might be located in a 'geothermal' area, for heat, power and liquid water; [55] who would have dreamed that the first Mars outpost might nestle comfortably at the foot of a volcano!

As an alternative to lowering the ascent stage (perhaps risky, since it could jam), it might be carried inside the descent stage with cargo on top. However, the cargo then has to be lowered a long way to the ground. More importantly, the cargo must lift clear in a great hurry if the landing is aborted; even so, if the ship were keeling over, the ascent stage mightn't get out in time. The pilots couldn't see out and would be dependent on TV and instruments; in my design optical fibres or a simple periscope would greatly extend the view of the ground below.

The next expedition reclaims the first one's descent stage, sealing and pressurizing the whole interior, replacing the domes and/or adding more units. (Gavin Roberts suggested new units be hexagonal, so they could be clustered with no space between them; they'd then be protected by sandbags and an outer wall of metallic Mars bricks.) The third expedition converts the second descent stage in the same way and joins up the two with a pressurized tunnel, putting their living unit cluster at the midpoint with a temporary tunnel to their own ship, giving three shelters to retreat to.

A central shaft would be put down from the centre of a four-descent-stage square—but not the huge nuclear excavation of the lunar mine complex: this will be a spaceship hangar, with storage bays behind blast doors. The hangar level would be near the surface, so chambers would blow upwards rather than into the base if a ship exploded; in a major emergency the lids could be blown off and the ships launched from the silos. Ordinarily rockets would be raised to the surface and launched from the central pad.* The four original descent stages would be fully cemented in, for blockhouses, launch and descent controls, and surface vehicle maintenance. Inhabited tunnels would be below the hangar level, with escape routes to the surface or the stored landers, depending on the nature of the crisis.

Since Mars has an atmosphere and a relatively high escape velocity (5kps), it isn't likely to be a source of materials for Earth. You can't launch electromagnetically from the surface of Mars. (Laser launch would be more efficacious than on Earth because the atmosphere is thinner and the gravity smaller, but it takes a lot of power.) As a result, conflict over planetary resources is unlikely. (Shaw has asked whether Mars might really become the 'Red' planet, in time.) In any case, an

---

*The great solid dome with curved panels in *2001* would have a function on Mars: to keep the weather out. I never figured out what the one on the Moon was for: it wasn't an airlock because it wasn't closed after the ship landed and, since the underground hangar was red-lit, presumably it was *supposed* to be in a vacuum.

Earth-Moon system federation should prevent nationalistic conflicts in deeper space; but as far as can be seen the Martian resources will remain virtually untapped until there is a true Martian colony to make use of them, or export them in a big way by beanstalk (see below).

The Mars scientific colony will be a far cry from the 'traditional' one painted by R. A. Smith for Clarke's *The Exploration of Space* [56] and described in *The Sands of Mars* [57]: huge domes of transparent plastic, buoyed up by internal air pressure. In the distance was the rocket-field with its winged shuttles and banked earth strip, standing out in vivid red against the blue-green vegetation of Lacus Solis—as I described it in my teens in an unpublished space-odyssey. One of the domes contained the cathedral of the Church of Mars, a sweeping piece of low-gravity architecture, with a shining metal spire which pierced the dome and rose, impossibly slender, towards the deep blue Martian sky in which the brighter stars were always visible ... (Actually, the sky is permanently pink with floating dust.) At night the city shone like a beacon, 'filled with the misty light of denser air'. And, of course, there were the aircraft, with their sturdy tractor undercarriages (Clarke's idea) and rocket-assisted takeoff (mine); and the Mars trucks with their pressurized cabins, bouncing on balloon tyres along roads knocked through the vegetation, or rolling across the brightly coloured, merciless but *smooth* desert.

We know now that Mars Rovers will have to negotiate chasms, dried-up river beds and flood plains filled with debris, crater ejecta fields strewn with sharp-edged rocks, lava flows, 'chaotic terrain' seamed with fractures, canyons scoured out by storms after melting of subsurface ice, crater walls, and steep ridges formed by dust deposition or lava upwelling before erosion. The huge but localized dune fields have crevasses and surface movements, and in storms they move bodily. Mars Rovers, lightly built and highly sprung, like spiders on wheels—balloon tyres, perhaps, or wire wheels like Lunar Rovers—designed for speed, rather than stability, to outrun advancing dunes (unlike the vehicles of Silverberg's 'The Feast of St. Dionysius' [58]), may bring forth a breed of crazy drivers. As R. A. Lafferty had it in *The Reefs of Earth*, [59] 'Well, the devil himself is on wheels, according to Puca fables. He's a mechanical thing that got out of hand. And this thing, moving in the middle of a cloud of dust or wild horses, was on four bicycle or cart wheels. It was coming through the chosky bottoms, and even in a short dry spell those bottoms get pretty dusty. The thing was perched above the wheels like a crazy cat-castle of shining silver and gold, or of brass and chrome. The castle itself, intricate with instruments, was making the awful noise, and the man sitting in the castle was singing the wonderful verses.'

Most long journeys will be rocket trips, with landers in polar orbit for emergency recoveries—perhaps two-stage landers instead of Buckley's MEL because they'd be dotting Mars with emergency descent-stage shelters like mountain bothies. Rocket-pogos may be used for individual surface transport, if dust isn't too great a hazard.

Mars will be part of the terrestrial-planets study programme, with no terraforming until it's been fully studied 'as is': data on Mars weather can be used for better understanding, prediction and control of the weather on Earth. John Kelk predicted computerized planet-wide weather mapping, mostly from Mars orbit (including interrogation of unmanned surface stations). Buckley pointed out that, since Mars has no radiation belts, there's no reason not to put the base in polar orbit. A Phobos base couldn't cover regions beyond 49°N or S, and even Deimos can't be seen on Mars beyond 75°N or S.[37] The orbiting station might be the first of the SIOS family, servicing landers and directing surface operations.

The natural moons of Mars will be visited at an early stage because of their scientific interest. Mariner-9 confirmed earlier observations, briefly but mistakenly discredited, that Phobos is spiralling in towards Mars. Due to tidal forces (not atmospheric drag as thought before Mariner-4) Phobos will crash onto Mars in about 100 million years[60] —a very short time, relative to the age of the Solar System. Dark, irregularly shaped and heavy cratered, Phobos and Deimos might be crystal fragments of a carbonaceous chondrite asteroid (see page 189) whose main body fell on Mars in the relatively recent past.[61]

The long axes of Phobos and Deimos point towards the planet at all times. Phobos could have been locked to Mars over 10^4-10^6 years, Deimos in 10^6-10^8 years[60]. But the cratering on both moons is 'saturated'; i.e., the distribution shows that new craters are being created as fast as old ones are being obliterated. To reach such a state of equilibrium, both moons must have been in space for 1.5 billion years at least.

Orbiter flybys confirmed that both moons had regoliths, tens if not hundreds of metres thick. 'Ghost rings' can be seen on Deimos, as on the Moon, but drowned in regolith instead of lava. [62] Much of the 'fallout' from impacts was in clusters of house-sized blocks. Phobos has long chains of secondary impact craters instead. The remarkable thing is that neither moon has a large enough gravitational field to generate secondary craters or ejecta blankets by the processes illustrated on the Moon, Mars and Mercury, [60] so these must have been caused by material which went into orbit around Mars and recollided with the satellites. Once a regolith forms, it's more difficult for debris to be ejected from it; thus both moons must have been orbiting Mars before bombardment formed their regoliths—and, from the depth of it on Deimos, that was a long time ago.

One of the earliest Viking photographs of Phobos showed a surface section marked with no less than sixty parallel lines. They might have been crater chains [63], but a close pass showed they were grooves [64] —concentrated in the northern hemisphere [65], concentric with the long axis, parallel at the big crater Stickney and absent opposite to it. [66] Phobos is close enough to orbit Mars three times a day, and until recently was the only natural satellite known to rise in the west (Jupiter has two); is it on the verge of breaking up? Originally it could have orbited at twice the present distance. [67] But, although the grooves go through the older, larger, degraded craters, smaller and newer ones are superimposed on them. On the cratering evidence, Stickney and the grooves are at least three billion years old. [66] If Phobos were carbonaceous chondrite, from which water is easily driven off by heating, then the Stickney impact might have caused deep fractures from which steam could escape explosively. [66] But, in the close passes, the size, shape, mass and density of Phobos were determined with great accuracy, and the moon isn't dense enough to be of carbonaceous chondrite. [68]

The grooves go through the walls of any craters, but not across their floors—although at least one can be seen within Stickney. [69] It's as if some very massive object had been rolling around with the Martian tides, crushing the low-density rock, perhaps bouncing in the other hemisphere to form crater chains. About the only class of object which would fit the bill might be a mini black hole electrostatically isolated in a protective sphere—the power module of a visiting starship, perhaps, parked to save the fuel to land it on Mars and bring it back up. If its owners never came back for it, eventually it might be immobilized by the regolith or tunnel into a crater wall and crush its way to the centre of the satellite. It would be interesting—*very* interesting—if Phobos samples showed a density markedly lower even than that indicated by the Viking flybys ... But, joking apart, samples would be of compelling interest and much easier to get than from Mars itself. Using backup Viking hardware, a mission could have been flown with a Titan-Centaur as early as 1981.[70] But there will come a time—and sooner rather than later, if there is a manned mission in 1986.

Knowing how these things go, the results will probably be so startling that manned research is called for. An observatory may follow because gravitational strains on big optical and radio reflectors would be tiny. A flare shelter below the surface would be followed by a deeper and more comfortable one against galactic radiation; but, with that done, the moons would no doubt be tunnelled extensively while a sizable population built up. Deimos would probably be the observatory, rather than Phobos: although the relative velocity of meteoroids near Mars is lower than in Earth's vicinity,[55] Phobos's 32kps orbital velocity is enough to make them a nuisance again.

Phobos may be mainly a staging post, for transfers from deep-space vehicles to surface landers. In *Islands in Space* Cole and Cox argue that to escape from Mars altogether would take 5kps ideally, say 5.64 in practice. It takes 4.3kps to get from Mars' surface to Phobos, and another 0.6kps for rendezvous; allowing for course corrections, the practical figure is probably 5.49 kps, so there's no energy saving per kilogram launched in stopping off at Phobos.[71]

There is, however, a big saving *in* kilograms launched. Shuttles are light on radiation shielding, carry few supplies and are generally much smaller than ships to Earth, especially Ehricke's HISVs (page 133). They can be returned to Mars by EML, the weight of shielding being much the same for entry from Phobos or from close orbit; while plug-nozzle landers don't have shields at all. Phobos is stable and comparatively large, yet its gravity is low enough for flimsy deep-space ships to dock on it—the same advantages which make the moons potential observatory sites. To avoid electromagnetic interference and other spacecraft pollution, the spaceport should be on one moon and the observatory complex on the other.

For a Phobos shuttle refuelled in close orbit, delta-v requirement would be 4.26kps instead of 5.49kps, increasing the 9100kg payload of a 45,500kg shuttle by 50%[71]. A laser-launch system would reduce the delta-v for the two-way trip to 0.6kps for Phobos rendezvous, with EML launch back, plus Mars touchdown requirements. Waveriders landing on prepared strips would cut out that last element. Ian Downie pointed out that considerable savings might also be achieved by analogy with the rocket sled technique (page 46) or even applying it directly, using some variant of EML or mag-lift track up the side of one of the great volcanoes. Nix Olympica is the highest but, because of its latitude, would be suitable only for interplanetary launches; but Pavonis Mons, 'Middle Spot' (Plate 4), is ideally located on the equator for launches to Phobos, Deimos or anything else in equatorial orbit.

In direct interplanetary entry, the kinetic energy of the Mars airstream isn't much greater than for Earth-atmosphere entry from orbit, so an orbital winged shuttle would be exposed to lower stresses than with Earth, but, since the atmosphere at ground level is only 1% as dense as Earth's, the lander would need to have ten times the wing area or land ten times as fast. Even a Waverider would touch down at 320-480kph, comparable with the present Shuttle on Earth. ('I don't know as I'd care to be the *first* person to arrive at that speed on the surface of Mars,' Nonweiler remarked.) If Mars is terraformed, however, the problem will be solved and conventional flight will become easy because of the $\frac{1}{3}$ gravity.

Nuclear explosions might create caverns for 'half-terraforming', but they seem unlilely to be used if we can rapidly terraform the surface—although they might be wanted if Mars weren't given a *breathable* atmosphere, or if it became the home of a group in exile (possibly self-imposed) or cut off from Earth. Roberts suggested Christians, and white south Africans were mentioned too! David Proffitt proposed vegetarians, health-food groups and other minority communes (but not antitechnology groups, presumably). Ian Downie suggested radioastronomers, not entirely in jest, considering their battle over frequencies with commercial interests on Earth. More seriously, the colony might be a 'guaranteed survival' project, to ensure continuation of the human race if Earth's habitability were to be destroyed by war or neglect.

Such a project would be similar to the interstellar colonies described in *Man and the Stars*. To become fully self-supporting, perhaps 6000 people would have to be shipped, with all the equipment need to maintain their technology. But, if Mars is colonized before it is terraformed, the dependence on rockets for surface transport requires higher technology than a colony on an Earthlike world; on the other hand, rapid ship and signal links with Earth give access to the full human range of data processing and expertise.

Would such a colony do much with the Martian surface? Most agriculture would have to be underground, fed sunlight *via* optical fibres. Floating surface farms were suggested, buoyed up with helium—but they'd have so little lift that even they couldn't avoid a storm. Glass domes over any surface farm would keep out the lethal solar ultraviolet, but erosion would be a problem. 'It doesn't take long to go through glass with a sand-blaster,' remarked John Kelk. During the big storms it's likely that little sunlight reaches the surface for months on end. Industry would probably go underground as well, since it doesn't have lunar surface advantages—on Mars we have atmosphere, higher gravity and less solar energy.

It was suggested that, if terrestrial society was breaking down, emigration rates to space wouldn't be maintained. James Campbell replied that the multinational companies would take over space resources as the economic base on which to wall themselves off and ensure their own survival, so the emigration route would stay open. In a truly massive break-down, however, a one-way Mars colony effort might be made using existing ships—as at the end of Bradbury's *The Martian Chronicles*. [72]

> The scene which met my eyes was so un-Martian that my heart sprang to my throat as the sudden fear swept through me that I had been aimlessly tossed upon some strange planet by a cruel fate.
>   Why not? What guide had I through the trackless waste of interplanetary space? What assurance had I that I

might not as well be hurtled to some far-distant star of another solar system, as to Mars?

I lay upon a close-cropped sward of red grasslike vegetation, and about me stretched a grove of strange and beautiful trees, covered with huge and gorgeous blossoms and filled with brilliant, voiceless birds. I call them birds since they were winged, but mortal eye ne'er rested on such odd, unearthly shapes.

The vegetation was similar to that which covers the lawns of the red Martians of the great waterways, but the trees and birds were unlike anything that I had ever seen upon Mars, and then through the further trees I could see that most un-Martian of all sights—an open sea, its blue waters shimmering beneath the brazen sun.

—Edgar Rice Burroughs, *The Gods of Mars* [73]

Since three-quarters of Earth's surface is covered by water, Mars actually has slightly more land surface than the Earth. Mutaforming might seem the obvious way to claim that surface, but the carbon-dioxide atmosphere is a real problem. Most reactions involving carbon dioxide are endothermic, absorbing energy instead of releasing it, as oxidizing reactions such as burning do. To follow one bold author (whose anonymity we preserve) and open Mars up 'by a simple operation which allowed us to breathe carbon dioxide' gets no marks except for effrontery. Adaptation would require cyborg modifications on a massive scale—new skin, new eyes, wing-like solar panels to power the air-regeneration system, artificial limbs and heart, and electronic senses whose input to the brain is controlled by the external computer linkage as fully as the functions of the body—a process whose psychological traumas Frederik Pohl explores in *Man Plus*, up to and including the nightmare on Mars when the computer's 'mediation' goes awry. [74] This operation is easier than lunar mutaforming and more likely to be attempted, but, for the reasons given in Chapter 5, the strategic approach requires better options.

Curiously enough, if there were *more* carbon dioxide matters would be easier. Enhanced greenhouse effect would raise temperatures, allowing plant life to gain hold and convert the CO_2 to free oxygen. Losses into space would be less rapid than from the Moon because Mars is not only further from the Sun but also more massive. In this event, it might be better *not* to convert the atmosphere, tolerating oxygen masks for the sake of Earthlike temperatures and pressures, which Mars could keep indefinitely.

After Mariner-9, it seemed Mars might cyclically go through such conditions without human intervention. The 'Long Winter' hypothesis was that water and carbon dioxide would be released from whichever polar cap was turning towards the Sun in Mars's 50,000-year precessional cycle, ending the super-winter of great dust storms and allowing liquid water on the surface again. Dark dust, from a planetary or asteroid source, spread on the present north polar cap, would absorb solar energy and increase evaporation, bringing forward the Spring by 12,000 years to give Mars an atmosphere as dense as Earth's within only a century of a runaway greenhouse effect being established. [9]

That atmosphere would still be virtually transparent to ultraviolet radiation; to remove that hazard would require at least partial conversion to free oxygen, enough to generate an ozone layer. There's enough oxygen over the poles now, from dissociation of water vapour, to provide 'useful protection'; but, for terrestrial life, only equatorial temperatures are even marginally suitable, and there the protection from ultraviolet is less than a twentieth of the required value. [9]

Mats of blue-green algae or of lichen are the only suitable candidates. Only the algae could gain a hold without free oxygen already in the atmosphere, but the lichens are the only form with a strong ultraviolet tolerance. The latter might have to establish the ozone layer while being fed oxygen by algae sheltered in crevices. However, the thick layer of dead cells which would form on top of the mat might be sufficient to protect the algae beneath, and genetic engineering could improve their characteristics for Mars still further. In theory, all the gene pool of the Earth could be drawn on to help by transformation (already demonstrated) or adding characteristics by transduction (theoretically possible with algae). [9] For such experiments, however, even the initial breeding programmes should be off-Earth.

As in the Antarctic valleys, the plants would be able to establish themselves only where permafrost lay near enough to the surface for moisture to migrate upwards in summer. Starting from scratch, the algae could give Mars a breathable atmosphere in 140,000 years; lichens alone would take ten

times as long. With artificial release of the atmosphere from
the polar caps the timescale would be nearer 10,000 years, and
other intervention, including genetic engineering, might improve it still further.

Unfortunately, the 'missing' CO_2, if it ever existed, is not
frozen at the north pole now. Around the polar cap the Viking
Orbiters found a huge belt of dark dunes, submerging the
landforms below; the absence of cratering indicated that the
fields are 120,000 years old at most, and it isn't clear whether
they're moving on to the cap or off it.[71] In *New Worlds for Old*
I therefore suggested that Mars had been terraformed already:
if a carbonaceous chondrite asteroid had disintegrated in the
atmosphere, like the Tunguz meteorite over Siberia in 1908
but on an even bigger scale, and if the dust came down on the
polar cap with the winds which form the spiral ridges, then
perhaps the Martian Spring came early and life had a long
enough run to turn most of the carbon dioxide into oxygen
—only to lose it into space and make the next Long Winter a
permanent one. Sample cores from the polar cap, where the
'unconformable contacts' of the layered terrain show that the
annual deposition of dust and ice *has* been interrupted in the
past, may tell us whether life on Mars destroyed its environment—ironically, by briefly creating an environment in which
we could have survived.

Without the CO_2, it's doubtful whether much can be done.
Heat transfer to the poles by advection may not work with
water vapour, although it generates a more significant greenhouse effect than CO_2 at Martian-terrestrial pressures,[9] and
it's far from clear whether a breathable atmosphere could ever
be generated. The only answer may be another source of
atmosphere, and Dyson has already suggested the ice moons of
Saturn.[77] Delivery would have to be gentle: there's no point in
bringing ices in bulk from Saturn if they vaporize, dissociate
and ionize on impact, going straight back up into space as a jet
of bluish-purple plasma! If the Martian beanstalk can be
established, with Deimos as a counterweight and precessing to
dodge Phobos, then the tricky drop through the atmosphere can
be circumvented; moreover, the Martian colonists can use it to
start exporting metals in bulk. In fact, since the moons of the
outer planets are low in heavy elements, Mars may have to
become 'the Pittsburgh of the Solar System', as Blish predicted, just to pay for the volatiles.

It now seems that Mars has a great deal of water; indeed, some planetologists consider it to be in that sense a frozen version of Earth, with huge quantities of ice beneath the crust. [78] Surplus water ice from Saturn might be separated out on Deimos for re-export to the inner planets, because seas would cut down the usable Martian surface area. But, with or without oceans, there will be a steady loss at the top of the atmosphere as water dissociates into hydrogen and oxygen and both are lost into space. As the plants continue to release oxygen from carbon dioxide, there'll come a time when Lowell's description of Mars comes true—the drying planet, the oases, and the great irrigation schemes against the encroaching deserts. As the deserts grow and plant cover shrinks (unless the technology and the will persist to bring in more ice), then there will be increasing artificial maintenance of the atmosphere, until Edgar Rice Burroughs, too, is proved right. John Carter may yet have to make his epic dash to save the great atmosphere factory of Barsoom.

In that epoch the impact basins like Hellas, furthest below the mean surface level, might be the last refuges of life on the surface and, if Mars has already suffered 'involuntary terraforming', then perhaps we should look there for survivors—unless the Russians are right, and after the storms the dust goes swirling back there like a great choking blanket. Whether or not life has retreated into the deep basins before, it's worth remembering that Mars can't be permanently terraformed. Someday, unless our persistence in renewing the air and water quite literally outlasts the Sun's, the great storms will come again.

VIII

Venus as the Abode of Life

Hesper—Venus—were we native to that splendour or in Mars,
We should see the Globe we groan in, fairest of their evening stars.
Could we dream of wars and carnage, craft and madness, lust and
spite,
Roaring London, raving Paris, in that point of peaceful light?
                    —Tennyson, 'Locksley Hall Sixty Years After'

... if there is a London on Venus the Londoners there must be
of singularly strong constitutions.
                    —R. A. Proctor, *The Expanse of Heaven*, 1886 [1]

'Venus is Hell,' said jesting Sagan, [2] and need hardly stay for an
answer. At ground level, temperatures average 700 K, higher
than on the sunward face of Mercury, 48 million kilometres
nearer the Sun. 97% of the atmosphere is carbon dioxide, so
much of it that surface pressure is 88-94 times that on Earth,
and although the clouds reflect 75% of the incident sunlight [3]
the greenhouse effect remorselessly traps and concentrates the
rest. Venus is close to Earth in size and density, and the
quantity of nitrogen in their atmospheres is about the same, [3]
but on Earth the CO_2 is locked up in the chalk beds. To make
chalk in those quantities needs liquid oceans; with Venus
cooked and Mars frozen, was the distance from the Sun the key
factor in Earth's 'success'? If so, then because the early Sun
was fainter than it is now, the exact distance would have been
critical: 6-10 million km either way would have wrecked
Earth's chances [4]—a sufficiently narrow band, perhaps, to make
Earth after all the only inhabited world in the Galaxy.

But then came Pioneer-Venus-1 and the mapping of 93% of
the surface by radar. Previous radar mapping from Earth
had all been of the same region and led to the supposition that
the whole of Venus was strangely flat (after Mariner-9 and
Mars we should have known better). 84% of the surface is

relatively flat, like a single granitic continental plate preserving the record of early bombardment, but there are three great outcrops of basalt—Aphrodite Terra, Beta Regio and Ishtar Terra, with four great volcanoes on them. The Lakshmi plateau on Ishtar is 2..8km above the mean surface and on its eastern edge the Maxwell volcano rises a further 9km, with a 100km-wide crater and deep clefts in its sides. The Venera-11 and -12 landers reported violent lightning, 25 flashes a second, and the Pioneer and Venera Orbiters together established that the lightning is centred on Beta Regio and the 'scorpion's tail' feature of Aphrodite. Almost certainly these volcanoes are still in eruption.

Venus has one great rift like Mars's Valles Mariner-is—1500km long, 150km wide and 2km deep with a deep parallel cleft on each side of it. On all counts Venus is much more like an active version of Mars than like Earth with its jigsaw of crustal plates; it's as if Mars were a frozen stage in the evolution of Venus rather than of Earth. But Mars has lots of water, and so does Earth ... and so presumably did Venus.

Hoyle and Wickramasinghe argue that Venus, Earth and Mars acquired their water and carbon dioxide from comets in the final phase of bombardment in the early Solar System, and that life may have come to Earth at the same time.[5] The alternative is that these compounds welled out of the planetary interiors after the crusts solidified. Harold Masursky suggests that it was the rapid rise of single-celled life on Earth which made the difference here—taking out the CO_2, laying down the chalk, increasing the weight of surface material which sank with water lubrication and generated the mobile crust we have today.[6]

On Mars, if life ever gained a foothold, perhaps the 'forward Spring' came even earlier than I thought and the dark polar dunes are a coincidence. On Venus clearly nothing of the sort happened because the CO_2 is still there and the water is missing. But, as far as we know, an Earthlike Venus would be viable after it had been artificially created. If life on Venus failed to take control at the outset, perhaps the key factor was the biggest difference between Venus and the other two planets: Earth and Mars both rotate in approximately 24 hours, but Venus takes 243 Earth days. Under even the beginnings of a CO_2 atmosphere, that factor alone may be enough to explain the evaporation of the oceans, so that then the 'runaway greenhouse' may have been due to water vapour. Surface temperatures may have reached an appalling 1800 K, melting the crust, which then oxidized as the water dissociated and the hydrogen escaped into space.[7] If so, to have taken up the calculated amount of 'missing' oxygen, the crust may have been oxidized in a continuous turning over down to 450km. That would tie with the gravitational/topographic evidence that the crust is much thicker than Earth's, and the roots of the volcanoes may be nearly 1000km down.[6] But it makes it unlikely that the Venus Orbiting Imaging Radar, postponed to 1988 at the earliest, will be able to detect former shorelines and dunes as hoped.

In 1949 *Astounding Science Fiction* published a remarkably prophetic account of a Venus probe mission by 'Philip Latham' (the astronomer Robert S. Richardson). Supposedly a gap in the clouds had revealed a mountain 40km high—higher than anything on Venus or Mars, but correct in being much higher than anything on Earth and implying quite different crustal processes. Misled by the even temperatures measured in the upper atmosphere, 'Latham' gave Venus a day of 37h 25.7min., much too short. But the most remarkable guess, for which he gave no reason, was that the rotation was retrograde—against the direction of revolution around the Sun, unlike all other planets except Pluto (although Uranus 'lies on its side'). 'This is of considerable cosmological importance, in indicating that Venus may have had a different origin from the other members of the solar system.'[8] In the same magazine in 1964 J. P. Kirton published a hypothesis to account for the rotations of Venus and Uranus, which would mean that Venus was 100-200 million years older than most of the planets[9] (see page 229). Intriguingly, the Pioneer and Venera-11 and -12 entry probes found isotopes of argon and krypton which were thought to have been flushed out of the inner Solar System too soon to be caught by the planets.[10]

Another remarkable datum given by 'Latham' was that windspeeds in the upper atmosphere were 480kph—almost precisely the figure confirmed by Mariner-10 in 1974. The upper atmosphere rotates retrograde as a whole with a period of four days, coming round from the nightside in parallel streams which split past a permanent high-pressure area at the subsolar point, forming recurrent ultraviolet features like Ys or Cs on their sides, with Earthlike convection cells downwind near the equator. In both hemispheres the displaced airstreams make huge spirals around the poles, much simpler than terrestrial circulation patterns. The apparent rotation was questioned, since it isn't easily explicable, but its reality is now definitely established; more so than in 1974, since an equatorial jetstream then detected by Mariner-10 had dispersed by 1978. It was suggested that it could explain the supposed flatness of the surface, since even 16kph winds at ground level could be as erosive as sea waves on Earth cliffs. But windspeeds at the Venera-9 and -10 touchdowns were only 2-4kph, while dust from probe impacts took 3-15 minutes to settle. In the Venera-9 and -10 surface photographs, sharp-edged rocks were prominent, obviously not eroded by high winds, and dark soil was apparently a result of chemical erosion.[11] High-resolution scans from Earth produced evidence of dust on crater floors, and in the rift valley Pioneer-Venus-1 found smooth spots which have been touchingly named 'ice ponds'; but it seems that the lower atmosphere is calm.

Venus has no detectable magnetic field, and the interplanetary field is compressed and twisted into magnetic 'ropes' within the ionosphere.[13] The height of the ionopause—the boundary between the ionosphere and the Solar Wind—varies from 250km to at least 1500km, depending on solar activity.[14] A possibly related effect, utterly extraordinary in itself, is that according to the Salyut-6 cosmonauts Venus twinkles like a star when seen from *above* the atmosphere.[15]

The clouds of Venus are neither water droplets nor ice, as supposed well into the 1970s, but sulphuric acid droplets in smooth layers like terrestrial smog. The first layer, from 70-56km above the surface, is at about 13°C; the Sun begins to dim at 66km and can no longer be seen as a disc by 63km up.[3] Horizontal visibility is then 6km. The layer from 56km to 49.5km contains unidentified liquid droplets as well as solid particles which are almost certainly sulphur; temperatures rise to 20°C. At the 1atm pressure level there's a clear zone with about 1.6km visibility, followed by dense clouds down to 47.5km, at 200°C. Another clear zone follows, above a 'pre-cloud' layer of droplets, only a few hundred metres thick. At 30km altitude the temperature is 310°C and horizontal visibility 80km; below that the Pioneer entry probes found the atmosphere 'immaculately clean'.[10] At 30km, it was suggested, sulphur and sulphuric acid vaporize and the acid dissociates, forming a 'soup' of sulphur compounds which recirculate up and are attacked by solar ultraviolet, to reconstitute the acid and the sulphur.[3] Oxygen and water vapour are attacked in the clouds and therefore traces are found only below them— confirming previous Soviet results. But Venera-11 and -12 found lower strata dense enough to fall as rain: the Pioneer probes may have come down on a particularly clear day.[10]

At 20km the light is reddened, temperature 380°C, and horizontal visibility 20km. At 16km the Pioneers began to record a new kind of glow near the surface, at first thought to be due to spacecraft surfaces heating up[16] but later suspected to be 'chemical fires'.[13] What could release so much energy in those temperatures and pressures remains unknown. 13km above the surface, all four Pioneer probes stopped sending temperature and total-sunlight data for reasons unknown.[14] At 10km visibility should be 12km, in red light only, and temperature 410°C. Below 10km the atmosphere was found to be in convective circulation; surface features should first become visible at 7km, and at ground level visibility would be 3km in optical conditions resembling 'a cloudy day on Earth'[3] (but in red). No evidence has been found for the predicted 'super-refraction', which in theory would let one see right around the planet, but Sagan's vision of the surface as Hell comes ever closer to the mark. The survival record down there is still only 110 minutes (Venera-12).

For longer missions balloons have been suggested, to float at altitudes where conditions are more tolerable. The best radar resolution yet achieved for Venus from Earth, using Arecibo, is about 16km; Venus Orbiting Imaging Radar could resolve features as small as 1km from 290km orbit,[17] although better results could of course be achieved at lower altitude. In 1978 it was announced that a 1983 Soviet orbiter would release a French balloon probe, 8-9m in diameter with a 150kg gondola, for a planned lifetime of 100 hours at 55km.[18] For extended radar mapping that isn't long enough and, by 1979, the proposal was for two balloons to stay up for weeks or months.[19] In 1981 the mission was dropped in favour of a Halley's Comet encounter after Venus slingshot.

All such balloon missions would be high in the clouds and, under attack by sulphuric acid, their actual lifetime might be six days at most.[20] They're out of sight of the surface, although downward photography would be invaluable; and at the mercy of the winds they're almost guaranteed to go round and round over the same terrain or pass places of interest at high speed and just out of range. There's therefore a great deal to be said for a Waverider mission. Airstream kinetic energies for direct entry over Venus are much higher than for Earth [21] —the Pioneer entry probes decelerated at an appalling 565g [14] —but a Waverider could take it gently and cut out the balloon probes' need for prior deceleration into orbit. During entry, it would continue to relay data to Earth; still more importantly, after entry it would descend in a spiral taking in most of the visible hemisphere, sending far more data on wind patterns than the Pioneer probes acquired in their one-hour oblique plunges. (Balloons can measure wind speeds only by tracking surface features, and then only for the airstream in which they're carried.)

To photograph the surface the probe has to go down to 7km, virtually into the worst conditions—but things get really interesting if it can stay 'alive' down there. Below the clouds, said Nonweiler, the atmosphere of Venus is 'embarrassingly thick'. Asked what a Waverider's landing speed would be on Venus after terraforming, assuming a surface pressure of 2-3 atmospheres, he replied: 'You could get out and walk beside it.' In present conditions, even before taking thermals into account (the lower atmosphere is in convection), the Waverider would probably have to drop anchor and winch itself down. Even to dive into the ground as a penetrator would need rocket thrust: the Pioneer Small Probes hit at only 35kph in free drops. It would be easier just to ride around, although to cover large areas it would be necessary to stay higher up, maintaining airspeed, and concentrating on radar studies. To get down to 7km could take years! At higher levels, however, the Waverider must avoid the contracting atmosphere spirals over the poles: the dangers of flying around the north pole in ever-decreasing circles are well known.

Operations on the surface of Venus, manned or unmanned, will be akin to deep-sea technology on Earth. Since the surface winds are low, hovercraft should be very effective, but at those pressures—equivalent to nearly 1km of water, three times the operational limit of Cousteau's Diving Saucer—the vehicles will be more like bathyscaphes than aircraft. Whether or not there is 'super-refraction', sonar is liable to be a major mode of navigation as it is in water. The dynamics of flight near the surface are interesting: even without 'flotation tanks', only 2%

of the corresponding wing area on Earth would be required; 91% of the propulsive thrust would be needed and flight speed would be $\frac{1}{3}$ lower, but payload per vehicle would be a good deal larger. For dirigibles, floated by helium, 3.4 times the propulsive thrust would be needed but only 1.64% of the gas lifting volume. [22]

For the same reasons, rocket lift from the surface would require 2-4 times the fuel needed on Earth. [23] The obvious answer is a base in the clouds—literally a 'Cloudbase', as in the Captain Scarlet series. It might be near the 1-atmosphere pressure level, to use Earth-orbital shuttles with aerodynamic modification only rather than complete redesign—in Bob Buckley's *World in the Clouds* the Cytherea Station is a huge saucer supported by helium cells, at the 1atm level. [24] To avoid sustained exposure to sulphuric acid, however, the base may have to go below 30km; temperatures and pressures would be higher but lift requirements less, and the airstreams less turbulent below the shear zones. Station-keeping over surface bases would be easier and could be achieved with propellers, electrically driven and supplied by powersats in high orbit. As on Mars, jet engines won't function in CO_2; and synchronous orbits are impossible because of the slow rotation—even if the Cloudbase went round in four days with the clouds—so at least two powersats would be needed at the Sun-Venus L1 and L2 points (see page 112).

If rapid atmospheric rotation extended all the way to the ground, landing and takeoff would be hairy but wind power would be plentiful. In ASTRA's 1975 discussions Bill Barr and Linda Lunan spent some time designing a safe wind-turbine for hurricane-force winds at the surface, assuming that with continuing erosion there would be a good deal of windborne rock. Unfortunately, even the plateaux don't go into the clouds—just into the lightning. As already noted, even a 16kph wind in the lower atmosphere could provide as much energy as wave power on Earth; but attractive as it is to imagine Waveriders tethered like kites and sending wind-power down their cables, there's a great risk of suddenly collecting too much energy altogether!

Until Venus is terraformed, surface bases are liable to be scientific only—although, human ingenuity being what it is, someone will probably think up a commercial use, if only for large-scale high-temperature and -pressure experiments. Sagan stipulated that terraforming should begin only after present conditions were fully explored, lest irreplaceable information be lost. [25] The trouble with that is that you can never at any particular time be sure you have *all* you need—especially in the high-temperature test-bed situation. But since Sagan's paper was written, in 1961, Venus has turned out to be 'Hell', as twelve years later he said himself. [2] Terraforming looks like taking a *long* time to affect surface conditions.

Robert Shaw remarked that it would be easy to terraform Venus in a hurry: 'Just turn off the gravity for 2-3 weeks.' The effect might be achieved in reality by a series of impacts so violent that the entire atmosphere was ionized and blown away into space; but, since there would be a great deal of fresh outgassing from the interior, very little might be gained. Sagan proposed a gentler conversion: only a microrganism could achieve significant photosynthesis before dissociation in the atmosphere of Venus, and blue-green algae seem obvious candidates. Some strains can survive in liquid nitrogen and others in hot springs at 80°C. On the ice crystals of the clouds, 'fixing' nitrogen from the atmosphere (with some genetic engineering) and taking up micrometeorite particles for trace elements, they'd absorb carbon dioxide and release oxygen. [25] Carried into the lower atmosphere by convection and roasted, they'd release water vapour and be carbonized. The changing Venus would suffer a gentle rain of soot, and the eventual oceans would be floored with coaldust. Between those two stages would come the tumultuous Big Rain, as temperatures dropped and the clouds fell.

Sagan's concept was so original and visionary that it's still widely cited years after being proved impossible in its original form. The micrometeorite trace elements are there, ironically enough, but nitrogen is only 1-3% of the atmosphere [3] and sulphuric acid droplets are too fine to be a substrate for algae—even if they were immune to the acid. There are bacteria which can live *in* sulphuric acid, but not on it, and even they need it diluted with water. There's water vapour *under* the clouds, but not *among* them, [3] and that rules out Bob Buckley's scenario in which Sagan's algae are replaced by a synthetic, free-floating plant form. [24] Extracting hydrogen and oxygen from pure sulphuric acid to make water doesn't seem possible for carbon-based lifeforms, even with genetic engineering. Algal operations will have to be inside Cloudbases, and that will slow things down a lot.

The possible approaches depend on the altitude of the bases. In the clouds the acid must be removed from the incoming atmosphere (perhaps by electrostatic precipitation), water vapour has to be added, and probably the nitrogen content needs to be enhanced. It would help if we could crack the precipitated acid, but pure ('oleic') sulphuric acid is almost totally non-conducting and can't be electrolysed; and, while thermal dissociation may be easy in space at the foci of big mirrors, in the Cloudbases it would take a great deal of electrical energy, with all the problems of disposing of waste heat in a hot atmosphere.

Below 30km the acid is less of a problem, water vapour is available, and in denser air it'll be easier to gather enough nitrogen. The problem is to cool down the incoming air by more than 200 K so that algae can live in it; no easy task without the heat sinks so readily available in vacuum, and needing a great deal of power in its turn—generating more heat. Perhaps the clouds might be seeded with expendable floating islands, foam structures impregnated with nitrogen and water, providing a substrate for the algae within and protecting them from the acid. Porous interiors offer much larger conversion surfaces than Cloudbase decks, unless honeycombed. As water and nitrogen were used up, the foam would become alkaline, reacting with the acid to form more water and so prolonging the life of the island.

Previously it has been suggested that deep-space transit costs could be cut by two big transfer stations in periodic orbit giving recurring encounters with Earth and Venus. Transit time would be six months on average, and two 'Swing Stations' would be needed to take advantage of every transfer window. [26] If the Earth-Moon L2 point becomes the arrival terminal for asteroidal volatiles (page 132), then Swing Stations could pick up bulk loads each time from a free-space skyhook; and, with a similar skyhook orbiting the Sun-Venus L2, connecting with atmospheric ones orbiting the planet, islands could be placed in the clouds without a fiery atmosphere entry.

If Mars had 25% of its surface covered with algae and was given a carbon-dioxide atmosphere with 1atm pressure, the air might be breathable in 10,000 years. [27] From Table 1 (see page 10), 115 million islands each with a processing area of 1km^2 could in theory give Venus a breathable atmosphere in 3,172,414 years; but, since islands are consumed in operation, many more would actually be needed. Researchers on the surface needn't feel their interests immediately threatened.

As the islands worked on the carbon dioxide, lowering the temperatures, the altitude at which the acid vaporized would descend until acid rain reached the surface and reacted with minerals there. On the way down it would have taken up all the water vapour and left the planet effectively dry. All the water vapour below the clouds even now, according to the Pioneers, would be only knee-deep if spread evenly as liquid over the surface—as compared with an average depth on the same basis of 3km for Earth.[14] Unconsumed acid would work its way down into the crust, with continuing reactions as it went, until the residues collected above impermeable strata. Much later, when temperatures fell below 100°C, water ice could be brought from comets or outer planet moons to give Venus moisture; but, as *it* worked down through the rock, it would be seized upon by the acid reservoirs with fresh releases of heat. The changed Venus might have lots of geothermal power, for a long time, before stable surface waters became possible.

The floating islands attack the acid, generating water. Since more than 90% of the atmospheric mass lies below the clouds, perhaps in sufficient numbers they can take up enough acid for the surface eventually to 'kill' the rest. Reactions with alkalis release water, and that plus what's locked up in biomass within the islands would be all there was, initially, available for true terraforming. Careful tests and calculations would be needed to make sure that enough acid was neutralized for the surface to react with the rest and prevent formation of deadly underground reservoirs. Plans to shield the sunward face of the planet, with webs across multiple-armed skyhooks rotating at Sun-Venus L2, would actually make matters worse by bringing down the acid rain too soon (unless of course the surface has enough metals and alkalis to neutralize it all). With the acid gone, island structures can be open—floating sponges rather than boulders; and they can start work in earnest on bringing down the temperature until algae can take hold and spread on the surface itself.

Serious thought would have to be given to the nature of the new world—if it isn't to be just crater pools, interspersed with vast sulphate flats thinly spread with algae and lichen; the topograhy of Venus doesn't allow half measures. The plains cover 60% of the surface, varying in height by less than

100m [28] though extensively cratered, apparently because of 'surface rebound' after impacts. [29] Pioneer scanning shows only two depressions comparable in area with the Ishtar and Aphrodite plateaux, [30] going 2-3km below the mean level. [29] Filling them and the fifty or so smaller ones would still leave 84% of the planet dry; but going beyond that involves flooding huge areas. One third of Earth's water cover would create a very watery world; half Earth's cover would submerge everything except the plateaux, Beta Regio, and a few nearby islands. Except for the scattered depressions, almost all the planet would be continental shelf, within the range of light-weight submersibles like the Cousteau Saucer. But Venus receives twice as much solar heat as does Earth: without greenhouse effect the poles (at least) would be habitable, [31] but a water-vapour greenhouse is even more efficient than a carbon-dioxide one. L1 sunshades might be needed to keep the greenhouse from running away again. Polar icecaps would help, reflecting sunlight back into space: the small axial tilt, the Ishtar plateau and the Maxwell Mountains could all be crucial in getting icing started, whether the water came from volcanic activity or was delivered from space.

The prospects for terrestrial life are striking. Off the continental shelves much of Earth's surface is unproductive because nutrients sink into darkness and cold, leaving clear 'ocean deserts' above. In the 116.7-day solar 'day' of Venus, there would be energy and time enough to stir up even 2km deeps, but most of the seabed would be much nearer the surface, like the huge commercial fisheries of Peru but on a planet-wide scale.

On the night side there might be an equatorial icecap, continuously thawing on one edge and advancing on the other, like a solid Gegenschein. Solar mirrors at Sun-Venus L2 could disperse it if it became a nuisance when impinging on Aphrodite or Beta Regio. More probably, and more conveniently, it would form two components in higher latitudes. Between 40° and 50°N, and 45° and 55°S, they could travel around the planet without obstruction. Human settlement might begin with a nocturnal civilization harvesting the descendants of imported fish round the edges, and processing on the ice. On the terminator a sea-farm culture would develop, moving into the sunlit hemisphere by one huge slow convection cell at a time as it adapted to dayside conditions. At the subsolar point a permanent cloud would help keep temperatures down, reflecting sunlight, but humidity would be high. Shaw suggested that the cloud would be a ring, a slow hurricane with a clear central eye, surrounded by elliptical circulation cells tending towards the heat sink of the dark side. Cloud cover would help keep up the brightness of Venus in Earth's morning and evening sky, alleviating the wrath of poets.

Adrian Berry has suggested that a Venus culture would have to be nomadic to escape the extremes of temperature, and might not be able to maintain its initial level of civilization. [32] If Venus is exporting seafood in bulk to the rest of the Solar System, however, there seems little need to drop to the level of the raft dwellers in Jack Vance's *The Blue World*. [33] The culture might develop airships up to floating cities, perhaps magnesium shells as Gerry Carter has suggested; lifting cells would be much smaller on Venus, even after terraforming, and Waveriders could still be launched with a good push.

If the atmosphere after terraforming is still too hot and stormy there might be seabed settlements farming the oceans from below, analogous to the 'Keeps' in Henry Kuttner's *Fury*. [34] During the night they could use solar mirrors at L2, 'geothermal' power and, if necessary, nuclear fusion to keep the sea productive and force the icecaps to go around them, although that might conflict with another possibility for semipermanence—a creeping city on the ice, lifting its tracks behind and setting them down before, like the one in the still stranger setting of Christopher Priest's *Inverted World*. [35] Permanent floes of refrigerated ice-clathrate with additives raising the freezing point (an idea considered for wartime aircraft-carriers) might be anchored over seabed cities, so reducing the need to use water-landing plug-nozzle ferries in place of Waveriders, although they'd float lower under 3-4 atmospheres' pressure than on Earth.

In a sense this chapter has been a digression from our main theme. Venus doesn't offer immediate strategic possibilities, not even the emergency survival option given by Mars. Until the planet is terraformed its only apparent uses are for research, although for all we know by early next century new technologies may make Venus a prime target. In the mean time, crucial decisions have to be taken nearer home. Both sides of that question were foreshadowed by William Harkness of the US Naval Observatory, writing on the transit of Venus across the face of the Sun, as seen from Earth, in 1882: [36] 'There will be no other [transit of Venus] till the twenty-first century of our era has dawned upon the earth, and the June flowers are blooming in 2004. When the last transit occurred the intellectual world was awakening from the slumber of ages, and that wondrous scientific activity which has led to our present advanced knowledge was just beginning. What will be the state of science when the next transit season arrives God only knows.'

The Workshop of the Solar System

Ours has been the first, and will doubtless be the last, party of whites to visit this profitless locality.
—Lieutenant J. C. Ives, discoverer of the Grand Canyon, 1859

So far, only one 'party' has visited Mercury, the Mariner-10 spacecraft in 1974. Before it ran out of attitude control gas, three flybys took place, thanks to daring use of techniques like orienting the spacecraft by sunlight pressure on its solar panels.[1] Almost everything we know about Mercury came from the Mariner-10 flybys: even the period of rotation was determined by radar only in 1965, and that proved to be a great if cruel joke. Mercury rotates in 59 days, two-thirds of its year, so its *solar* day is 176 days, two of its years. Straining to make out markings on the small, distant disc, astronomers had been fooled into thinking that Mercury kept the same face towards the Sun all the time.

It wasn't clear whether the rotation was in exact Sun-lock at perihelion (Mercury's orbit is markedly elliptical), or in overall Sun-lock over two Hermian (Mercury) years. The latter is correct: the same two points on Mercury's surface take turns to receive the greatest roasting when the planet is nearest to the Sun. One lies in a huge impact basin, appropriately named Caloris; the other 'heat pole' is 'chaotic terrain', apparently due to focussed shockwaves from the Caloris event. Mariner-10 met the planet at Caloris Basin sunset, and, because the probe's subsequent period was 176 days, the illumination was the same for the second and third encounters. (In *Solar System*, by Ryan and Pesek, the half-hemisphere maps from Mariner photographs are engagingly titled 'Mercury West One' and 'Mercury West Two'.[2]) Because the second pass was over the south pole, the total coverage of the surface was 37%.

The mass of the planet couldn't be determined from Earth because Mercury has no known moon. Asimov has calculated that the outer limit for a stable satellite orbit is where the Sun's gravitational pull is $\frac{1}{30}$ that from the planet, in Mercury's case only 2093km from the centre, which he describes as well within the Roche Limit where a sizeable satellite would be pulled apart by tidal forces.[3] (Indeed, since Mercury's diameter is 4800km, the moon would be orbiting underground.) Mariner-10 found Mercury's mass was higher than generally expected: about 4.5 times the mass of our Moon[4] for about three times the volume. The effect would be to move Asimov's 'safe zone' out, but the Roche Limit likewise, so satellites are still not to be expected. The density implies a nickel-iron core like those of Earth and Venus, and—despite the negative results for the Moon and Venus, the near-zero field of Mars and Mercury's slow rotation—Mercury has a relatively powerful magnetic field, compressed by the Solar Wind right down to the surface on the sunward side. With, as a result, no radiation belts, and no atmosphere apart from the Solar Wind over the sunlit hemisphere, there's no protection from solar-flare particles and cosmic rays. As on the Moon and Mars, settlements will almost certainly have to be below ground.

The cratering on Mercury proved that all the inner planets, including Earth, had been subjected to the 'final bombardment phase' in the formation of the Solar System. Mercury's *maria* are thinner and more patchy than the Moon's, and their crater counts imply that they formed during the bombardment instead of up to a billion years later, as on the Moon.[5] After the pounding ceased, the crust split to form great scarps not seen on any other planet: Discovery Scarp, for instance, runs for 500km and is 3km in height, cutting craters, hills and plains. Unlike Earth, Venus, Mars and the Moon, all of which show or at least hint at crustal spreading, Mercury's crust appears to have contracted; and it is argued that the core may have cooled, contracted and solidified, 'freezing' the magnetic field.[6] It seems that Mercury has a Man-in-the-Moon-like hemisphere and another more like Farside; this may support the long-standing conjecture that Mercury was originally a moon of Venus or, more accurately, a twin planet. When eventually we have a Mercury orbiter, it will be interesting to see whether Mercury's centre of mass is displaced to the *maria* side like the Moon's.

James Strong suggested a 'clamshell' orbiter with closed reflecting panels protecting it in sunlight and opening to radiate heat in shadow;[6] but the only modification to the basic Mariner design was to tilt the solar panels on their long axes so that sunlight struck them obliquely[1] (adopted in preference to the V-configuration shown in Plate 11 of *New Worlds for Old*). Since then the Helios probes have gone millions of kilometres nearer to the Sun with a conventional layout. In 1976 a Shuttle-launched Mercury orbiter was proposed for 1987,[7] but no funding has been allocated.

Ed Buckley predicted that the first manned landings on Mercury would be made near the terminator, as on the Moon, so that temperatures would be fairly low and hazards easily seen. Extended stays should be around 100°W or 60°E, safely on the terminator at perihelion; so touchdown should be at aphelion, and conditions would (we'd hope) be least demanding and geologically most stable. Caloris and its antipodes get 2.5 times the overall solar radiation of intermediate longitudes,[8] and at perihelion they take ten times the illumination on the Moon,[1] itself 20% higher than at Earth's surface.[9] The overall movement of the Sun is west to east, so the preferred site would have the less prestigious 'Mercury West Two' address, on the longitude of Sobkou Plantitia.[2] The very low axial tilt means high latitudes never have the Sun high in the sky at all; and sites like Boreas Plantitia, which takes in the north pole and extends westwards from 90° longitude, would be the safest on the planet—although even there the rotation plays a trick with the Sun that has to be watched for (see below).

Strong suggested a more dangerous strategy for unmanned rovers, landing in Caloris Basin or the chaotic terrain opposite, at the midpoint between aphelion and perihelion when they're on the terminator. A rover would have to move east at only 3.7kph to stay on the terminator throughout the Hermian day;[6] but it's asking a lot to get across the Caloris Mountains ringing the basin, or even the hummocky plain of Odin Plantitia which breaches them, while moving in long shadows. The chasms of the chaotic terrain would be still more difficult—if not impossible—and control would almost certainly have to be from orbit overhead rather than from Earth; moreover, for eight days around perihelion, just when the Sun is at its biggest and most fierce, the planet's rotation goes through simple sun-lock to halt the Sun in the sky, then move it back westwards. The rover on the sunset terminator gets a roasting and the sunrise one is plunged into a night as severe as the Moon's.

Buckley's Multi-Environment Lander can be used for Mercury without modification: although surface gravity is near that of Mars, escape velocity is lower and there's no atmosphere, so the extra tank module isn't required. However, long-stay shielding from cosmic rays and emergency solar-flare protection would need an underground base. The extra fuel module might therefore be used to increase the payload; and the penetrator technique might be used to implant deep shelters as on the Moon (pages 128-9).

So near the Sun, Mercury provides a fascinating laboratory: it resembles Earth in having a magnetic field, Venus in having a slow rotation, and the Moon in having no atmosphere. Mercury studies should reveal interactions with the Solar Wind, etc., which affect the other planets more subtly. The Sun itself could be intensively studied, as from Skylab but at much closer range, and this time the observers would be shielded by many metres of rock instead of the rather chancy protection of Earth's Van Allen belts. (Unfortunately neither of Mercury's poles has 'Mountains of Eternal Day' like the Moon's ideal sites for solar observatories.) Solar effects on comets, at their nearest to the Sun, could be studied for data on the *outer* Solar System (see Chapter 12).

It seems Mercury has Moon-like soil, rich in dark glasses with high iron and titanium content, [10] although the regolith is either patchy or pierced by protruding rocks. [11] Going by the planet's density, we would expect Mercury to be richer in metals and heavy elements than the Moon. There's no atmosphere to impede electromagnetic launches and, although surface gravity and escape velocity are higher than the Moon's, so too are solar power levels. The 88 days' darkness could be inconvenient, but by the time Mercury is industrialized nightside power-supply from solar-L2 powersats or mirrors will be a standard technique. Since nightside temperatures fall to $-173°C$, [1] and can be brought lower in insulated systems radiating to space, the Caloris Basin may see some exotic industries with 88- to 176-day production cycles.

The only problems with Hermian resources are the energies required to reach and export them. Without its Venus sling-

Plate 5   Terraformed Venus. Since much of Venus' surface is flat, relatively little water would have to be imported (after the atmosphere had been modified) to make Venus a watery, Earthlike world—although its weather patterns would be unlike Earth's. Painted before Pioneer-Venus-1 radar-mapped the surface from orbit, this view shows Alpha Regio and Beta Regio without the great volcanoes. Ishtar Terra, with the great Maxwell Montes, would be in the area under cloud at upper right, which then had not been scanned from Earth. (*Roberts.*)

Plate 6   Multi-Environment Lander over Io. The MEL could be used on the Moon, Mercury, Pluto and the moons of the giant planets, and, with extra fuel tankage, on Mars (see page 149). But on Io, Europa and Ganymede its operation could be only unmanned, unless the moons can be shielded using artificial magnetic fields (see page 214). (*Buckley, based on Pioneer imagery.*)

Plate 7   'Gothic arch' Waverider in Jupiter's upper atmosphere. The fins on the upper surface are not stabilizers but booms for atmosphere-sampling probes projecting into the slipstream. The ammonia-crystal plume rising out of the depths may be 50km high, or more. (*Buckley, based on Pioneer imagery.*)

Plate 8 'Caret wing' Waverider approaching Titan's haze layers. Landing probes designed for surface conditions are carried as 'deck cargo', protected during entry through the atmosphere without requiring streamlining. Unmanned 'gliding entry' missions could be used to develop Waverider designs for commercial use in the next century. (*Roberts, based on Voyager imagery.*)

Plate 9 O'Neill habitat with Daedalus engine. Mobile habitats will need more compact and robust structures for industry and agriculture; in this variant they have been built from the core cylinder as 'wings'. The habitats' radiation-shielding will let them penetrate Jupiter's powerful radiation belts. Europa is crossing the face of the planet, and the equatorial ring can be seen near Ganymede. The scene is a century or more from now, and it's supposed that the redness of the Great Red Spot has continued to fade, as it has done during the 20th century. (*Roberts, based on Voyager imagery.*)

Plate 11   Jupiter   industrialized   (see Chapter XI). A free-flying Solar-Wind scoop is being redirected back to Uranus at the end of its mission, with the help of a close pass by an artificial magnetic-field generator at the Jupiter/Europa L2 point. On the night-side of the planet a 'mini-sun' lights up the clouds for hundreds of kilometres in all directions. *(Roberts, 1979.)*

late 10 ‗   Mobile habitat showing Daeda-ıs engine bell and thermal/radiation shield-ıg. The 'wing' design of Plate 9 has been xtended into a complex polygonal structure ıcorporating larger deuterium/helium tank-ʒe. The imaginary outer-planet moon in the ackground is similar to Ganymede, with ːooved terrain and older, larger craters in ırious stages of erasure, but with less ırface ice visible. *(Roberts.)*

Plate 12   Industry on Triton (see pages 233-34). This prophetic painting anticipated the discovery of cloud-features on Neptune and of subsurface oceans, heated by tidal forces, on Jupiter's Galilean moons: Neptune/Triton interaction is believed to be even stronger. (*Buckley, 1975.*)

shot, Mariner-10 would have needed a Saturn V launch, or else either a solar sail or ion-drive. [12] The 1973-74 two-planet window was a particularly suitable one, not to recur until 1987[1] (hence the orbiter proposal). Even the 1985 and 1988 launch windows involve longer flight-times, and a Mercury orbiter would stretch the Shuttle/Centaur combination to its limits. [12] Payload could be improved by *multiple* Venus flybys—e.g., in a 31-month transfer with three Venus flybys after the 1985 launch—but manned visits are likely to wait until Daedalus engines make all transfer routinely hyperbolic. But Mercury-Venus conjunctions are relatively frequent, and transit time for industrial payload usually doesn't matter as long as deliveries are regular, so Venus slingshots may be used in the EML export programme—with or without skyhook assistance—until Venus terraforming is completed. The new inhabitants of Venus are likely to object to the occasional misdirected payload penetrating the atmosphere to add to their landscape, and unfortunately it's much easier to hit a planet than to stage a close flyby.

If Mercury was originally a moon of Venus, there may be volatiles such as water bound up in the rocks (our Moon's rocks, it would seem, formed initially much nearer the Sun). Carbon, nitrogen and hydrogen compounds and water in particular would make settling Mercury and 'half-terra-forming' much easier than if they had to be imported from the asteroids (see Chapter 10). Hoyle and Wickramasinghe have suggested that Venus, Earth and Mars acquired their volatiles from bombardment by comets [13] and, if so, or if Mercury did form at its present distance from the Sun, then the rocks will be more Moonlike; although near both poles there are small, steep-sided craters which could act as 'cold traps' and preserve some ices from sublimation. [8] But, whatever their availability, Mercury is too near the Sun for open-surface terraforming.

'Orboforming' is, however, possible. Dyson has suggested that Earth could be made to spin faster or slower, with metallic windings on the surface and orbiting, solar-powered EMF generators. [14] With a total energy-collecting surface 100 times the area of the Earth, the satellites could stop the planet's rotation in 2500 years. Or, speeding up the rotation instead, centrifugal force at the equator could balance the pull of gravity in 40,000 years. The timescales for Mercury would be shorter, since the planet is less massive and solar generators would be more efficient.

Mercury's rotation could be slowed to 88 days, so that it did after all keep the same face always to the Sun. The great heat and cold in the respective hemispheres could both be put to work, perhaps in joint operations; dayside solar stations might power darkside industries, shedding their waste heat into space. Steps would no doubt be taken to protect the useful high-grade vacuum at the centre of the darkside, in the Solar Wind 'tail' of the planet. With still higher technology (see Chapter 12) the planet might be moved closer to the Sun to increase the day/night differentials. The terminator regions would be 'libration zones' in which the Sun rose and set over 88 days; such conditions might be exploited for slow-moving low-gravity processes of some kind.

Speeding up the rotation would make solar energy more uniformly available over the surface, with orbiting mirrors to supply energy during the shortened night. If rotational velocity were just short of disruption at the equator, a continuous EML band there, permanently subsolar, could fire off payloads at large velocities to other parts of the Solar System. Alternatively, the spin might be increased to just above disruption speed, with a restraining band holding down the equator: payloads from the mines fed on to it would take off and float slowly outwards, to be captured and processed by orbiting factories.

Such large-scale conversion would make Mercury the 'Workshop of the Solar System'; processing usually goes to the raw materials, and Mercury's matter and energy resources are richer than the Moon's. But production facilities could be extended by habitats moving sunwards for energy, and, unless there are essential processes on the planet, its fate could then be sealed. With Dyson's scenario taken to its logical conclusion the planet would be broken apart, its resources used up, and the habitats dispersed to new orbits, probably further from the Sun. Adrian Berry has suggested a still more drastic measure, that Mercury should be sacrificed to provide shielding material during the destruction of Jupiter.[15] It seems a shame: there is a case for conserving the planets as symbols, not just for sentiment but as a reminder that uncontrolled expansion can't be continued indefinitely. The issue bears directly on the philosophy of the emerging Kardashev-2 civilization and will be addressed in Chapter 13.

Your Considerate Stone

Sure my heart is nearly broken,
From the clear daylight till the dawn,
And I'm afraid I'll never be able,
For to plough the rocks of Bawn.
—*Irish traditional*

Anthony You wrong this presence; therefore speak no more.
Enobarus Go to, then; your considerate stone.
—Shakespeare, *Antony and Cleopatra*

It's always been supposed that Mars, Venus and Mercury would be the targets for manned spaceflight, after the Moon; but apart from their scientific interest they're second-generation or later 'strategic' targets, and have no direct bearing on Politics-of-Survival questions. The strategic approach points instead to the asteroids which surround the inner planets and occasionally threaten them.

Asteroids are divided into the Main Belt, between the orbits of Mars and Jupiter, and the 'Earth-grazers', divided technically into the 'Apollo class', which cross the orbit of the Earth, and the 'Amor class', which don't. But the term 'Earth-grazer' is valuable, because it focusses attention on the specific threat to us.

In 1979 Drs Alvarez, Asaro and Michel discovered relatively high concentrations of iridium in sediments deposited worldwide 65 million years ago. Their interpretation is that Earth was struck by a body massing about 13 trillion tonnes, which would have thrown a hundred times its own mass into the atmosphere. Such a volume of dust, 1600 times that ejected by Krakatoa, could have blocked off sunlight from the Earth's surface for three to five years,[1] causing worldwide loss of plant cover and a 'Great Dying' of the larger herbivores and carnivores—both classes of the larger dinosaurs. Small mammals, probably nocturnal in any case, survived on rotting vegetation, carrion and fungi, as well as by prolonged hibernation, to take over as the dominant lifeform on Earth. The ocean food chain would similarly have been disrupted, causing the disappearance of marine reptiles.

The asteroid might have been 7-10km across and made a crater 150km in diameter, five times the size of the Vredevoort impact ring in Africa. 'Vredevoort events' don't occur more than once in five million years, on average,[2] but there's evidence of a 250km crater in Antarctica, under the ice,[3] and in the history of the Earth the 'Great Dying' of the dinosaurs is, although exceptional, not unique. Smaller 'megadeaths' in geological time seem to be associated with reversals of the magnetic field, even when marine species are involved,[4] so maybe impacts *cause* the apparently random reversals every 100,000 to 10 million years—perhaps by disrupting the dynamo currents in the core.[5] If so, then, since the average separation is 170,000 years, we may think ourselves lucky that there hasn't been one for 700,000 years.[6]

That one, presumably, wasn't a sea impact, or we might not be here. In 1966 Enever pointed out that a sea impact would be much worse for all concerned.[2] When an asteroid strikes a continent, little or nothing survives on that land mass, but the crater reradiates much of the impact energy into space. A sea impact (as three out of four would be) causes huge tidal waves which sweep the lowlands of the world, and generates a terrifying image: an actual crater in the sea, punched through the Earth's crust to the rising magma. As the water tries to close over the pit it simply vaporizes, adding more and more vapour and energy to the tortured atmosphere above. There has never been a storm like it in the existence of Man—the most violent annual hurricanes would be just eddies on its perimeter. Sufficient numbers *might* survive to continue the human race, but collapse of civilization seems certain. John Baxter makes a brave try at describing the effects in *The Hermes Fall*,[7] but probably overestimates the resilience of high-technology culture; he doesn't describe the process of recovery.

As of 1978, 38 Earth-grazers were known, 19 'Apollos' and 19 'Amors', compared with 7 in 1951; a year's search with a 48in (122cm) Schmidt camera would probably double the number, and the figure for bodies down to 100m diameter could be as high as 100,000. All those currently known will hit Earth, Venus or the Moon over the next 100 million years, a frequency which Brian O'Leary rather casually dismisses as 'rare';[8] there have been three major events in the last thousand years, one on the Moon and two on Earth in 1908 and 1947. Another body flew up the middle of the US in 1972 and left the atmosphere without striking the ground. However, most of the bigger objects entering the atmosphere are very loosely structured, probably originating from comets. Isaac Asimov termed 19-tonne masses 'city-busters',[9] but almost without exception they disintegrate in flight; and the brightest recorded fireball, the 200-tonne Sumava 1974, would have been too fragile to stick together under Earth-surface gravity.[10] The 1908 Tunguz object exploded near the ground, apparently disintegrating completely into dust, and Ian Ridpath suggests that it was a carbonaceous chondrite[11] (see below); had it been an active comet nucleus, ice and all, large fragments would almost certainly have cratered the ground below.

But the Tunguz event had all the other features of a big impact: the explosion was high in the megaton range and devastated a huge forest region. On the latitude of Leningrad, had it been $4\frac{3}{4}$ hours later it would have been the biggest disaster in the history of civilization—even the explosion of Théra hit only coastal settlements. The Sikhote-Alin object in 1947 created 106 craters up to 28m across[12] and, since five tonnes of meteoritic iron were subsequently collected, it was apparently from the Main Belt rather than from a comet. The 1972 object over the US had a mass between 30 and 4000 tonnes, depending on composition, and since it didn't disintegrate or fragment, despite coming into dense enough air to generate sonic booms, the upper value is more likely.[13] Arthur C. Clarke wrote of an imaginary 1000-tonne impact: 'It was as if a great war had been fought and lost in a single morning.'[14] But in our present situation the real fear for human survival is that such an event might precipitate the last war of all.

One of the most feckless arguments on this subject is that 'the chances are millions to one'. As just over half the people who've played Russian Roulette can testify, the small chance that a given chamber will go off is a mathematical fiction: similarly for the asteroid and the Earth there's one day which counts and the rest, no matter how numerous, are immaterial. Nor can anything, at present, alter the odds on the day itself—asteroids hardly ever have misfires—but in twenty years' time there could be a chance for us to do so and in fifty years, all being well, the odds on impact could be reversed.

Adequate preparedness goes a long way beyond just retaining nuclear missiles, avoiding disarmament so that all the world's warheads can be used against an incoming asteroid: the chances of finding, reaching and affecting one have all been grossly overestimated. Earth-grazers are found by the trails they make on time-exposed photographic plates—and, dark, small objects as they are, the range of detection is only a few million kilometres. Asteroids on collision courses won't form noticeable trails on such plates, and half of them will approach the daylight hemisphere like the Tunguz object and not be photographed at all. Moreover, an astronomer who's been up all night taking a time exposure normally goes to bed. The velocities of passing Earth-grazers average 30kps [15] but can range between 8 and 65kps according to the configuration of the encounter. At average velocity, the object will be here from the distance of the Moon in under 3.6 hours; unless the observatory is on a mountain the odds are that the astronomer will never wake up, much less develop the plate. But even if the asteroid is detected and recognized immediately at ten times that distance, and the world's political and military leaders accept the fact, how many missiles—designed to hit targets on Earth, fixed with respect to the launch sites—could be reprogrammed for a target 1-10km across, closing at up to 76kps, in the final plunge, in time to do any good?

The major destructive effects of a nuclear explosion are caused by atmospheric shockwaves, and in space even the heat flash is for the most part transformed into X-rays. Current theory is that enough of the approaching asteroids' surface would vaporize to generate a sideways thrust. [16] Since a close flyby is even harder in guidance terms than a direct hit, and the asteroid's path may have to be shifted by up to 6000km, it could go down in history, if there *was* any more history, as the least effective military operation on behalf of the environment since the bombing of the *Torrey Canyon*.

If a manned ship could get to the asteroid, destruct charges might do some good. The hardest thing to believe in *The Hermes Fall* is that there's time, a booster available, and a big enough fuel reserve to achieve a rendezvous with an Apollo spacecraft. In the *TV* series *Men into Space* a larger Moon-rocket reached an incoming asteroid and destroyed it with conventional explosives planted on the surface; but the force of the explosion would be spent into vacuum, and even the remark by one of Baxter's characters, 'To a hydrogen bomb, that thing's just a pebble',[7] is untrue unless it can be planted well below the surface. Even then, unless the asteroid is a Tunguz object ready to shatter completely into dust, the best that can be achieved is to split it by shockwaves and internal resonance.* If a billion-tonne asteroid shattered into a million pieces, each of them would mass 1000 tonnes and inflict as many casualties as Clarke's 'great war fought and lost'. Together they would firestorm a continent—the effects might be worse than a big, centralized impact on land, although better than one in the sea.

To deal effectively with the hazard, we shall have to track all the potential Earth-grazers in orbit around the Sun, reach any which pose threats *before* they're on collision course, and deal with them not by sudden violence but by changing their orbits or by dismantling them completely. Fortunately the Earth-grazing asteroids are the next strategic approach target, and industrializing them will let us take 'big impacts' off the Politics-of-Survival list.

We left the Starseeds, or their equivalents, in orbit around the Earth-Moon L2 point at the end of the powersat construction phase. Orbiting factories are in a major growth phase with materials supply from the Moon and, as the Moon goes in for deep mining settlements, more personnel are required. They'll need bulk supplies of carbon, nitrogen and hydrogen compounds, and if as suggested Island One is to be stationed at L2 as the counterweight of a lunar beanstalk then even more volatiles will be required to build the stalk and fit out the habitat for occupation. From now on such operations should be 'Free on Earth' so, while some of the Starseeds may go into 2:1 resonance orbit to work on habitat hulls, and most of them will probably be wanted urgently nearer Earth as testbeds for the orbital factory programme, one or more should be assigned to the first convenient Earth-grazing asteroid.

---

*I tried to draw attention to these points in a story called 'How to Blow Up an Asteroid'. It was so heavily rewritten by the magazine concerned that I can't point to it without embarrassment. This note is just to disown the absurdities and prejudices grafted in.

Cole and Cox pointed out in 1964 that a mission to Wilson-Harrington, an ambiguous object (Amor-class asteroid or short-period comet) discovered in 1949, would require a delta-v from close-Earth orbit of only 3.94kps, compared with 6.01kps for a Moon landing and 10.7kps for a Mars landing with atmospheric braking over Mars and Earth. [17] The mission would take six weeks, using cryogenic propellants. Geographos and Eros, two of the most famous Earth-grazers, could be visited for 7.56kps on direct transfer. But the bulk of the delta-v for Geographos lay in the 13° plane-change to reach its inclined orbit, so a Venus flyby, Geographos landing and return to Earth could be achieved for only 5.5kps—less than the 6.01kps required for a Moon landing, let alone the 15.85kps needed for Venus itself. [17]

Ironically, however, the easier the transfer, the less convenient the result. The closer the asteroid's orbit is to Earth's own, the longer the 'synodic period' before a given configuration recurs and the longer the 'waiting time' before a return launch window to Earth. Asteroid 1976 AA, which passed Earth at about 19.3 million km and was described as 'one of the easiest places to get to in our Solar System, apart from the Moon', circles the Sun 20 times in 19 Earth years and won't be near Earth again until the 1990s. [18] Eros, although harder to reach, generates launch windows every two years; [19] and Toro, which ranges in a remarkable 'swing-station' orbit between those of Mars and Venus, passes the Earth at 12 million km every 53 months, alternately to sunwards of the planet and behind it. Initially such targets will be preferred, if they're carbonaceous chondrites like 1976 AA. Both Eros [20] and Toro [21] appear to have mixed compositions and are relatively unpromising.

Many Earth-grazers may be cometary nuclei, trapped by the planets into short-period orbits around the Sun and stripped of their ices by solar radiation. The fireball evidence and the dramatic dissolution of the Tunguz object suggest that their materials were never compressed in any significant gravity field. Yet meteorites which reach Earth's surface have obviously been thus compressed, apparently within different bodies, and probably come from the Main Belt asteroids whose diameters range up to 1000km. [22] At one time they were thought to be debris of a planet which might have fragmented as recently as 16 million years ago. Asteroids aren't observed in retrograde orbits, however, ruling out a core explosion; and a noncentral one would have exposed Earth to a lethal radiation flux and bombardment; even the Sun would have flared with the energy of the impacts. [23]

Although the total mass of the asteroids is uncertain, no estimates put it higher than 10% of the Earth's and many are as low as 0.1%. Only 112 are known with diameters over 100km, and many of their spectra suggest stony-iron composition, like the denser meteorites. These may be the remaining cores of 'planetesimals' which melted and differentiated internally, but collided too violently under the influence of Jupiter to stick together and grow to planetary size. The other asteroids would be mostly shattered crustal fragments. Chondritic material would have formed the mantles of the planetesimals and only in those nearest the Sun would 'chondrules'—embedded, fused spheres of silicates—be absent. Carbonaceous chondrites, rich in water and naturally synthesized organic compounds, would have formed as the outer layers of all planetesimals further than 2.3AU [21] from the Sun. The main body of the Belt lies beyond 3AU, and the proportion of carbonaceous asteroids rises from 50% at the inner edge of the Belt (2.1AU) to 95% in its outer regions [22] (3.3AU at least).

Asteroid distribution has been influenced by collisions and close encounters, by the pulls of the planets and particularly that of Jupiter. 'Families' apparently originate from single collision events, [24] and 'jetstreams' are produced by mutual attraction. [25] Jupiter's pull divides the Belt into three main bands, separated by 'Kirkwood gaps' where the orbital period is in resonance with Jupiter's; its outer moons are evidently captured asteroids, and the Sun-Jupiter L4 and L5 regions contain 'Trojan' asteroids which can also be regarded as captured. One of the Trojans, Hektor, rotates too fast to hold together even at stony-iron density, and may be double; [26] the 243km asteroid Herculina has been deduced to have a satellite 42-49km in diameter; [27] similar sightings have been reported at almost all times when asteroids have passed in front of stars; [28] and 400 million years ago the Canadian Shield was struck by twin objects dense enough to form the East and West Clearwater Lakes. [2, 29] Apparently, when two planetesimals collided and shattered, the cores often remained in orbit about each other. Later collisions and slingshots would tend to split up the partnerships; Eros, for example, is apparently alone, like all the other Earth-grazers, although silicates and nickel-iron on its battered surface suggest that it's a particularly ill-used core fragment. [20]

Since the first strategic aim is to secure volatiles for the Moon, the habitats and the lunar beanstalk, the surface composition of our target asteroid will have to be studied spectroscopically beforehand to make sure we get a carbonaceous one. A varied surface like Toro's might do at a pinch, but there are enough problems in landing on an asteroid to make us want the first one to be desirable territory all over. It's been calculated that asteroid rotations should stabilize in 10-100,000 years, and collisions won't usually make their axes precess; [30] but Chinese astronomers report that Eros has a nutational wobble [31] despite the great age implied by its extremely rough surface. The shapes of the asteroids, their low gravities and their relatively rapid rotations, give them all the worst characteristics of space habitats—with no docking ports. Icarus has the shortest known rotational period, 2h 16.4min, [32] but even Eros at 5.27h is rotating fast enough to make effective gravity lower at the equator than at the poles—where it's estimated to be only $0.001g$. Worse still, Eros is 37km by 16km and rotates about its short axis, so in effect there are two very high mountains whirling round on its equator.

One reason for Lunar Orbit Rendezvous in Project Apollo was that, had the entire Apollo craft had to land on the Moon and lift off again, the vehicle would have been much taller than the simple Lunar Module; someone compared it to trying to land the Empire State Building without being able to see the landing gear. Cole and Cox proposed to try it on an asteroid because the low gravity would make landing easier and safer: an illustration from GEC showed a vehicle about 21m tall sitting comfortably on an asteroid surface with rigid landing gear and no anchorage. [17] For lunar $\frac{1}{6}g$ the LM legs were crushable, not hydraulic, partly to reduce overall weight but also to absorb kinetic energy instead of rebounding. In an Eros landing the upward reaction from the surface would be equal to the momentum at touchdown (proportional to the *mass* of the ship), less whatever energy was absorbed by the landing gear, while the effective *weight* to counteract it would be about a thousand times less than on Earth. 'And all I ask is a tall ship and a star to bounce her off ...'

Throw in a triaxial rotation for the asteroid ... and if you really fancy yourself as a pilot make the ship 21m tall with rigid legs. For my money, you'll still be off the surface and trying to recover attitude control when the long axis of Eros comes round like the biggest fly-swatter in the Solar System.

James Strong suggested landing on the axis of rotation,[33] but apparently Eros presents difficulties in that respect. The probe or ship could throw out anchors to catch on surface irregularities, then winch itself down. The anchor point would have to be very near the pole, or the descending craft would acquire side motions. In 'How to Blow up an Asteroid' (see page 187) I had cables shot from the landing gear, tipped with explosive pitons, but that won't work on the dust or regolith which covers most asteroids. Robert Shaw suggested a 'thistle-down' spacecraft, mesh ball, or series of loops like the Lunar Rover wheel, flattening itself against the surface and releasing adhesive at points of contact. The vehicle would have a separable ascent stage so that future dockings could be made into the collar left behind. Without the adhesives, it could be the only practicable unmanned asteroid rover. But whatever the landing gear, the best way to approach an asteroid is in something big enough (like a Starseed) to carry small landers, highly manoeuvrable, from which you can see what you're doing.

In mining carbonaceous chondrite material for volatiles, the easiest way to get the products home would be as unrefined rock, launched by mass driver. If water and so on are extracted at the asteroid, then containers have to be provided for transit. But, since the Starseed is much more than just a mining unit, processing experiments will start at once and the resources of other Earth-grazers will come in for increasing scrutiny. An 'ordinary' chondrite body 1.6km in diameter would contain more than 20 million tonnes of iron;[34] but the planetesimal core fragments should be made up almost entirely of iron and nickel, which is in short supply on Earth; a fragment 900m in diameter could contain up to 30 *billion* tonnes of iron. Such asteroids are rare, but some are among the Earth-grazers and pose the biggest threat to us; in mastering them, we establish the foundation for a huge expansion of our industrial civiliza-tion. Between here and the Belt and in its inner sections we can expect at least half the asteroids to be 'ordinary' chondrites, for which J. A. Wood compiled a table from meteor analyses[17] (Table 5), of many of the elements, common and exotic, on

Table 5

Component	% weight	Element concentrations / million silicon atoms						
SiO_2	38.29	He	0.11	Se	17	I	0.05
MgO	23.93	Li	50	Br	32-2	Cs	0.12
FeO	11.95	Be	0.64	Rb	7	Ba	4.00
Al_2O_3	2.72	C	20,000-2000	Sr	20	La	0.4
CaO	1.90	N	90	Y	3.6	Ce	1.1
Na_2O	0.90	F	300	Zr	65	Pr	0.2
K_2O	0.10	Ne	0.0015	Nb	1	Nd	0.8
Cr_2O_3	0.37	Cl	1000	Mo	2.5	Sm	0.3
MnO	0.26	Ar	0.4	Ru	1.6	Eu	0.1
TiO_2	0.11	Sc	30	Rh	0.27	Gd	0.4
P_2O_5	0.20	V	160-900	Pd	1.1	Tb	0.06
H_2O	0.27	Co	1200	Ag	0.13	Dy	0.3
FeS	5.89	Cu	190	Cd	0.064	Ho	0.08
Total silicates	81.00	Zn	120	In	0.0013	Er	0.2
		Ga	12	Sn	1.1	Tm	0.04
Total metals	13.11	Ge	19	Sb	0.1	Yb	0.2
		As	4.7	Te	1		

which industrial civilization depends. Quantities might seem to be insignificant, until the masses of the asteroids are take into account. Gold and the platinum group of elements (not listed above) are together present in 50-60 parts per million by weight, in both iron and stone meteorites. Thus a typical 1000m-diameter asteroid, whatever its composition otherwise, should contain 25-30 thousand tonnes of platinum-group metals—current Earth value is at least \$2 million per tonne. Delivery of just one iridium or platinum-bearing asteroid to Earth would have a dramatic effect on the values of rare metals ('especially at the point of impact').

The point is that we can process asteroids in their entirety for the materials they contain. Surface gravity is trivial for all but the largest, and there's no atmosphere to impede processing or payload launch. Large-scale metal processing will be on-site because zero-*g* techniques have been mastered in Earth orbit; and there's no point in shifting ore back to Earth when it doesn't need the silicates while, to the asteroid community, the oxides are 'oxygen-ore', as Jean Sendy called it. Even more precious to the chondrite outpost is the 0.27% by weight of water; apart from its rôle in life support, it may be relatively rich (like cometary nuclei[35]) in deuterium for fusion power and Daedalus engines. Better yet, carbonaceous chondrites are 13-20% water by weight,[1] and that water *is* deuterium-rich—up to 35% more than standard terrestrial samples from Lake Michigan[36] —while their 'bituminous' matter is 4% nitrogen by weight and rich in carbon, as their name implies.

As Stine points out, the key economic factor in exploiting the asteroids is delta-v, not cargo trip time.[37] From Earth's surface to orbit, delta-v is 8kps; from the Moon's surface to Earth orbit, about 5.48kps; from Eros to Earth orbit, about 3.66kps;[1] from a typical Belt asteroid to Earth orbit, 8kps again.[38] But in delivery to Earth's surface by Waverider or capsule those last three figures are each reduced by up to 3.2kps; and, using solar-powered EMLs, launches are free. The linear variety may have to be anchored to an asteroid for stability, but a rotary EML can spin freely in space and take time to spin-up stably, although the high g-pull may restrict its use to launching raw materials or refined metals.

For minimum-energy transfers to Earth, waiting time between launches and flight times would typically be about 18 months, but are unimportant for unmanned cargoes as long as there are enough asteroids being mined around the ecliptic to ensure steady deliveries to the Earth-Moon system.[37] By the same token, a long time can be taken to remove the rarer elements, after the main ones have been extracted. Schwigl-hofer and Shaw suggested encasing the asteroid in a big plastic balloon, shielded from the Sun by an occulting disc. The asteroid's surface would be melted by lasers and the tempera-ture raised until the first of the wanted materials vaporized and sputtered onto the balloon, which would then be removed and replaced; the temperature would then be raised and the next element or compound collected; and so on until, 'to go from the sublime to the ridiculous', the asteroid was complete-ly used up. Even the silicates boiled off could be put to use—see below.

Launch by EML of refined metals and finished products remains preferable to shifting asteroids bodily into the vicinity of the Earth. Such moves might be performed with hydrogen-bomb thrust, although rock asteroids may be too fragile,[17] but the dangers involved are all too clear. Even when habitats are moved around the Solar System there will certainly be absolute computer overrides, under government seal, to prevent any large body being put even temporarily on a course threatening an inhabited planet or satellite. Cole and Cox actually suggest deliberately placing asteroids in high Earth orbit as a new form of deterrent, and at odds with the generally liberal tone of their book go on to argue that the US must generate such threats to prevent others from doing so [17]: 'It does not appear probable that any Earth nation other than the United States that had the scientific and technological resources to discover nuclear energy would have resisted the temptation to use it in conquering the world'!

The evolution of the asteroid culture will be conditioned by the materials available for power generation and propulsion, since helium is scarce and helium-3 for Daedalus still more so. Significant finds of radioactive elements might lead to un-shielded fission in reactors on asteroid surfaces, although robots would have to be used for even the most trivial maintenance—nickel-iron asteroid mining might be completely automated. In the absence of atmosphere the steel would receive only hard radiation, not contamination, and would be safe to handle by the time it reached Earth. Optical computers and fluidic control systems would be used in preference to electronics, which are affected by intense radiation. Manned fission rockets of the NERVA type might then evolve, and cargo EMLs might be fission-powered, since solar cells aren't effective at that distance from the Sun and mirrors need to be eight times bigger.[40] Finds of mercury or caesium would favour ion-drive, although without them or the radioactives local transport may after all be based on LH_2/LO_2 chemical rockets.

An SF commonplace used to be the 'Belter' civilization, which confined itself to the asteroids as much as possible and resented the fuel expenditure for trips to the planets, but the concept was exploded by Jerry Pournelle.[38] Delta-v to get from an asteroid at 2AU to Ceres, usually the 'Belt capital', would be about 3kps—no better than the trip to Mars. Moreover, the Ceres-asteroid synodic period, giving the 'waiting time' between launch windows, is seven years, a year worse than for Mars, and the minimum-energy trip takes 1.8 years—as compared with the $1\frac{1}{2}$ years' waiting and flight time for similar trips to Earth. The closer the orbital radii of any two asteroids, the longer the interval between launch windows.* Even with 'torchships', the Belters' traditional Continuous Acceleration Transfer ships, delta-vs would be so high

---

*The news was no surprise to Professor A. E. Roy's 1964 first-year class, who were set a problem beginning; 'A and B are two asteroids in

and trip times usually so long that interasteroid commerce would be futile: Earth would be the capital of the Belt culture, because it's the easiest place to get to most frequently—much more so than Mars. Pournelle concluded that, since Jupiter/ Earth launch and return windows are still more frequent, and since the moons have frequent mutual launch windows, a Galilean-moon civilization was more likely than a Belter one. We know now that asteroid technology will be needed to reach the Galilean satellites (see Chapter 11); but an asteroid civilization will be radial with the Earth-Moon system as its cultural focus.

Such a civilization could be a very high one, perhaps the finest—in cultural terms—since ancient Greece. In an altogether more acceptable part of their discussion, Cole and Cox remark on the increasing regimentation of life—in the US as elsewhere—and the potential for diversification offered by asteroid colonies. Ehricke and Dyson think the major promise of space is the return to small independent societies, like city-states in ancient Greece, which can maintain a feeling of identity and cope with social problems because the numbers involved aren't overwhelming. Any future cultural explosion similar to the Renaissance would have to come from such groups, on comets or asteroids, because planetary societies will be too bureaucratized to allow them. [41] In Brian Aldiss's *The Eighty-Minute Hour* Earth is totally organized under the Computer Complex which is introducing for its convenience the 80-minute hour of the title. The colony on Mars is still free, but 'across the gulfs of space, a mind that was to human minds as human minds are to those of other primates, an intellect vast and cool and unsympathetic, regarded the Red Planet with calculation, and slowly and surely drew up its plans for reorganisation'. [42]

Cole and Cox suggest that if initially the asteroid researchers and miners are family groups (Starseeds!), extended missions will be acceptable. Next, as small asteroids are brought

---

circular coplanar orbits with the following elements ... An absentminded prospector goes from A to B, then finds he has forgotten his Geiger counter. Determine the waiting period before he can return to collect it, and the duration of the return flight, assuming minimum-energy transfer orbit.' Both periods proved so long that one student remarked: 'He'll die of the horrible pangs!'

towards the processing facilities of larger ones, general mobility evolves. Daedalus engines would be required rather than mass drivers: capturing even a 1km Earth-grazer would waste 19.5 million tonnes of material using mass drivers.[43] Looking ahead a few years, one can imagine asteroids coming sunwards to have more solar energy for life-support and industry—and to be placed to receive the products of the Belt. Since they'd be fully stocked with volatiles, there may never be *lunar* habitats at L4 and L5. Other communities will be moving outwards, to claim the giant planets; and so the asteroid civilization comes into being.

The first colonies will obviously be converted mine shafts, or the habitable parts of a mine complex, as on the Moon. Among the larger asteroids Ceres may not be differentiated, not having an iron core, and large-scale processing methods such as underground nuclear explosions will no doubt be used. In time there will be large 'half-terraformed' caverns with Earth-surface conditions—apart from the low gravity. Flying will be even easier than on the Moon.

J. D. Bernal and L. R. Shepherd suggested that small asteroids could be made habitable by tunnelling into the interiors and adjusting the spin rates. 'Gravity' would increase from zero at the centre and poles to $1g$ (or $\frac{1}{6}g$, perhaps) at the equator. Mobile asteroids might prefer no spin, to make manoeuvring easier, but if so gravity will be very low throughout. Such colonies now appear doubtful: more probaby habitats will be built during large-scale processing. Cole and Cox suggested melting an iron asteroid right through with mirrors, after which embedded water tanks explode and blow up the asteroid into a great cast-iron hollow cylinder.[17] With spin put on, a habitable world could then be created with an equatorial sea, an Earthlike atmosphere circulation system, and a cylindrical 'sun' down its centre scattering sunlight out of a column of dust or gas.

The only problem is the method of manufacture. As Oscar Schwiglhofer pointed out, at the moment of explosion the water vapour will force its way to the surface along any path of weakness. Any nodule or gas pocket (surely unavoidable, in the low gravity) would cause a cataclysmic break-out of high-pressure steam into space, followed by the collapse of the (now wildly tumbling) molten cylinder.

Robert Shaw suggested that, instead, a stony-iron asteroid

might be hollowed out by 'termites' chewing round the centre, processing out the iron and delivering it to the surface for launch; the rock-dust collects at the centre, loosely glued together with water, and the oxygen is released to pressurize the cavity. When the process is completed the habitat is spun-up and the dust, primed with seeds and bacteria, spatters onto the walls as a coating of fresh soil. Gavin Roberts suggested that, after melting, an iron asteroid might be moulded into a cylinder by central spreaders, like hands shaping a pot. (It would avoid getting the inner face rusty, as well as the dangers of the Cole-Cox method.) Better yet, if the asteroid could be put under gentle, continuous thrust, one could begin melting it at one end and casting it into steel cable and basalt ribbon, spun like a cocoon. Thus the habitat is built out of *refined* material, whose properties are accurately known, and therefore is more reliable.

Perhaps the best suggestion was to brace a balloon with prestressed cable and build the habitat like Island One, out of the silicate shells cast off one by one as an asteroid was processed by the balloon-and-laser technique. By reducing balloon diameter midway the habitat could be given a double hull for safety, with metal coatings between them like a vacuum flask. As Sheppard has pointed out independently (page 117), it would be far lighter than iron, steel or unprocessed rock, and shielding properties would be splendid. In pairs, with Daedalus engines, they could go *anywhere*. Perhaps the inhabitants won't live on the inner face, but keep it for farming and recreation; since under drive there will be 'gravity' nose-to-tail as well as radially, dwellings may be huge disc-shaped airships like the floating habitats proposed for Venus (page 175). Cast out of light-metal alloys, needing little lifting volume in $\frac{1}{6}g$, they'd align themselves to the prevailing 'gravity' and could be moved around the interior at the occupants' whim.

With paired cylinders and the engines to move them, the asteroid culture won't be content to move sunwards and bask there. Only a few kps away in terms of delta-v lies the high-radiation environment of Jupiter, unapproachable by conventional spaceships but rich in deuterium, helium-3 and bulk volatiles. In the opposite direction they can go as close to the Sun as Icarus—which glows red-hot at perihelion—or further, behind hemispherical rock or metal shields. Beyond

Jupiter lie three more giant worlds, with their systems of moons, and one very enigmatic small one; beyond them the system of comets, and outer System resources still only guessed at.

It has sometimes been suggested that such communities would have to be rigid, ruthlessly disciplined from above, with all deviation a threat to survival. Cole and Cox point out that all such systems are unstable: they must perish either by revolt or by some unforeseen crisis to which they lack the flexibility to respond. Instead, asteroid communities must be examples of 'macro-life', where people, animals, plants and microorganisms are all seen as units analogous to the cells which make up a living being, each with needs which have to be met to ensure the survival of the whole. In the social models they adopt, asteroid communites may be testbeds for the attitudes which must evolve on Earth if *that* huge spaceship is to survive. But, beyond that, life in the asteroids must be satisfying and worthwhile if the communities are to last, and the 'Belters' may choose to extend it beyond the Solar System. Even voyages lasting for generations (if no better propulsion is available) might be acceptable, because the habitat itself is home and there's no compulsion to go back to Earth or the Sun. Nor does another planetary system have to contain an Earthlike world for them to find it attractive: they have the technology and the will to make little worlds, in their own image.

A civilization of mobile worlds could colonize the Galaxy.

Taming the Giants

There will certainly be no lack of human pioneers when we have
mastered the art of flight. Who would have thought that
navigation across the vast ocean is less dangerous and quieter
than in the narrow, threatening gulfs of the Adriatic, or the
British straits? Let us create vessels and sails adjusted to the
heavenly ether, and there will be plenty of people unafraid of the
empty wastes. In the meantime, we shall prepare, for the brave
sky-travellers, maps of the celestial bodies—I shall do it for the
Moon, you, Galileo, for Jupiter.

—Johannes Kepler, *Conversations with the Star Messenger*,
1610[1]

Classically, a star shines by its own light, while a planet shines
by reflection. This is true for Jupiter in visible light, but the
great planet emits $2\frac{1}{2}$ times more heat than it receives from the
Sun, apparently because it's still contracting after its formation
4.6 billion years ago. Tracking data analyses after Pioneer and
Voyager encounters found no evidence for any solid core
within the planet; and, although some scientists still feel there
'must' be a silicate/metal core down there, what one calls
'solid' at 30,000 K or over[2] is moot. The heat works its way to
the surface by convection, just as energy does from the core of
the Sun, and Jupiter is generally less like a planet than a failed
star—too small, at 0.1% of the Sun's mass (about three times as
much as all the other planets put together), to sustain fusion
reactions. In 1969 it was thought that Jupiter would burn at
only five times its present mass,[3] but more recent estimates
give ten times Jupiter's mass as the value at which fusion
reactions would occur during contraction, and at least seven
times *that* for a stable ('Main Sequence') star.[4] But, with what
we know now about Jupiter's continuing contraction, how
much of the smaller stars' output is due to similar processes?

One explanation for the absence of the predicted neutrino flux from the core of the Sun could be that, even in stars as massive as ours, fusion reactions may not be continuous. The densities of Jupiter's four major satellites, all of them in the Pluto-Moon-Mercury size-range, decrease outwards from the planet—just like the planets going outwards from the Sun—due to heat given off by the primary during formation; and the major revelation of the Voyager flybys was that these 'Galilean' satellites qualify as a miniature planetary system in more subtle ways.

Io, the nearest of the Galileans to the planet, was already known to be active. Its shadow on Jupiter's face was hotter than the surrounding clouds, suggesting that it has an atmosphere; and its orange surface was brighter when it came out of eclipse by Jupiter, as if frosted over. A hydrogen atmosphere was confirmed, electrically charged by sodium ions; it extends along the orbital plane at least as far as the Jupiter-Io L4 and L5 points, and out of the plane far enough to stream planetwards, enveloping Jupiter itself.[5] Intense radio 'bursts' occur when Io is at right angles to the Sun-Jupiter line, and it was deduced that there must be a 'flux tube' of ionized gas in the planet's magnetic field, linking Io's northern and southern hemispheres to the Jovian atmosphere. Cutting across the lines of the planetary field generates a potential of 400kV between the leading and trailing hemispheres, and halfway through each 42-hour 'month' the magnetic and electric potentials are reversed because Jupiter's magnetic field is tilted from the equatorial plane. To neutralize the previous charge, multimegaton lightning bolts leap along the flux tube to Jupiter and back.[6]

Io's surface is a riot of reds, oranges and yellows, sulphur deposits and compounds spewed out by active volcanoes. Eight were in eruption during the Voyager-1 flyby, and seven (but not the largest) were still going during the Voyager-2 encounter four months later.[7] It seems that much of the internal heating comes from tidal forces, and that below the crust there may be an ocean of liquid sulphur. The crust could be 20km thick, with eruptions powered by sulphur vaporized by rising magma, or as thin as 1km—in which case sulphur dioxide would be the driving agent.[8] Sagan suggests that the colours may be sulphur allotropes crystallizing at different temperatures: black, orange, then white, working outwards. (It had been suggested that the brightening, which occurs in about half the observed eclipses, might be surface composition changes rather than frost.[9]) Rock lavas of differing sulphur content could explain the colours but not the staggering energy of the eruptions:[8] the highest plume seen by Voyager-1 was 280km high and 1000km wide, and ejection velocities must be 1600-3200kph.[10] Ejecta fall back to the surface in great arcs: by the second Voyager encounter the huge feature informally known as 'Sullivan's Hoofprint',[2] associated with one of the plumes, had already lost its cloven appearance.[7] The map of Io may have to be redrawn every 21-42 hours, and it's by no means certain that any surface features are permanent—although the relief seems greater than a floating crust of sulphur and sulphur-dioxide ice could sustain.

> *The sulphur mines on Io were on strike*
> *when we arrived. I can't say I'm surprised.*
> *Seventy-five men had just been killed*
> *in the fiercest eruption ever seen there.*
> *I hardly recognized the grim volcano*
> *with its rakish new crater and a leaning plume*
> *two hundred miles high—like an ash tree,*
> *someone said. Meanwhile the landscape burned,*
> *not that it never burned before, but this*
> *was roaring, sheeted, cruel. Empty*
> *though not perfunctory funeral rites*
> *had been performed; not a body was found ...*

Edwin Morgan, 'The Moons of Jupiter'[11]

Near the flux tube Voyager-1 confirmed the 400kV and a current flow of five million amps, twenty times the combined output of all the power stations of Earth.[7] There may be industrial potential there, in more senses than one, but Morgan's miners won't be prospecting for 'the best sulphur ... the most perilous' just yet. The volcanoes arc not more violent than Earth's, taking gravity and atmospheric drag into account,[12] but that'll be little consolation when a new eruption breaks: on a small world with low gravity, safe distances will be a long way off, if there are any. The major barrier, however, remains the radiation belts which close the inner Jovian system altogether to conventional manned operations. On all counts, but especially radiation counts, Io is living up to its reputation as the most dangerous place in the Solar System.

If Io was amazing to the Voyager observers, Europa was

astonishing. It's the brightest of the Galileans, but nobody was prepared for a world *completely* covered with ice. Europa is a smooth, glittering ball, patterned with cracks less than 100m deep but hundreds or thousands of kilometres long and 20-40km wide. One appears to go right around the moon in a sine-wave.[7] In close-up they strongly resemble Landsat photos of cracked and refrozen pack ice on Earth, and the inference is that Europa is covered with ocean, tidally heated and thickly encrusted with ice, smoothed from below: its surface is as free of prominent craters as Earth's. It has to be water—other ices (being denser than their liquid equivalents) would sink, until the ocean was frozen from top to bottom. Ridges and hummocks 50m high, near the equator, appear to be the only features elevated at all above the terrain. The world-sea of Europa may be 60km deep.

> *Boots and boats—in our bright orange gear*
> *we were such an old-fashioned earthly lot*
> *it seemed almost out of time-phase. We learned*
> *or re-learned how to skate and ski, use snowshoes,*
> *fish through ice-holes though not for fish. Soundings*
> *and samples were our prey. We'd never grade*
> *in years, far less in weeks, the infinite*
> *play and glitter of watery Europa,*
> *waters of crust ice, waters of deep ice,*
> *waters of slush, of warm subcrustal springs,*
> *waters of vapour, waters of water.*
> *One day, and only one, we drilled right down*
> *to something solid and so solid-hard*
> *the drill-head screamed into the microphone*
> *and broke, the film showed streaks of metal shards*
> *whizzing across a band of basalt or*
> *glimmery antediluvian turtle-shell*
> *or cast-off titan miner's helmet or—*
> *it must have been the metal scream that roused*
> *our thought and fear and half desire we might*
> *have had a living scream returned. Lightly*
> *it sleeps, the imagination ...*[11]

In recent years there's been a contest between Jupiter and Saturn as to which has the largest natural moon in the Solar System, the fourth largest solid body; Triton, the giant moon of

Neptune, is now another contender.[13] Ganymede won the first round, the Pioneer flybys, by proving to be larger than Mercury; and the Voyager-1 Titan flyby showed that Ganymede was indeed 100km larger. Only Triton is still in the contest with Ganymede.

After the Pioneers, Ganymede's apparent density suggested the entire interior was liquid water! Now it's more accurately known to be $1.9g/cm^3$, and presumably the core is rocky.[7] But there's a great deal of ice on and below the crust, with evidence of movement, and there could be a liquid-water mantle like Europa's even though, as on Earth, some continent-like masses rise through it, or, as on Mars, volcanic activity has intermixed lava with the crustal ice.

Voyager-1 found Ganymede was cratered: its surface is less active than Io's or Europa's, but still dynamic. The newest, smaller craters are brilliant white where ice has been exposed or thrown out onto the greens, blues, browns and purples of the lava plains; but older, intermediate-sized ones are degraded, and the biggest ones are only circular scars. Close-ups revealed why: huge arcs and bands of deformation, lineated like the ridges of the Martian poles. In finer detail, photographed from 145,000km, the patterns overlie the older craters and themselves are overlaid by later lines of stress.[14] From 85,000km, Voyager-2 found the concentric ridges of a huge, erased impact like Callisto's (see below) but even bigger, while the intricate patterns were found on the cratered terrain as well as the lava fields. Assuming they are stress marks, that wasn't too surprising: as *Spaceflight* casually remarked, quoting NASA, 'Pieces of the crust have *moved* relative to one another since the Voyager-1 encounter.'[17] (My italics.)

> *Galileo would have been proud of Ganymede.*
> *Who can call that marbled beauty dead?*
> *Dark basins sweeping to a furrowed landfall,*
> *gigantic bright-rayed craters, vestiges*
> *and veils of ice and snow, black swirling grey,*
> *grey veined with green, greens diffused in blues,*
> *blue powdered into white: a king marble*
> *rolled out, and set in place, from place to place ...*
> *I remember I drowsed off, dropped my notes,*
> *with the image of Ganymede dancing before me.*
> *They nudged me, smiling, said it was a judgment*

for my wandering thoughts, what had got into me?
That satellite had iron and uranium.
We would be back. Well, that must be fine,
I teased them; had it gold, and asphodel? [11]

Callisto is by far the most heavily cratered of the satellites, but
still there's evidence for an active surface phase. Few if any
craters are more than 100km in diameter, although the terrain
is so saturated with smaller ones [16] that Callisto looks virtually
the same from all angles.[7] The only conspicuous large feature
is an orange plain 600km across, [15] surrounded by concentric
ridges at 150km intervals out to a final diameter of 2600km. [18]
The absence of a *mare* basin or a raised rim might mean the
impact came close to shattering the moon altogether: planetary
surface rebound has also been suggested, to account for the
shallowness of craters on the Galilean moons and on Venus. [19] Or,
if the impact was actually on the other side of Callisto, perhaps
the converging shockwaves formed 'frozen ripples' instead of
'chaotic terrain'. But the similar still larger ring pattern on
Ganymede suggests surface and subsurface erasing processes,
even if they stopped early in Callisto's history.

The surface appears a much more thorough mixture of ice
and silicates than patchy Ganymede—it's been described both
as 'dirty ice' [18] and as 'frozen slush'. [15] If Io's active sulphur
chemistry has parallels with Venus, Europa with its water
cover resembles Earth and Ganymede's lava fields recall Mars,
then Callisto may tell us what the fifth planet would have been
like had it not been for Jupiter's disturbing presence. There
may be few heavy elements, but the prevalence of ice—hopefully including heavy water, to yield deuterium—will make
Callisto a prime target. Some (rather simplistic) studies have
suggested that the Solar System's future may consist of a power
struggle between Earth and Callisto: [20] its orbital radius allows
the most effective gravitational braking on transfers to the
Galilean moons from Earth, [21] but the crucial factor is that, as
it's the only one outside Jupiter's 'supralethal' radiation belts, it
alone can be reached by conventional ships.

Scarred, cauterised, pocked and warty face:
you grin and gape and gawk and cock an ear
at us with craters, all blind, all deaf, all dumb,

toadback moon, brindled, brown and cold,
we plodded dryshod on your elephant-hide seas
and trundled gear from groove to groove, playing
the record of your past, imagining
the gross vales filled with unbombarded homes
they never had till we pitched nylon tents there ...
Frail and tough as flags we furnish out
the desolation. Even the greatest crater,
gouged as if a continent had struck it,
circled by rim on rim of ridges rippling
hundreds of miles over that slaty chaos,
cannot forbid our feet, our search, our songs. [11]

Jupiter's magnetic field is generated by currents in the liquid hydrogen layer overlying the crystalline, metallic hydrogen at its core, giving it a complex quadrupole and octopole structure near to the planet, although the overall field is a dipole like Earth's. Its middle region, which has no counterpart in Earth's magnetosphere, contains a plasma cloud rotating rigidly with the planet in 10 hours, locked to the magnetic field lines [23] and generating a sodium cloud 'wake' over the *leading* hemisphere of Io. [24] The outer field, which may have a spiral structure indicating an outward plasma flow, pulsates 'like a huge jellyfish' under pressure from the Solar Wind—Pioneer-10 crossed its boundary, or rather was passed by it, no fewer than 17 times on the way out from the planet. [25] If it could be seen from Earth it would look about as large in our skies as the Moon, and Pioneer-10 recrossed its 'tail' well beyond the orbit of Saturn. Particles trapped within the field seem to come from Jupiter and Io, rather than from the Sun as with Earth's radiation belts; and, with the overall field strength 20-30 times Earth's, they have much higher energies. In the most energetic zone, the torus enveloping Io, they travel at up to 10% of the speed of light; [2] the intensity is comparable to a continuous high-altitude nuclear explosion; [26] and even a momentary exposure would give 100 times lethal dosage for humans. [27]

The whole inner belt is a torus aligned with the magnetic equator, at 10° to Jupiter's axis of rotation and the orbits of the Galileans. It extends to 1,298,000km above the ionosphere (1,359,400km from the planet's centre), so all the big moons except Callisto are immersed in it. Densities and energies of outer belt particles are hundreds of times lower, even in the most intense zone—a flat sheet in the equatorial plane.[27] Callisto's orbital inclination of 0° 15′ to that plane may be enough to limit dangerous exposures to the bimonthly passages through it.

The initial reaction to the radiation readings was dismay. In May 1974 Pournelle summarized the arguments for a Galilean civilization,[28] but withdrew them two months later in the light of the Pioneer data.[29] In 1975 Ben Bova endorsed the verdict: 'Pioneer-10 destroyed all the science fiction stories that picture human colonies on the inner moons of Jupiter. The giant planet's fierce radiation belt makes human habitation of all but the outermost Galilean moon totally impossible; unless someone comes up with some truly staggering radiation protection.'[30] R. C. Parkinson argued that Callisto's volatiles, especially the water ice, could provide a resource base for *unmanned* exploitation of the planet.[21] Using gas-core nuclear propulsion, unmanned tankers could supply liquid hydrogen from Callisto to the Earth-Moon system more cheaply than it could be brought up from Earth, and could finance 'mining' Jupiter for helium-3 despite the very high delta-v from the atmosphere to Callisto. In very general terms, these assumptions also underlie the predicted power struggle between Callisto and Earth for the asteroids.[20]

The irony is that it was Ben Bova's predecessor, the late John W. Campbell, Jr, who suggested to me the use of cast lava as an ideal hull material for large cylindrical spacecraft, two years after Cole and Cox proposed asteroidal iron.[31b] Hulls blocking off primary cosmic-rays with energies of 10-15GeV per nucleon, even heavy nuclei such as iron,[32] are not going to be troubled by the 30-35MeV peak energies of the protons and electrons in Jupiter's inner belt,[27] however numerous. Nor, with Daedalus engines, does it matter that transfer energies between the Galilean moons are comparable with those for interplanetary missions:[28] the deuterium and helium-3 expenditure to place a habitat in close orbit around Jupiter is minimal, and the object is to recover both materials in bulk.

Helium makes up 17% of the Jovian atmosphere, and most of the rest is free hydrogen, but since both are colourless and don't liquefy or freeze even at the bitter 120 K of the cloud tops, the planet's appearance is dominated by hydrogen in combination with the 1% of other elements.[27] The bright bands are ammonia clouds: the dark 'belts' are the true visible 'surface', 20km below, and their colouring is due to compounds such as ammonium hydrosulphide. In the next layer below there are water-ice crystals, and still further down—just above the liquid hydrogen level, and revealed through 'blue holes' in the clouds—there is a water-vapour layer, at Earth-surface temperature but at twenty times the pressure.

Before the temperatures of the cloud tops were measured, astronomers took it for granted that Jupiter still retained much of the heat of its formation, indicated by the atmospheric activity,[33] and they were right except that the heat comes from continuing contraction. Polar flattening, due to the rapid rotation, brings the poles nearer to the internal heat and gives temperatures virtually equal to those at the equator, so gravity and convection effects dominate, forming calm polar 'caps' surrounded by extremely complex weather. In lower latitudes, as rising material spreads north and south, it's diverted into jetstreams parallel to the equator, with or against the rotation,[27] while the visible equatorial zone rotates five minutes faster than do the planet's other visible bands and the interior. There's violent shearing and turbulence between rotation zones and between opposing airstreams within them, at relative speeds of hundreds of kilometres per hour.

The most famous rotational storm on Jupiter, the Great Red Spot, has persisted at least since 1664 and is larger in surface area than the Earth. The band due south of the Spot contains features obviously related to it: upwelling white ovals, as large as the Earth, with the same internal structure and anticyclonic rotation as the Spot itself.[34] The ovals have lasted at least since 1939:[15] in the equatorial zone they're elongated into plumes stretching for tens of thousands of kilometres, and they too form 'families', dating back at least to 1964.[35] The plume heads rise out of deep blue-grey holes and form cumulus-like tops;[7] in Plate 7, to appreciate the scale, the rising plume may be 50km high. The Red Spot and its short-lived small cousins[25,35] resemble the mixtures of organic compounds, including amino acids, formed in the laboratory when 'primal atmospheres' are subjected to simulated lightning. Jupiter certainly has lightning: on the night side Voyager-2 saw hundreds of flashes, up to 32,000km in length.[10] Life might evolve in the water-bearing layers below, especially in the calmer polar regions. But a more prosaic hypothesis is that, in the highest clouds, phosphene breaks down to release red phosphorus.[25]

Deuterium has been detected and may be as abundant as 700-800ppm[36] (parts per million), and Jupiter should still have the abundances of the primal nebula in which helium-3 is believed to have been relatively common. But, to confirm that Jupiter does have the resources to open up the Solar System and take us to the stars with Daedalus engines, atmosphere-sampling probes are needed. The Galileo entry probe would have separated from the Orbiter 150 days before entry and hit the atmosphere at 48.2kps, decelerating in seconds at 400g.[23] The parachute would have deployed before the first visible clouds, the bright bands of ammonia crystals, and entry would have been in the equatorial zone to improve the chances of sampling them. During an hour of data sending, taking the probe 130km below the high clouds to the water droplet layer at 20 atmospheres' pressure, transmissions would have been relayed through the orbiter, already turned onto a parallel course by a Europa flyby. Immediately afterwards the orbiter would have braked into capture orbit and, over the next twenty months, during four long elliptical revolutions around the planet, it would have had slingshot encounters with all the Galilean moons, each modifying the orbit for the next.

As of December 1981, however, the news was that Galileo had been postponed to at least the late 1980s, if not indefinitely.

For the strategic approach, a Waverider Jupiter probe would be much more important than Mars or Venus missions, and gliding entry has more to offer than ballistic probes. Normally the problem is maintaining contact with the relays: since Jupiter rotates so fast, there's no point in designing a probe for endurance if the orbiter will be setting on the horizon. Even to maintain contact for an extra half hour, down to the 73atm level, a relay would have to be close enough to the planet and/or moving fast enough to be ejected from the Solar System altogether, like the Pioneers. Grand-Tour missions and TOPS probes, outer planet missions long-since cancelled, would have allowed penetration to 100atm (equivalent to Venus's surface) and 300 atm respectively.[37]

For the strategic approach, prolonged data-gathering is needed 0-90km *above* the visible clouds, at 0.01-1atm, where the deuterium and helium-3 collectors will operate. Instead of plunging almost vertically downward, a Waverider can glide at up to Mach 6 in the same direction as the orbiter or flyby relay. Sample intakes would have to be well above the upper surface to reach the airstream: in Plate 7 the fins are booms, not stabilisers (which aren't functional on the back of a Waverider). The Jovian ionosphere, which is multilayered and 600km deep,[38] can be explored *only* by gliding entry—Galileo would have gone through it in little over 12 seconds—and only a Waverider can send ionosphere data in real-time when other spacecraft wculd be cut off by surrounding plasma. As the relay draws near the horizon the Waverider can take a steep dive into lower layers, preferably through some prime scientific target like the Red Spot, a blue or brown hole, or a white oval.

'I have not the smallest molecule of faith in any form of aerial navigation other than ballooning,' remarked Lord Kelvin, and balloon stations are the only type discussed in detail in the Daedalus report,[39] geared to fuelling a 50,000-tonne interstellar probe within 20 years. However, Solar-System operations can be run on a very large scale with much smaller quantities: habitats don't need to move between planets or Galilean moons on hyperbolic transfers, and fast transfer ships won't be massive. Practical considerations then favour flying factories, although they'll have to be very large. To separate deuterium by conventional means would require a very large compressor, with a great deal of waste heat to disperse, followed by an expansion turbine, to liquefy the hydrogen-deuterium mix, and a fractionating column to take off the 'ordinary' hydrogen. On Earth, that column would have to be at least 12m high[36] (but what would it be at 2.5g at the Jovian visible surface?). It could be replaced by a cold trap at 23 K, the Daedalus team found. Then the helium would have to be liquefied to separate the helium-4 by way of its superfluidity characteristics.[39] That might be done in space at more leisure, if there were enough demand for 'ordinary' helium to make it worth shipping up (see below).

Effective compression could be generated in high-speed flight. Waverider lends itself to external combustion in the supporting shockwave, and for the first time since we left Earth there's chemical energy available in the atmosphere. A chlorine jet ignites spontaneously in a hydrogen atmosphere in sunlight, as Hal Clement pointed out in *Mission of Gravity*;[40] but oxygen is equally effective, more controllable and usable at night. Schwiglhofer argued that because of hydrogen's low density arc heating would be the best solution. Flying against the rotation of the planetary magnetic field, helped by a retrograde 290kph airstream parallel to the equator, and using superconducting coils, there might be enought induced EMF to maintain the arc without using onboard power at all! But flying against the rotation partly cancels its major benefits to shuttle operations; for example, direct high-speed flight greatly simplifies shuttle rendezvous. There are enough problems in gravity $2\frac{1}{2}$ times Earth's and in a low-density atmosphere without having to 'land on' the underside of a 212m hot-air balloon![39] The approach to a Waverider factory can be made as in the midair refuelling of aircraft; and, if it misses, the shuttle has enough airspeed for the factory to slow for another attempt. Furthermore, boom contact and landing can be in the lee of the upper surface.

The biggest advantage of powered flight is in avoiding turbulence. In general, the bright areas are rising gases and the brown ones are descending; velocities are uncertain, but supposedly balloon stations with 10% excess lift could rise out of danger at 25m/sec.[39] But, with 290kph horizontal streams *in opposite directions*, Voyager photos showed resultant turbulence features typically 100km across; and above the visible clouds clear air turbulence must surely be widespread. In the air that once-dreaded killer can now be detected,[41] and could be avoided by a cruising Waverider where a balloon would have to take its chances: at a minimum diameter of 212m, supporting an 85-tonne nuclear-powered factory, those chances don't seem too good.

Straightforward docking and the avoidance of turbulence will both be vital if the factories are to be manned or even just visited occasionally. Because the magnetic field is offset from the planet's geometric figure, it generates an 'eccentric cam effect': a particle-free zone to 7140km above the clouds on one side of the planet,[25] within which manned shuttles could transfer between close-orbiting habitats and the factories without being exposed to the radiation belt. Some human beings can operate at 2.5g—standing up in a fairground rotor is a well known test of strength—and formation aerobatic teams like the Red Arrows work with extreme precision at considerably higher gs. High-g acclimatization can be provided within habitats by driving around the inner surface in the direction of spin: inside Skylab, in zero-*g*, the astronauts simulated gravity by running round a ring of lockers.

From the upper atmosphere, to get into close orbit around Jupiter takes 42kps, and to escape altogether needs 60kps, but Jupiter's 12.6kps equatorial spin provides a quarter of the orbital velocity and a 290kph airstream in the same direction supplies 0.08kps; supersonic factory flight can add 1-3kps more. From the calm over the upper wing surface, the shuttle can enter the slipstream and reach an airspeed of 10kps on ramjet thrust [39] —but a further 19-20kps is still needed. For ssto the minimum propulsion system would be the gas-core nuclear 'scramjet' (page 45), whose ordinary hydrogen reaction mass is already separated and purified by the factory; payload could be enhanced by use of external tanks, but then there's the problem of getting them down through the atmosphere. If not already filled with hydrogen, which would really be taking coals to Newcastle, they'd need pressure-bracing with some other gas, which gas is unlikely to be needed below in quantity unless the factory is flying on halogen or oxygen jets.

Beanstalks might seem the answer were it not for the intensity of Jupiter's gravity well; but even if suitable materials could be developed the solutions are not very promising. Synchronous orbit would be at a radius of 162,000km, 90,600km above the clouds, and, while the moon Amalthea at 181,000km might be borrowed as a counterweight to reduce the huge beanstalk mass required, the stalk would be threatened by satellite 1979 J1, its co-orbital 1979 J3, and the equatorial ring discovered by Voyager-1. Flying with the rotation in an eastward-moving airstream would decrease the radius for synchronization *with the factory*, but not even a ramjet at the theoretical limit could reach much more than a third of the airspeed needed to use 1979 J1 or J3 as a counterweight, 57,000km above the clouds [47] —and they're on the outside of the ring, which may well originate from them. Skyhooks are workable in theory, but the tip velocity would be at least four times that required for pickups from Earth—and the ring is still a problem.

Shaw suggested atmosphere-mining in orbit, just within the upper atmosphere. A PROFAC system (Propulsive Fluid Acumlator) has been proposed to collect liquid oxygen on the fringe of Earth's atmosphere [42]; some of it has to be expended through a plasma thruster to counter atmospheric drag. However, PROFAC's velocity would be about 8kps; a similar satellite orbiting Jupiter would have to move at least six times as fast. If the problems can be overcome, Shaw asked, why not move faster still—in forced orbit, using hydrogen jets to prevent the satellite swinging away from the planet? Cargoes would no longer need an extra 20kps just to reach close orbit: if released unpowered at the right moment they'd return, for capture by retrofire or EML rings, to the moons from which the factories were launched. If forced orbital velocity were raised to 60kps, from the 50-plus they'd have if dropped from a Galilean moon, we could send payloads straight out of the Jupiter system for nothing.

The safety factors are obvious. With forced orbit (and only with forced orbit), engine failure doesn't mean total loss of the factory, which would otherwise sink into Jupiter's depths, at unbelievable expense. In normal operations the engines would be switched off periodically, timed to bring the factory back to the launching moon for refurbishing and maintenance. If it simply passed near Callisto, maintenance crews could visit it and return at low relative velocity, before it dropped back naturally to operating altitude. A unit in difficulty would return to its moon; and, in a total, untimed thruster failure, a solid rocket burn in space would raise perijove far enough out of the atmosphere for the unit to be safe in elliptical orbit until a tug could reach it.

In the Daedalus study, PROFAC mining was discarded because it couldn't meet the 20-year target. To extract a combined 50,000 tonnes of deuterium and helium-3 in that time, 28 tonnes of Jovian atmosphere have to be processed every second.[39] Even for the strategic approach to the Solar System, PROFAC maý be too limited: the energy of the incoming gas is proportional to the square of the airspeed, and at 60kps, nearly eight times as fast as over Earth, a given processing system could handle at most $\frac{1}{64}$ of the quantity. But initially the system might fuel habitats for the drop to close orbit if supplies from Earth's Moon weren't available.

In the early 1960s Asimov pictured the future dependence of society on computers, and therefore on liquid helium to supercool their key components. Since the inner planets have lost their original helium, the computer centre of that civilization might be on Amalthea, where helium could be mined from Jupiter's atmosphere.[43]

Ironically, however, Amalthea's mass and escape velocity are too *low* to make it a convenient base: at any time there would be many manned and unmanned spacecraft orbiting the moon, but they'd need continuous station-keeping to avoid collisions. In *2001* the *Discovery* was originally to be left in orbit around Amalthea for rescue (page 53), but the idea was dropped because, at sufficient altitude to avoid perturbation by the moon's irregular shape, the Galilean moons could tweak orbiters away.[44] Voyager-1 confirmed that Amalthea is deformed towards Jupiter by tidal stress:[13] it measures 161 by 129km, and is bright red, presumably because of sulphur deposits ejected from Io's volcanoes. Three brilliant white spots are probably impact craters. 1979 J1 and J3 can be expected to look similar, since they too are in a sulphur ring which orbits Jupiter from just outside the silicate one to a radius of 400,000km, just within Io's sulphur cloud.[45] Even from Amalthea, Jupiter would totally dominate the sky.

> I took a book with me to Amalthea
> but never turned a page. It weighed like lead.
> I squatted with it like a grey image
> malleted into the rock, listlessly
> reading, staring, rereading listlessly
> sentences that never came to anything.
> My very memory lay paralysed
> with everything else on that bent moon,
> pulled down and dustbound, flattened, petrified
> by gravitation, sweeping Jupiter's
> more than half the sky with sentences
> half-formed that never came to anything ...[11]

The other problem with Amalthea or 1979 J1 is just the converse of what makes them attractive as bases—proximity to Jupiter. Minimum-energy transfer from Callisto orbit to Amalthea takes 12.9kps. Since Amalthea and 1979 J1 are deep in the radiation belt and would be reached only by habitat, and the velocity saving for a forced-orbit PROFAC would be small, we might as well go on to close orbit.

It's important to realize that we're dealing with what is in effect a miniature Solar System. 'Once when an assistant had unluckily broken a slide showing the orbits of Mercury, Venus, Earth and Mars about the central Sun, I, for the occasion, substituted a slide showing the orbits of Jupiter's four moons about their central planet. No one noticed the change,' wrote R. A. Proctor in *Other Suns than Ours* (1887).[46] From Callisto surface to Io surface needs 9.4kps, and from circular orbit around Callisto to orbit around Ganymede, Europa and Io take 2.1kps, 3.7kps and 6.0kps respectively[28] —in general, comparable to transfers between the inner planets. In most cases Hohmann interplanetary transfers would be adequate for habitats, although with Daedalus engines they can be moved around swiftly, if necessary, without daunting expenditures of fuel (page 57). Within the Jupiter system there's no problem: even minimum-energy transfers take days rather than months. Even better, the moons' orbital periods are 'commensurate'—Europa's period is nearly twice Io's and is half Callisto's[13] —giving frequent, recurring, regular launch windows. The plunge from Callisto to close-Jupiter orbit is like a voyage to the outer planets in energy terms, but minimum-energy transfer takes 70.8 hours, less than from Earth to the Moon. Since the asteroid habitats would come to Jupiter for strategic purposes, they'd probably move all the way in as soon as collecting techniques had been proved and the first 200 tonnes of propellant had come to hand.

With such forceful reminders that the Galileans are a small solar system in almost every sense, the habitats won't be content with operating from Callisto to close orbit, leaving a ring and six moons untapped in between. (1979 J2, diameter 70-80km—twice J1's—orbits at 223,000km radius, between Amalthea and Io.[47]) An artificial magnetic field would need to be very powerful to divert the high-energy particles into new radiation belts around the Galileans, high enough for habitats to orbit below them and use ordinary shuttles. Otherwise Buckley's Multi-Environment Lander, boldly shown over Io in Plate 6, is barred from three of the ten environments for which it was designed. Superconducting ion scoops were suggested as hydrogen collectors for Earth's Moon[48] (see Chapter 5), but to tame and divert Jupiter's intense belts would require either more powerful scoops, unforeseeable in terms of present technology, or perhaps more numerous ones—but, by the time of the move to Jupiter, the asteroid culture will be masters of the technique, and 'making the moons safe for democracy' may well be possible.

Such a project would actually increase the intensity of the inner belt, since the moons strongly absorb radiation and produce a statistical drop in flux all along their orbits. In Io's orbit, for example, intensity drops to 'only' 1000-100,000 times that in Earth's belts.[49] In order to open up the inner Jovian system to conventional spacecraft, Shaw suggested breaking up the outer moons to form rings between the Galileans: the giant moons themselves occupy the commensurability gaps where small particles' orbits would be unstable. (Rings beyond Callisto would be no good because inner belt particles wouldn't impinge on them, and rings within Io's orbit are unlikely to be much more help than the present one.) Inter-moon delta-vs would be increased in avoiding the ring plane, but the extra fuel expenditure would be minimal compared to the savings in not having to move whole habitats. Transfers under the rings would be favoured; the space below the shadow side of Saturn's rings is the most radiation-free yet found in the Solar System.[50] Rings might be safer for Galilean surface colonies than artificial magnetic fields, which *could* break down; but only if the moons really permit sufficiently dense rings between them. There's no point in exchanging a radiation blockade for a meteroid barrage.

However, since the outer moons can be reached by manned spacecraft even now, they may not be available for destructive exploitation. In theory, with slingshot braking they could be reached from Earth with 6.6kps delta-v, less than for Main-Belt asteroids,[28] but avoiding the inner radiation belt makes it more than 12kps (11.58 for close orbit around Callisto).[20] Once asteroid technology is established with the Earth-grazers, the Starseeds or SIOS might bypass the Main Belt and go straight for the outer Jovian moons. Habitats can be built there because the moons *are* captured asteroids: their orbits are highly inclined to Jupiter's equator and the outer four are retrograde—the orbits are sufficiently elliptical to intersect like interwoven hoops.[51] Between the inner four—Leda, Himalia, Lysithea, Elara—transfers are more frequent, cheaper, and *much* faster than between the inner planets. Between Ananke, Carme, Pasiphae and Sinope minimum-energy transfers are more frequent than between Belt asteroids, but transfers between the inner quartet and the outer one are costly. They all have more frequent launch windows to and from Earth than Belt asteroids do, and with Callisto's ices to draw on they can use gas-core nuclear engines until Daedalus propellants are available. The possible drawbacks are: solar mirrors would have to be still larger than in the Belt; they're so clearly divided into two families that they may be from just two original asteroids, perhaps limited in resources; and at 15-100km, much larger than the Earth-grazers, exploiting them may require different or modified technology. But because of their size they're capable in theory of supporting very large human populations, in near-zero g, within tunnels and half-terraformed caverns: Asimov has pointed out that spheres of that radius, hollowed into levels 15.25m apart, could *each* hold populations as large as Earth's.[52] By the time the Galilean consortium proposes to demolish the outer Jovians it may be very much too late. There may be smaller moons on which Earth-grazer technology, minus solar cells, could gain a foothold: Leda, Jupiter XIII, is the smallest at 15km across—a still more elusive Jupiter XIV has yet to be confirmed (reports [53] that it had been found by Voyager-2 were due to confusion with 1979 J1 [47]). George E. Hale on the discovery of Jupiter VII, 1905:[48] 'You must warn Perrine not to go too far, or it may become necessary to establish special funds to keep track of all the new satellites as they are delivered to us from the plates of the Crossley reflector.'

In the longer term, mining Jupiter might give life within the planet a long-awaited boost. Deuterium in the atmosphere would form heavy water lower down, harmful to carbonaceous life;[54] but, as it rose back into the upper atmosphere to be dissociated, selective removal could only be beneficial. Helium, being neutral, could be removed with impunity. Life in the water-vapour layers, perhaps confined to the polar caps, might be stimulated to expand and adapt to more turbulent latitudes. The total mass of deuterium and helium-3 would be enough for 10,000,000,000,000 Daedalus probes,[55] or a similar number of habitats moving at 1% of lightspeed, and it's hard to imagine even a total evacuation of the Solar System needing so much in the foreseeable future.

Even the removal of all the helium-4 as well wouldn't reduce Jupiter's mass by significantly over 17%. James Campbell pointed out that advances in computer science—e.g., optical systems—may reduce Asimov's estimates of demand for liquid helium. Other uses of superconductivity and super-fluidity may put helium cities on the Galilean moons or even in completely supercooled orbiting habitats, but 17% of Jupiter's mass is near 70% of all the other planets put together, and again it's hard to see why so much might be wanted. What might be done with it and the other 83% of Jupiter *where it is* is another matter.

'Vacancies', or holes in the structure of solids and liquids, are eliminated under high pressures. Water ice, which has a very open tetrahedral lattice of oxygen atoms, collapses progressively through seven different forms at pressures up to 100,000atm:[56] Blish used them in his classic Jupiter story 'Bridge' to build a huge structure for gravitational research on the supposed solid surface.[57] Chemical properties change because, for instance, tetravalent atoms now have more than four neighbours. In benzene, for example, electrons are shared over the whole molecule in a kind of metallic state. All group-IV elements are similarly affected, except carbon, which forms diamond at 100,000atm and should collapse to a metal at 3.7 million atmospheres. In 1968 it was said that the development of a stable megabar press (1 million atmospheres) would be as revolutionary as the first creation of synthetic dia-monds.[56] Several megabars' pressure had already been achieved by 'dynamic methods' (explosives), but for only a few millionths of a second. Bonded diamond powder was a possible structural material for the press up to 3 million atmospheres; beyond that, boron nitride might be still harder in a nonmetal-lic diamond-lattice form.[56] At 320,000atm NASA scientists report formation of metallic xenon, with oxygen and krypton as the next possibilities.[58] At the Earth's core (3 million atmospheres) all materials should be metallic except diam-ond (and boron nitride?); in 1977, Soviet sources reported creation of metallic hydrogen at those pressures in the labor-atory.[59,60]

Fantastic as it may seem when the survival record on the surface of Venus is less than two hours at less than a 'mere' 100atm, these experiments open up the possibility of exploring, within Jupiter, conditions which exist nowhere else in the Solar System. At the upper boundary of Jupiter's liquid hydrogen core, 24,000km down—less than halfway to the centre—pres-sure is already 3 million atmospheres and experiments can be performed over areas and volumes which could never be achieved in the laboratory; we can't predict what industries may eventually arise at these and greater depths.

Far above, another industry has been suggested for the moons of Jupiter. Like Earth's Moon, the Galileans may make a name in shipbuilding, perhaps producing vast hulls of solid hydrogen to be consumed by fusion motors;[61] or the more conventional tanks and staging of Daedalus vehicles. But—unless the outer Jovians steal a complete march on the Main-Belt asteroids and are then prepared to spend their substance to stay ahead—the mobile habitats which claim the outer planets, the cometary halo, and the nearer stars will be built among the asteroids and come to Jupiter for fuel. Dyson has speculated that, with electromagnetic launch systems, ships could eventually be sent out of the Solar System at half the speed of light.[62] They too will probably start from the Jupiter system, on the trail of Daedalus-type probes which burned their way out of there a century or more before, consuming more deuterium and helium-3 than all of the strategic approach put together.

> *Is it beauty, or minerals, or knowledge,*
> *we take our expeditions for? What a question!*
> *But is it What a question? Is it excitement,*
> *or power, or understanding, or illumination*
> *we take our expeditions for? Is it specimens,*
> *or experiments, or spin-off, or fame, or evolution,*
> *or necessity we take our expeditions for?*
> *We are here, and our sons or our sons' sons*
> *will be on Jupiter, and their sons' sons*
> *at the star gate, leaving the fold of the sun.*[11]

'There is perhaps not another object in the heavens that presents us with such a variety of extraordinary phenomena as the planet Saturn: a magnificent globe, encompassed by a stupendous double ring: attended by seven satellites: ornamented with equatorial belts: compressed at the poles: turning upon its axis: mutually eclipsing its ring and satellites, and eclipsed by them: the most distant of the rings also turning upon its axis, and the same taking place with the farthest of the satellites: all the parts of the system of Saturn occasionally reflecting light to each other: the rings and moons illuminating the nights of the Saturnian: the globe and satellites enlightening the dark parts of the rings: and the planet and the rings throwing back the Sun's beams upon the moons, when they are deprived of them at the time of their conjunction.'

—Sir William Herschel, 1805. [63]

Before the Pioneer-Saturn flyby, radio and optical astronomers disagreed over whether Saturn was hot internally, whether there was a solid core and if so how big, and whether there was a magnetic field and radiation belts. Now we know there is a core, with three times the mass of Earth but with the same diameter, molten, and mostly iron.[64] The outer core is a hot, highly compressed layer of methane, ammonia and water, nine times the mass of Earth but less than 10% of Saturn's total. Overlying it, a shell of metallic hydrogen generates a magnetic field with overall strength 1000 times Earth's (twenty times Jupiter's),[50] but at the top of the clouds the field intensity would be slightly less than on the surface of Earth.[64] Like Jupiter's, Saturn's magnetic field has south at the 'top'; but, although its centre is displaced 2400km north within the planet,[50] it's aligned almost perfectly with the axis of rotation, unlike Earth's and Jupiter's, and knocking out hypotheses that the two axes *have* to be different.

Deep within Saturn, helium is apparently condensing and settling out, so the planet is contracting and, like Jupiter, emits about $2\frac{1}{2}$ times as much heat as it receives from the Sun. As on Jupiter the atmosphere is mostly hydrogen, and there are three layers of cloud—ammonia ice at the top, then ammoniahydro-sulphide ice, then water ice;[50] and then presumably water vapour and the possibility of life; and below that liquid hydrogen. Again as on Jupiter, the equatorial ammonia clouds are higher and colder,[64] and Voyager-1 found that the whole equatorial zone rotates 1800 kph faster than the interior. [65] Wind speeds there are four times those on Jupiter, erasing convective features and keeping the zone relatively bland.[66]

At the time of the Pioneer encounter there was extensive high-altitude haze and the planet as a whole looked bland, but, when the Voyagers followed, spring had come to the northern hemisphere and there was a great deal to be seen. There were white ovals (as on Jupiter) with sizes up to 3000km,[66] but also brown ones which, judging by their spiral structure, were storms[67] like a red spot, 6000km long,[65] in the southern hemisphere. Jetstreams create 'chevron' patterns as on Jupiter, but in considerably higher latitudes (to 78°N as against 60°); but, although the wind patterns are symmetrical in the nothern and southern hemispheres, the bands aren't correlated with the winds as on Jupiter. The most conspicuous non-Jovian feature, a sinuous dark band within a bright ribbon at 47°N, marks the one big transition between the eastward equatorial winds and the westward polar ones. Perhaps the oddest similarity to Jupiter is that the hydrogen-to-helium ratio is just the same, 9:1, despite the supposed condensing-out of helium within the planet;[65] that's good for the strategic approach, but does mean that the internal heating mechanism isn't fully understood. Another enigma is that the radio 'bursts' detected earlier are actually coming from the planet, each Saturn day at local noon, from mirror-image points at 80°N and S—the most active auroral zone, where magnetic fieldlines link into the Solar Wind.[68]

In 1889 R. A. Proctor calculated that, below the winds of the visible atmosphere, there must be a latitutde (N and S) where at local noon the interior is instantaneously at rest with respect to the Sun *in space*, although the velocity vectors of rotation and revolution immediately cease to be parallel and the illusion of trapped rotation vanishes.[69] The magnetic field lines there must momentarily come to rest in relation to the Sun: are the radio bursts connected with that? As regards the general north-south symmetry of the atmosphere, it's worth noting (again from the 19th century) that when a point goes into the shadow of the rings it doesn't see the Sun again (except through the gaps) for fifteen years.[70] Latitudes in shadow during the Pioneer pass in 1979 were mostly still in shadow during the Voyager encounters in 1980 and 1981, and things may be very different in there.

Beyond the atmosphere, the radiation belts trapped in the magnetic field are ten times the size of Earth's but have only 1% of the intensity of Jupiter's because of absorption by the rings. The space below the rings has the lowest radiation count ever measured in space, and passing through the Saturn system Pioneer-11's total dosage was equivalent to only two minutes in the Jovian belts.[64] As with Jupiter, Saturn's magnetosphere fluctuates under varying pressure from the Solar Wind and, since its mean distance is beyond the orbit of Titan (1,221,600km), the giant moon is inside the boundary about

80% of the time. It seems that the charged particles in the belts come from the rings and satellites, but many of them are reabsorbed; and the orbits of Enceladus, Tethys and Dione are all low-radiation tori within the charged-plasma cloud from Enceladus to beyond Dione's orbit.[66] Shortly before Pioneer-11 passed under the rings, a 'precipitous' drop in radiation counts indicated a near-collision with a previously unknown satellite; designated 1979 S1, this 'Pioneer Rock' was subsequently identified with 1980 S3, photographed by Voyager-1, and now has the provisional number S11.

The classification system for Saturn's moons, once simply numbered outwards, is now extremely complicated. Problems began in 1966, when the rings were edge-on to Earth and Dollfus reported an innermost satellite, 'Janus (S10)'. Glimpses in later years suggested there were actually several inner satellites; and, when the rings were again edge-on in 1979, a large number of sightings accumulated, later integrated with spacecraft photos to give 17 moons, [66,68] with four more indicated.

Table 6

Temporary Designation	Provisional Designation	Name/ Nickname	Diameter (km)	Orbital Radius (km)
1980 S2	S15	'A-ring shepherd'	60	137,670
1980 S27	S13	'Inner F shepherd'	140 × 80	139,353
1980 S26	S14	'Outer F shepherd'	110 × 70	141,700
1980 S1	S10	'Leading co-orbital'	220 × 160	151,422
1980 S3	S11	'Trailing co-orbital'	140 × 100	151,472
	S1	Mimas	390	185,600
	S2	Enceladus	510	238,100
	S3	Tethys	1050	294,700
1980 S13	S16	'Tethys L4 Trojan'	60	294,700
1980 S25	S17	'Tethys L5 Trojan'	50	294,700
	S4	Dione	1120	377,500
1980 S6	S12	'Dione L4 Trojan'	60	378,060
	S5	Rhea	1530	527,200
	S6	Titan	5150	1,211,600
	S7	Hyperion	410 × 220	1,483,000
	S8	Iapetus	1440	3,560,000
	S9	Phoebe	200	12,950,000

Relatively compact compared with Jupiter's, Saturn's system of moons has been photographed throughout by the Voyagers. Except for Titan, Iapetus and Phoebe, described later, their subtle differences are outweighed by their similarities—Edwin Morgan probably won't find scope for another set of poems. Where masses, and hence densities, were determined, all except Titan were little denser than water ice; even Titan is no denser than Ganymede, which we know to be partly ice.[66] All (except perhaps Titan) display bombardment craters, and several testify to large-scale collisions. Mimas has a crater 135km across, a full third of its diameter; while Tethys has a 400km crater into which Mimas could fit bodily. The S10 and S11 'co-orbitals' are obviously fragments of one broken moon, likewise (almost certainly) the shepherds with the narrow, twisted F-ring between them; while Hyperion— extremely irregular, with its long axis *not* pointing towards Saturn—may have fragmented within the last 10 million years.[71]

Like Jupiter's moons, Saturn's have sorted themselves out into commensurate orbits. Mimas, Tethys, Dione and Enceladus form one system of recurring configurations, while Hyperion and Iapetus are locked to Titan, and Rhea's elliptical orbit allows interaction with both groups;[63] for the origin of the Dione and Tethys 'Trojans' there is so far no explanation. Their surfaces may have been modified by inter-moon tidal stresses: even Rhea, heavily cratered, has one hemisphere markedly different from the other, with evidence of slurry flow from the interior. With colour enhancement, Rhea shows light wispy streaks, quite unlike the grooved terrain on Ganymede. Similar features, possibly due to snow welling through cracks, are spread across one smooth, dark hemisphere of Dione, while the other is extensively cratered. Dione has also long, sinuous fault-like valleys, like Enceladus, Tethys, Mimas and S11; probably tidal stresses melted interior water after formation, cracking the surface. But Enceladus seems to have been through at least five evolutionary, phases, including grooving like Ganymede's. Parts of the surface are virtually crater-free, probably less than 100 million years old, so probably tides caused by both Saturn and Dione are still smoothing the surface: methane geysers and water outbreaks could account for the broad outermost E-ring, in which Enceladus is embedded.[66]

'When we in fact see how this majestic arc is suspended over the equator of the planet with no visible means of support or connection, our mind can no longer remain at ease. We cannot become reconciled to this phenomenon as if it were some simple fact, we cannot describe it simply as the result of observations, and we cannot accept it without seeking for an explanation for it.'

So wrote James Clerk Maxwell in 1859,[72] and it would be nice to have a possible explanation for even the outermost ring, since on current models of Saturn's formation the others would still have been inside the planet when initial contraction stopped.[73] The probes confirmed the existence of rings outside A, B and C, as amateurs had reported for years, and the tenuous ring D, which extends from C down to the atmosphere, but didn't resolve their detailed composiiton or explain their existence. What they did find was tens of thousands of ringlets making up the visible structure:[68] the narrow outer rings F and G are distinguished only because they're separated from the main body—and even *they* have finer rings within them. The discovery of the A- and F-ring 'shepherds' led to predictions that the rings would be full of tiny satellites, but Voyager-2 found not even one.[66] Some ringlets are sharply kinked, for no obvious reasons; the 'shepherds' were blamed for the braiding of the F-ring, but Voyager-2 absolved them; many others are elliptical, and the whole outer edge of the dense B-ring is in 2:1 resonance with Mimas and precesses in a huge ellipse at right-angles to the Saturn-Mimas line. Worse still, in the B-ring, radial spokes come and go, apparently composed of fine dust which is scattering sunlight, in defiance of the laws of orbital motion but corotating with the magnetic field; they are perhaps connected with radio emissions, which suggest high-voltage lightning within the rings.[74] As Maxwell wrote to Lord Kelvin, 'I should not recommend anyone to lease a building stance on any of the rings without security that his property may not be spun out into spirals of unknown extent within a few hours. Arctic ice packs are secure in comparison.'[75]

Travel around the Saturn system should generally be cheaper than between the moons of Jupiter, but delta-vs will be increased if transfers have to avoid the equatorial plane, and the D-ring will make 'mining' Saturn's atmosphere dangerous. Robert Shaw's forced-orbit satellite would have to pass twice under the rings on every circuit, exposed to a continuous meteor infall (the effect of collisions within the rings is that the whole system gradually loses energy,[72] with steady drainage into the atmosphere). In other ways, the operation should be more effective than Jupiter-mining: gravity is lower, the equatorial current is faster, and upwelling 'white ovals' are rare in the equatorial zone—they may occur only when the rings are edge-on to the Sun,[63] when overall illumination is 15% greater,[73] and disperse from the leading edge, unlike Jupiter equatorial plumes driven back by counter-rotating streams.

Equatorial winds in the direction of rotation favour flying factories or 'aerostats', but to launch cargo past the rings they'd have to stay north or south of the equator, and the north equatorial band has been seen to be notched, indicating extensive turbulence.[63] Since the equator is significantly inclined to the orbital plane, cargoes might be launched directly to other planets more easily than to the moons. Phoebe, the outermost moon, could provide high-energy boost, guidance, or deceleration of incoming cargo shells, with an artificial magnetic field or laser stations, because its orbit is retrograde in the plane of Saturn's orbit around the Sun. Waveriders might swing round Phoebe and then Titan, to re-reverse their direction, and drop straight into Saturn's atmosphere.

Since most of the system is ice, Phoebe may be a major resource site. Its orbit always suggested a captured asteroid, and Voyager-2 found it much larger and darker than expected —reflecting only 5% of incident light, less than our Moon, and with surface features darker still. It's spherical, however, unusual for a body 200km across, and has a 9-10 hour noncaptured rotation, suggesting a gigantic cometary nucleus.[66] The long-standing mystery of Iapetus, the next moon inward, was that the leading hemisphere is far darker than the other: but the dark material has the same albedo as Phoebe and could well have come from there. It has a noticeable reddish tinge, which Sagan suggests may indicate organic compounds;[68] Phoebe may be a huge carbonaceous chondrite and the Saturn system's main source of heavier elements. But there are dark-floored craters in the bright hemisphere of Iapetus, suggesting that the material wells out from the interior or that it is the ice which is the deposit; however, there are also bright craters in the dark hemisphere.

When the asteroid culture comes to Saturn it may well start with the outer moons, as with Jupiter's, for low gravity, no atmospheres (EMLs usable), low delta-vs to escape altogether —and lower collision hazards than nearer the planet. Ice can be acquired from Iapetus, initially; and as development moves inwards the snowball moons may be the next target because EMLs can be used there, avoiding Titan. This is just the reverse of earlier predictions, but then everything about Titan is like that.

When Titan's atmosphere was discovered it was interpreted as methane, and many artists followed Chesley Bonestell in painting a frost-bound landscape under a clear blue sky. Clarke predicted that Saturn might be reached before Jupiter because nuclear-powered ships could fill their fuel tanks with methane on Titan.[76] Early in the 1970s high-altitude red clouds were discovered, and in 1975 Ed Buckley reinterpreted the classic views (*New Worlds for Old*, Plates 14 and 15). Gavin Roberts produced an alternative view (an earlier version of Plate 8) assuming that the cloud cover was complete, and has proved right except that Titan is much more orange than he supposed. The probes found opaque clouds 50km above the surface, with three layers of blue haze at 200, 375 and 500km.[65] Voyager-1 saw almost featureless parallel bands and a darker polar hood, but by 1981 spring had come and a dark ring had formed around the pole. Voyager-1 indicated that only 1% of the atmosphere is methane and 99% nitrogen;[65] in that case plenty of methane is missing from the predicted abundances and there could be a methane ocean 1km thick at the surface, at 91 K and a pressure of 1.5atm;[68] also, there could be liquid nitrogen at the poles.[77]

The other possibility is that the methane has been synthesized into organic compounds. Voyager-1 detected hydrogen cyanide, one of the basic molecules in abiogenic synthesis of organics, and Sagan and Khare have been able to duplicate the spectroscopic properties of Titan's clouds by energizing 'primal atmospheres' of nitrogen and methane.[66] Voyager-2 detected at least ten organic compounds including propane and acetylene, and the atmosphere may after all be 12% argon; such a high proportion would again suggest depletion. Darrell Strobel, who engagingly described his Voyager experiment to ASTRA as 'a hobby', suggested that, instead of the methane ocean, Titan's surface may be 3km deep in hydrocarbon snow.[73] The energizing agent may be solar ultraviolet radiation, although there's also the frequent exposure to the Solar Wind, since Titan has no protective magnetic field.[77]

It's generally accepted that Titan is a frozen stage in the

chemical evolution of Earth-like worlds. When the atmosphere was thought to be methane, it was hoped that greenhouse effect might give surface temperatures where life could evolve: to see the next stages we may now have to wait until the Sun flares briefly at the end of its stable lifetime. But, since Titan has no obvious strategic uses as it is except for slingshot manoeuvres, and since anything that was triggered by the death of the Sun would almost immediately be snuffed out again, human curiosity might cause a solar laser to be turned on Titan to light the 4.6-billion-year chemical fuse. In 'How Beautiful with Banners', the classic story of the 'old' Titan, Blish imagined a chance human intervention 'beginning that long evolution the end of which, sixty millions of years away, no human being would see'.[78] Titan as it really is lets us put it under the sunlamp and give life there as long a run as we have had so far.

There's another form of atmosphere depletion: the nitrogen has almost certainly come from ammonia dissociated by solar ultraviolet, allowing the hydrogen to escape into space.[73] Even now Titan's orbit is completely surrounded by a torus of neutral hydrogen stretching outwards for a million kilometres, past Hyperion, and inwards to the orbit of Rhea.[65] When Titan is inside Saturn's magnetosphere the magnetic field lines rotate past it at 200kps, creating a leading hemisphere wake like Io's: and no doubt when Titan's in the Solar Wind there's a trailing wake instead. While the Titan one has no obvious uses, tori might deliberately be generated from the smaller moons: Robert Shaw suggested vaporizing the surfaces with nuclear explosions and collecting the plasma in orbit using charged spherical grids, manufactured from asteroids by vapour deposition on the surface of a balloon and then 'taking away the balloon you first thought of'. (His penchant for drastic methods led to suggestions that he was out to terrify rather than terraform the Solar System). Scoop vehicles would comb the tori in retrograde orbits from Phoebe, and the residues would be recycled by their moons in due course.

Exploiting outer planets and their moons on such scales may seem absurd. But deuterium will always be rare compared to ordinary hydrogen, and helium-3 rarer still, and beyond the Asteroid Belt solar cells are ineffective and mirrors increasingly unwieldy. To save the key isotopes for power generation, interplanetary flight might shift increasingly to the methods described in Chapter 4; and heavier elements and more exotic isotopes may be harder still to come by. In such circumstances, measures may have to be taken to preserve the rings of Saturn: it would be tragic if they were to disappear, like whales. Future generations may count themselves fortunate if the ring particles prove too small for on-site mining and too large for electrostatic collection: even within ASTRA some people were quite prepared to have the rings consumed for their resources. ('Why do you want to keep the rings?' 'They're pretty'. 'That's not a very good reason.') With them, the only conservationist argument carrying any weight was that the rings are 'the best advertisement space travel ever had'. In reply to suggestions that pictures of the rings *before* Man reached them would suffice, Roberts invoked the Trades Descriptions Act.

If the rings are preplanetary material which never coalesced, they may be unique in the Solar System and of inestimable scientific value—and sampling methods will have to be devised to find out. From there to large-scale exploitation may be just a matter of time, unless the ice, rock or metal components of the rings have no practical use or are too slight to be worth collecting. The rings' best defence is that they absorb radiation. But in 1966 Kozyrev found evidence in Saturn's spectrum for the greenhouse effect of an atmosphere over the sunlit face of the rings;[72] Pioneer-11 found hydrogen there, confirmed by Voyager-2, from dissociating water vapour. That atmosphere may be scooped, because otherwise it will escape into space; and from there it's a small step to heating the rings ahead of the orbiting collectors with giant mirrors. As the rings grow dimmer, the gay Irish fiddle tune 'The Frost Is All Gone' gradually turns into a lament.

But if Lawton's dust hypothesis is correct (see Chapter 12), and there's a steady infall of valuable materials from the outer Solar System, then a variant of the same process may preserve the rings after all. The dark leading hemispheres of Enceladus and Iapetus and the dark band on Tethys are interesting, because our moon accumulates material mostly on the leading hemisphere.[79] If, as predicted, small particles in the ring-seither stick to larger ones or are swept out by radiation pressure,[72] quite a lot of dust may already have been trapped by the rings. If, however, we trap the gases over the upper face and reintroduce them, in the shadow of the planet, they'll tend to refreeze on to ring particles and trap dust in the process.

Orbiting scoops, staggered according to the rates of infall, could collect the gases over the rings and release them in fragile containers, to reenter the rings and burst in shadow; swinging back below the rings, the scoops would gather the dust thrust out by radiation pressure. The whole vast area of the rings would be a gigantic dust collector and, since the ices are continuously recycled, their brightness would be preserved by Man, where even nature would allow it gradually to diminish.

If these things come to pass, there will be a high-technology Saturn civilization exporting to the rest of the Solar System. Chris Boyce saw it as a component of the asteroid culture—the surface of Titan may never be worth terraforming because of the great distance from the Sun and the slow rotation; the other moons could be made habitable only below the surface, and habitat-dwellers might find their hollow worlds more comfortable and—because of the possible gravity variations—more interesting: a constant-*g* environment like a planet or a moon might be seen as constricting. A true interplanetary culture would be developing and, if it hadn't alread happened, the move out to Saturn might see the emergence of mobile habitats as independent economic units, soon becoming politically independent states.

> Well, 'the winds hae swung the warld' since then, and the
>   tides hae gane out and in,
> And the Moon has vanished many times but it's aye come back
>   again,
> Tae shine upon the Carlisle road and cast its spindly beams
> Through space and time and Universe, and it's kennel't up
>   men's dreams.
>
> Oh, the Moon shone bright one Sunday night, not many
>   days ago,
> When Neil Armstrong frae the USA, tae the Borders he
>   did go ...
>   —Buff Wilson, 'Rounding the Moon', 1969

Pioneer-10 is out there now, in the border country not just of the Earth-Moon system but of the Solar System itself. In July 1981 it was at 25 AU, more than halfway from the orbit of Uranus to that of Neptune, [80] still fully immersed in the Solar

Wind which, at launch in 1972, was thought to end not far beyond the orbit of Jupiter. Although it won't pass near the outer planets, Pioneer-10 has already demonstrated that they are, in a sense, within the atmosphere of the Sun: the boundary or 'heliopause' may lie as far out as 100AU, or more than four times Pluto's mean distance.[25] Pioneer-10 isn't likely to remain operational to such distances, and is anyway going back along the Sun's orbital track around the Galactic Centre, but by conserving power it can probably be followed out to Pluto's orbit, 15 years after launch. Pioneer-11 is now moving towards the Apex of the Sun's Way, where the heliopause should be closest, but because of the five-year detour to Saturn it's unlikely to be tracked even to the planetary borders. Voyager-1 is going in the same general direction and will be at 40AU by 1990, but the Reagan administration is reported to want to switch off Voyager-2 even before the Uranus and Neptune flybys,[68] so Voyager-1 tracking is even more at risk.

The boundary planetoids and planets (Chiron, Uranus, Neptune, Triton, Pluto and Charon) may not have formed directly from the condensing disc of matter around the proto-Sun but more slowly, out of collisions amongst the great family of comets. Hoyle and Wickramasinghe have argued that their accretion times were of the order of 300 million years;[81] if the Kirton Hypothesis (below) is correct, the timescale for Uranus is spot on but Neptune's formation would have been 100 or 500 million years later still—the latter date, 800 million years after the formation of the System, coinciding with the final bombardment sustained by the inner planets and the satellites of the giants.

Kirton's conjectures (the details are in *New Worlds for Old*) are that planets' rotations take up the direction of orbital motion at formation, and that the plane of the Solar System turns right over through 360° during two 'Galactic Years' (revolutions of the Sun around the Galactic Centre).[82] The Sun's orbit around the Centre would be elliptical, and the 2:1 rotation of the orbital planes would be analogous to Mercury's 2:1 trapped rotation in orbit around the Sun. Since the 'Galactic Year' is about 200 million years, the axis of a planet formed 300 million years after the inner worlds would now be on its side in the orbital plane, and that's just the case with Uranus.

Radio observations in 1974 confirmed earlier suggestions that Uranus's 'brightness temperature' was considerably higher than expected, at 120 K[81] not much colder than the high clouds of Jupiter (150 K)[25] and hotter than Saturn's turned out to be (90-100 K). At first greenhouse effect was suspected, but by 1978 the emissions, apparently from the 10atm pressure level, had increased in strength by 30%.[83] Either the temperature is rising sharply as Uranus' north pole turns into sunlight, or there's a difference in internal composition with latitude due to convection currents—i.e., there's internal heating. There's evidence for a magnetic field extending as far as the orbit of Oberon, outermost of the five known moons.[84] The generally accepted rotation period of 10.8 hours has been challenged, as it would cause too much polar flattening: the new estimates are 22-23 hours[85] and 14-16 hours.[86] The latest amazing idea, which has emerged from high pressure/temperature simulations with gas cannon, is that inside Uranus and Neptune methane could dissociate and form Earth-sized masses of diamond or graphite.[87]

But the big Uranus sensation was the 1977 discovery, as the planet passed in front of a star, that it has at least five rings of dark fragments, apparently coarser in constitution than Saturn's. They're extremely narrow, four of them less than 10km across—much narrower than even Saturn's F-ring at 800km, but more regular. The outermost ring, Epsilon, was suspected of being double, like Saturn's ring A, but in later occultations it was found instead to have precessing sharp edges in the form of a Keplerian ellipse.[88] Four more rings were discovered, bringing the total to nine, and they're all known to be ellipses, although three are near-circular.[89] Dynamical analysis suggests a sixth satellite, as large as the innermost known one (Miranda), but still closer to the rings.[51]

The discovery of the rings gave Voyager-2's redirection to Uranus such high priority that Pioneer-11's Titan flyby was dropped, to test-fly the Voyager trajectory instead. In January 1986 Voyager-2 will make a north polar approach to Uranus: the options are a close flyby of one moon and the planet, or a more distant encounter when all the moons are on the same side of Uranus.[90] Neptune encounter would follow in September 1989. If the Reagan administration does instead switch it off, the estimated saving is $220 million over the eight years,[68] 0.0001 of what that same administration proposes to spend *annually* on preparation for a war which is supposed never to happen. It would imply a judgment that there is no future, so we needn't trouble ourselves to assess the possibilities.

'Who can say but what your new star, which exceeds Saturn in his distance from the Sun, may exceed him as much in magnificence of attendance? Who can say what new rings, new satellites, or what other numberless phenomena remain behind, waiting to reward future industry?' wrote Sir Joseph Banks to Herschel on the discovery of Uranus in 1781.[91] Despite its distance, the planet may have a great deal to offer mankind. If they're built up of cometary materials, both Uranus and Neptune may contain a great deal of deuterium, and there's reason to think they have higher helium-to-hydrogen ratios than the Sun, that the helium-3 to helium-4 ratio also may be different,[92] and that the relative abundances of elements heavier than helium may be greater.[83] Flyby and atmosphere-entry missions may tell us a great deal about the processes of element formation in stars, and the details of the Sun's initial condensation. Both planets may eventually become major sources of those essential isotopes; once again, the length of the journey doesn't matter—even on minimum-energy transfers —once a regular transport-line of unmanned cargo carriers is in operation.

The weird moons of Uranus and Neptune are likely to be useful in such operations. A normal approach to Uranus (in the orbital plane) will always put a spacecraft into polar orbit, while an approach from north or south of the orbital plane can give direct or retrograde equatorial orbit, respectively, in the 21-year northern-hemisphere autumn (the opposite in spring) but *also* will give polar orbit in the summer/winter modes. To get to the moons requires what would be a polar-orbit approach, for any other planet, and can be done with the help of a Jupiter flyby and out-of-the-Ecliptic Jupiter-Uranus transfer, plus a plane change ranging from 0° at the equinoxes to 90° at the solstices.

The innermost satellite, Miranda, will therefore have a key rôle if, as suspected, it has a large orbital eccentricity and inclination.[93] It could then act as a staging post for incoming spacecraft between the equinoxes: capture would be economical, since Miranda lies so far down the planet's gravity well, lunar shuttles could be fuelled from the planet, and Miranda's movements are commensurate with those of Ariel and Umbriel, so that transfer windows would be frequent. Minimum-energy flyby past Ariel, the next moon out, could effect the equatorial plane-change for transfers to any of the other moons.

In Chapter 5 I mentioned mining the Solar Wind for hydrogen with superconducting ion scoops.[48] The outer worlds aren't likely to need hydrogen to manufacture water, since ices of all kinds appear plentiful. Nevertheless, paradoxically, Uranus will probably be the base of operations when we decide to do something about the Solar Wind on a large scale. Virtually all the Sun's output of energy, and matter in the Solar Wind, goes out of the Ecliptic; scoops on a few airless moons and asteroids would hardly make a dent in it, and free-flying ones in the Ecliptic plane would be undesirable because of the effect their huge magnetic fields would have on each other, passing ships, and even planets. For Solar-Wind exploitation the moons of Uranus are the only natural termini, since approach and departure in any season *have* to be out-of-the-Ecliptic. Any significant stay in the Uranus system provides a free plane change in Ecliptic longitude for each given launch configuration and, while it wouldn't be efficient to wait eleven years, say, to get a 45° plane change, a steady stream of launches over 84 years could fill both Ecliptic hemispheres with scoops sweeping up the Solar Wind in a grid pattern. Each unit would end its collecting run with a Jupiter flyby, shifting into the Ecliptic plane for delivery before a second pass around Jupiter sent it back to Uranus for maintenance.

Helium-3 will no doubt be in demand, and the Solar Wind contains in addition ions of many useful elements; but most of the collectors' input will be 'ordinary' hydrogen and helium, which may not be useful in such quantities. Perhaps the scoops could carry fusion reactors and systematically 'breed' what they picked up into the more useful isotopes. More exotic manufacturing would be possible by focussing the input into high-energy proton and α-particle beams over periods of years, if appropriate. With a Daedalus interstellar mission calling for 30,000 tonnes of helium-3, plus deuterium, a large-scale interstellar programme would be a colossal undertaking, but the Uranus culture needn't be daunted—it can send off ion scoops backed by fusion reactors and automated factories, telling them not to come back until they have starships ready for launch. Uranus would be a good launch-point also for out-of-the-Ecliptic interstellar targets—using lunar flybys to finalize the outgoing trajectories, since otherwise one would have to wait up to 42 years for the plane of the Uranus system to pass across the target.*

By comparison, Neptune's rôle will be secondary, since it can supply materials only from its own substance. But any industry based on Triton, Neptune's giant moon, may be competitive with those of the Galileans or Titan because launch velocity into circumsolar orbit is lower than theirs: because of Triton's retrograde revolution about Neptune, it's apparently possible to launch into direct, circumsolar orbit at *less* than the moon's normal escape velocity.[94] Although less convenient, the velocity advantage could be increased by EML launches from orbit if Triton's methane atmosphere is confirmed—at the moment it's in doubt.[95] This might be about the only case in the Solar System where the presence of an atmosphere was bad news; but Triton capture is highly effective. A Jupiter or Saturn swingby could place a minimum energy probe in orbit around Neptune, using Triton's pull for final braking, in 22 years—four years less than it takes to get to a Uranus orbit using similar methods.[96]

As a result, Triton may provide us with a remarkable bonus. Shaw pointed out that, if as Lawton suggests the outer planets receive an infall of dust trapped by the interacting gravitational fields of the Sun and other stars, Triton would be able to capture dust at very low relative velocities in some parts of its orbit. Cyclic freezing and thawing could form 'laminated terrain' like the Martian polar caps, rich in rare elements and isotopes if the dust has been created by recent supernovae (see Chapter 12). Neptune's orbit is much more nearly circular than Mars's, but at those distances a small eccentricity has a big effect—the distance from the Sun varies by 81 million kilometres, more than twice Mars's variation. Neptune's axial tilt is nearly 29° and Triton's orbit is inclined 20° to the equator, so there's almost certainly a precessional cycle giving a wide range of seasonal effects. If Triton has significant internal activity like the Galileans (there's *plenty* of tidal

*An old Highland skipper, watching his boat being loaded, was asked by a Spanish visitor if there is a word in Gaelic corresponding to '*Mañana*'. 'No,' he replied, 'there is not a word in the Gaelic conveying such a sense of *urgency*.'

interaction with Neptune[97]), gases injected into the atmosphere may be deposited—perhaps suddenly, when the moon is
eclipsed by the planet. As David Proffitt, a keen climber,
remarked, 'Instant snow-steps yet, but keep moving.'

Sudden atmosphere freezing would have a fractionating
effect: dust brought down with the condensing gases would
be left behind when they sublimed again. Seasonal processes
would form laminated terrain at the poles, at least, while
volcanic plumes like Io's might bring down dust deposits in
rings. Shaw suggested seeding the atmosphere with crystals or
large dust particles to promote snowfall, which would be easier
to collect and process than hoarfrost; and in suitable terrain a
snowfield might be dusted with aluminium, to reflect more
sunlight and keep it from subliming again, in order to start a
glacier. Once established, the glacier itself would create
snow-forming conditions, and processing plants could work the
ice at its foot. Unlike our Moon's, Triton's productivity could
be enhanced by rocket exhausts and other gases added to the
atmoshere by human activities. If Triton does have a subsurface ocean, even more remarkable processes might operate
—and Ed Buckley painted those intriguing derricks on Triton
(Plate 12) years before the Voyager flybys of the Galilean
moons.

Plate 12 features another remarkable prediction of Buckley's. Although in 1948 Dollfus reported surface markings on
Neptune, but no belts,[98] many experts maintained that there
would be no visible activity on the blue disc. In 1975-76,
however, Neptune's brightness increased markedly in the
infrared, while no corresponding change due to solar activity
was seen on Uranus. High-altitude tenuous clouds of methane
or argon seem to be the explanation.[85] At the same time,
Neptune's surface was found to be much warmer than
expected, at 163 K,[99] part of which may be greenhouse effect
and part tidal heating by Triton; and the accepted rotation
period of about 16 hours was shown probably to be wrong,
with 19-27 hours as the new range of values.[85]

Buckley didn't incorporate another prediction already two-
thirds fulfilled. In his 1971 lecture on 'the new look of the
Solar System' (which led to the *Man and the Planets* project) he
argued that Saturn's rings might not be unique, only conspicuous: all the giant worlds might well have them. He showed a
sketch of Jupiter with a single equatorial ring—discovered

eight years later!—and his 1973 painting 'Golgotha Moon' showed dark, chunky rocks orbiting Uranus—although further out than the rings found in 1977. Since Neptune has two known satellites, and since Saturn is now known to have seven rings, Uranus nine and Jupiter one, we could follow Tolkien's numerology and suggest that Neptune should have three. But star occultations suggest not rings but satellites at 50,000 and 37,000km,[100] the two predicted resonances for rings.[101]

Not only has Triton, possibly the largest satellite in the Solar System, an inclined and retrograde orbit, its smaller companion Nereid has the most eccentric orbit known in the Solar System;[102] while Pluto has the most extraordinary planetary orbit, highly inclined to the Ecliptic and at times coming closer to the Sun than does Neptune. For 20 years out of every 248, as at present (1982), Neptune and not Pluto is the outermost known planet. It has been suggested that Pluto was a satellite of Neptune which interacted with Triton, reversing Triton's orbital motion as Pluto itself was thrown clear; or that Triton was a stray planet, perhaps even of extrasolar origin, which entered the Neptune system and usurped Pluto's place; while, if Pluto was indeed responsible for the measured planetary perturbations, by its apparent size it must contain dense material unknown to contemporary science. Ingenious variations were put forward on the theme that the apparent diameter was only the reflection of the Sun on a smooth ocean (of liquid methane) or an ice field. But, with every attempt to determine Pluto's diameter from star occultations, results were negative and the estimated diameter had to be revised downwards still further.

In July 1978 it was announced that Pluto has a satellite. Charon is 1200-2000km across,[103] and Pluto's own diameter lies between 3000 and 3600km.[104] Pluto's mass is about 0.0023 of the Earth's[105] and its density is therefore about that of water—like Saturn's moons. A composition of frozen volatiles seems most likely (methane frost has been detected), and yet there are contrast features on the surface, from which the rotation had already been determined before the discovery of Charon—dark patches, possibly coinciding with depressions, and spectral suggestions of silicates.[105] In 1980 a methane atmosphere was detected.[106]

The interplanetary importance of Charon is that Pluto in its present form couldn't have been a satellite of Neptune: satellites of satellites are unstable and crash down onto their primaries. [106] Furthermore, Pluto doesn't have mass enough for either of the postulated Triton slingshots. Harrington and van Flandern suggest that a stray planet two to five times as massive as the Earth passed through the Neptune system, disrupting the orbits of Triton and Nereid and fragmenting Pluto as it was thrown clear; [107] but, if so, when? In *New Worlds for Old* I suggested that the tenth planet, if it exists, might be a stray captured by the Sun very early in its history, so that the Bode's Law distribution of the known planets might be explained in terms of gravitational resonance. If this is the case, and if Kirton is right, and if the Neptune-'X' encounter was soon after Neptune formed, it's remarkable that Triton has survived so long to testify. Triton's orbit is decaying due to tidal drag, and in a few more million years the moon will be gone. [13]

In 1972 Brady suggested that the tenth planet was in a retrograde orbit, inclined at 60° to the Ecliptic. [108] It wasn't found as predicted, and in *New Worlds for Old* Lawton called it a false alarm. Yet *Charon's* 6.38-day orbit is retrograde, inclined at 65° to the orbital plane, and Pluto's rotation is locked to it. [105] Pluto may belong with 'X' rather than with Neptune's family, and Brady may have been at least partly on the right lines.

All this has interesting implications for Chiron, the 'miniplanet' discovered by Charles Kowal in 1977. Chiron's orbit ranges between those of Saturn and Uranus, like a stray asteroid, but it's remarkably large at 160-640km. It might be a survivor from a series of collisions which turned Uranus on its side [109] —the only explanation for that apart from Kirton's hypothesis—but this seems unlikely: Chiron may have had close encounters with both Jupiter and Saturn, modifying its orbit, during the last 2500 years. [110] Over the next 3 million years (2900 revolutions), there's a 1:8 chance that it'll be expelled from the Solar System by Saturn, and a 7:8 probability that, instead, the orbit will contract due to interactions with Jupiter. [111] The present 'chaotic' orbit suggests that Chiron is new to the planetary system, altough as Kowal points out it's 100 times the size of a typical comet nucleus[112] —like Phoebe. [66] The timescale for major evolutions in its orbit, of the same order as Triton's, suggests a connection with the Triton/Pluto-Charon mystery.

Seen from Pluto, Charon would be at least $4\frac{1}{2}$ degrees across,[105] fixed in the sky, and as bright when full as our gibbous Moon although at least 81 times larger. There would be no shortage of daylight, for out there the Sun is still hundreds of times brighter than our full Moon—more than enough to read by;[113] but the surface is at 48 K or colder, approaching the range in which even hydrogen would liquefy. For explorers, that may a considerable problem. Before Luna-2, there were fears that the lunar crust might be chemically unstable and ready to explode on contact with terrestrial material; the favoured explanation for the Viking 'biology' results was that the soil was reacting dramatically to its first liquid water in untold years. There were fears too that the nuclear-heated Viking might melt its way down into permafrost and disappear. On Pluto that would be certain unless steps were taken to prevent it. But the steps might have to be proverbially large ones: even a well insulated boot might not just melt into the snow but trigger a major explosion. One small step for a man could turn into a giant leap indeed.

Even projecting mountaintops (nunataks, in Antarctica) mightn't be safe for a landing. In a conventional rocket landing, ices raised to a temperature previously unknown might ignite in a colossal explosion or a conflagration that swept the planet; or ice might close around the rocket and trap it for ever—even a vehicle lowered from a rocket which returned to orbit would have to be fantastically insulated if it were not to sink into a bubbling pool which froze over behind it. Shaw suggested touching down on very cold helium jets, with a plug-nozzle refrigerated with liquid helium.* (Liquid hydrogen *could* theoretically be used, but it's dangerously near the environmental temperature and, since helium has to be used for touchdown, switching to hydrogen refrigeration afterwards doesn't seem worth the risk.) A trade-off decision would have to be made between refrigerating a large surface, for a stable, broad-based vehicle, or minimizing the area in contact with the ground and holding the ship upright with gyros. Landing legs, conducting heat from the main body of the ship, seem quite unusable.

Four such ships in a box pattern could be the legs for a

---

*He also remarked that an ion-drive ship, with heat-radiating panels, might blind Plutonians even from orbit!

permanent base. The underside of the platform would have to
be refrigerated as well, however, and all waste heat would have
to be radiated upwards from the centre, right out of sight of the
ground—otherwise the surroundings would soon become a
highly dangerous slush; even so, convection in the newly
discovered atmosphere might be a problem. All exploration
vehicles would have to hover on helium jets, and it's hard to
see how someone in a spacesuit could ever risk standing on the
surface, unless there's plenty of sufficiently stable, accessible
rock.

Pluto's contribution to a Solar System civilization is difficult
to assess. Since the planet is deficient in heavier elements and
has little or no helium available, deuterium would seem to be
its only promising export. If there are extensive dust deposits,
the story would be different—and if there's a continuing heavy
infall, no doubt an atmosphere-circulation system will be
artificially established to make the planet a more efficient dust
collector with precipitation on glaciers, etc. And there may be
unsuspected 'cold chemistries' on those remote icefields and
rocks. Ian Downie pointed out that, with carbon compounds
verified, an amazing tower could be built between the trapped
faces of Pluto and Charon. For consistency it should be called
the Styx, but its builders might be forgiven if they mixed
mythologies and called it Bifrost. Stresses on it would be low,
but it would have to be well built if it were to last the five
billion years until the Solar System's Ragnarok, when the
Earth falls seething into the Sun, life on Titan reaches Blish's
hinted-at apotheosis, and the Frost Giants come to claim their
inheritance.

If the outer worlds' culture is based on rare and heavy elements
in infalling dust, Chris Boyce predicted, it's only a matter of
time before demand outstrips supply. If Lawton's dust infall
doesn't occur, heavy element shortages could become a problem much sooner. Boyce therefore suggested an extremely
dangerous process he called 'pinpoint novae', focussing very
high-energy laser beams deep into the giant worlds from
synchronously orbiting satellites, to trigger fusion reactions in
the atmospheres. A very powerful magnetic field would
contain the reaction and draw the products up the plasma shaft,
separating in the longest imaginable mass spectrometer, for
collection at the synchronous station. In theory, the process

could synthesize any desired elements and isotopes, including ones too short-lived to be found even in dust from recent supernovae. The danger is that the plasma beam's focus might alter, to devastate rings and moons beyond. Runaway reactions can be discounted: the giant worlds, even Jupiter, are too small for natural fusion in their cores, much less near the visible surfaces. But the effects on the surrounding atmosheres would be dramatic; we're back in the realms of planetary engineering and that opens up the prospect, amazing as it might seem, of terraforming the giant worlds themselves. As the old Chinese proverb has it, 'With enough fire you can cook anything.'

In *The Next Ten Thousand Years*[114] Berry proposed to build a Dyson sphere (see Chapter 13) with fusion reactors in the atmosphere of Jupiter converting hydrogen to iron, which would be launched out electromagnetically to build a sphere around the Sun. Mercury and the Galilean moons would be used to build a mini-sphere around Jupiter, to shield Earth and other planets from the glare of the fusion reactions, whose energy release would equal that of the Sun. But surely in that situation Jupiter's gaseous mass would disperse explosively into space: if the heavy elements could be retained they might be enough to build several Earths, but it's a colossal waste of 99% of the planet's mass, and no one's likely to suggest it as a way of building new worlds. As a way of building a Dyson sphere it seems useless. Buckley suggested, instead of shielding the planet, using fewer reactors, so that as mini-Suns they generated bearable temperatures on the Galileans. It would then take a very long time to build a Dyson sphere, so why extend the fusion process as far as iron? Most of the energy release comes from reactions between lighter elements. If the cut-off points were oxygen and nitrogen, a breathable Jovian atmosphere would begin to form.

At first, free oxygen would combine with atmospheric hydrogen as soon as it was released. Shaw pointed out that it could generate lift for the flying reactors if released in underside lifting cavities, so the unit might be a gigantic Waverider riding on a continuous water-forming explosion; however, almost all the energy of the fusion reactions has to be shed upwards, out of the atmosphere (partly to avoid blasting Jupiter away and partly to provide 'sunlight' to the orbiting civilization), from a parabolic radiator on the upper surface in the 'lee' of the wing, while it maintains a supersonic high angle of attack. Shaw suggested energy release to the rear to simplify the process, but that doesn't satisfy the other requirements. However, if 'pinpoint novae' could be sufficiently finely tuned not to poison the environment for later use, then physical converters could be dispensed with, using the magnetic shaft just to channel the energy upwards and allowing the oxygen and nitrogen to disperse.

The Galileans may need terraforming or filter screens for their nearside faces because of ultraviolet, gamma- and X-radiation from the Jovian 'suns'. Oxygen atmospheres would form protective ozone layers but, since the moons aren't massive enough to retain them, they'd spread along the orbits in concentric rings, like the present atmospheres of Io and Titan. Could Jupiter hold such rings of oxygen, and nitrogen for plants, in sufficient density to be breathable in concentration at the surfaces of the moons? Even with protective layers, Shaw suggested, anyone on the moons who looked directly at the 'suns' might be blinded. That would be a pity, if true, since the weather patterns around them would be interesting, to say the least.

In theory, the whole planet could be converted into water; but later stages would be so violent that Shaw suggested speeding up the rotation, increasing the polar flattening so that, when the core disrupted, the physical explosion would boil up at the poles and leave the converters in the equatorial band unscathed. Dyson's way of speeding up the rotation of a planet with a magnetic field requires a solid surface:[62] in theory, the conducting strips could be laid on Jupiter's metallic hydrogen lattice by boron nitride vehicles, but in practice, thinking of the sheer *scale* of it, it seems unlikely. 'Pinpoint novae' would reform if disrupted; but apparently the issue need never arise.

If Jupiter became mostly water, driving helium to the top of the atmosphere for the PROFAC collectors, then, since liquid water is much denser than gaseous hydrogen, the planet would shrink dramatically, Right? *No*—because most of the hydrogen in Jupiter is compressed into liquid or crystal form. Jupiter's overall density is 1.3 times that of water, so taking out the helium and converting the 83% of hydrogen into water initially generates a sphere which is slightly larger than Jupiter is now, because for most practical purposes water is virtually incompressible. But within Jupiter, at megabar pressures, presumably the water would dissociate into hydrogen and oxygen, which would then differentiate to form an oxygen core overlaid by a very hot liquid hydrogen layer, indistinguishable from the present one, below the liquid water layer. *So there's no point in converting the whole planet.* All we need do is convert the upper layers until the present water-droplet layer condenses and a breathable atmosphere forms over it. Then we can shut down the fusion reactions and begin terraforming in earnest.

Meantime, a large number of asteroid habitats would no doubt have come into orbit around Jupiter to share the heat from the planet. In the later stages of conversion they might argue that the fusion process should after all continue, to maintain the energy output for their and the Galileans' benefit. But if that faction prevailed, preventing terraforming, the returns would diminish as the heavier-element reactions began to dominate, and the energy release dropped. It would be better to move those Jovian habitats into circumsolar orbits or, if their main marketplaces are the Galileans and the outer Jovians, high-inclination Sun-synchronous orbits, or halo orbits about the Sun-Jupiter L2, with big mirrors to meet their energy needs. Here we have the explicit beginning of a conservationist Kardashev-2 civilization (see Chapters 1 and 13), deliberately making the best use of the System's matter and energy *short of* destroying its existing planets.

The methane and ammonia in the Jovian atmosphere would dissociate in the conversion process, releasing carbon dioxide and nitrogen, with care not to form poisonous nitrogen oxides. Residual ammonia would rapidly be 'fixed' by bacteria when terrestrial life was introduced, while methane in an oxygen atmosphere forms carbon dioxide and water. It's been suggested that Jupiter's colours are due to complex organic compounds, particularly in the Great Red Spot and the transient little ones, and these would be destroyed unless means could be found to preserve them. There's no chance of such compounds or of life arising during terraforming, because free oxygen totally inhibits abiogenic synthesis of amino acids. (We're assuming here that there's no life in Jupiter already!) There would be a tendency, because of the steep gravity gradient, for all heavier elements to sink to the bottom of the ocean; the internal heat would eventually bring them up again, but unless the settling process could be arrested it would be necessary meantime to 'prime' the ocean surface with trace elements, synthesized by the fusion reactors, so that the waters could sustain life.

Alternatively, the ocean might be seeded with dust from the asteroids; Shaw suggested that the easiest solution might be to deflect comets to collide with the planet. It may be possible, however, to collect heavy elements in the surface layers during the terraforming process: James Campbell suggested creating artificial continents with submerged shelves and seeding over them to prevent losses to the deeps. Shaw added that free-floating marine life such as kelp should then be introduced at the same time as plankton, etc., and artificial islands buoyed up by gas pockets in decaying vegetation (there's a Scottish loch where this happens naturally, and Lake Titicaca has inhabited reed 'islands'). Still the areas between the continents will be clear 'ocean deserts', as on Earth, unless seeding is to continue indefinitely or means can be found to recover nutrients falling into the deeps, *eventually* to come up again by convection. (Earth's ocean deserts will almost certainly be reclaimed by fusion-power plants on the seafloor, creating artificial thermal upwelling of nutrients into the sunlight: on Jupiter the thermal process is natural but the 'seafloor' will be thousands of kilometres down!) Ideally, artificial continents should be created as early as possible in the terraforming process (in the present water layer), to catch as much as possible of the heavier elements in the present clouds; and that gives another reason to stop short of disrupting the core, since the continents could scarcely survive it.

When the planet is terraformed, new heat sources will be needed in the Jovian system. Big mirrors will be adequate for the Galilean settlements, and the water world will have big icecaps in any case, but unless it's decided to let it freeze over heating will be needed. It might be allowed to freeze, except for artificial atolls heated by underwater reactors, to prevent loss of trace elements and nutrients to the deeps. Instead of ocean deserts there would be ice plains between colonies (crossing boundaries between rotation zones would be an exciting experience). To start a new colony, one would melt a large area, put in an artificial atoll with a mountain barrier, sink the reactors to the required depth in the centre, seed the water, and set up house. However, Jupiter would require external heating even so, to keep the atmosphere from freezing, so the surface might stay liquid. The solar reflectors' total collecting surface would have to be several times Jupiter's cross-sectional area; an inclined artificial ring might do it, if one or more of the Galileans were moved inside the Roche Limit and fragmented—a large orboforming task; but the shadow would make some latitudes (north and south) alternately uninhabitable, and the benefit would vary from maximum to zero during the revolution of the nodes. Alternatively, orbiting fusion reactors may have to provide Jupiter with at least one artificial 'sun'. Whether the Galileans can then remain habitable is another question.

On the other hand, Jupiter would still rotate in about its present ten hours, and surface gravity would be much the same. Gravity and Coriolis effects on weather would therefore be larger than Earth's, and there would be wind- and wave-power systems in the lagoons' outer defences: even so, mutaformed people may live *under* the lagoons, with only lily-pads at the surface for recreation, still partly supported by water—lily-pads are porous—but using only the flimsiest, lightest artefacts: anything heavy would sink the pad or break through it. When a storm struck, the pads would be driven below the surface to safety, as they are on Earth, rising again afterwards. Under each lagoon there would be a huge plate (Gerry Carter's magnesium shell again?) and nuclear heating plants like Cerenkov-blue suns, far down, to prevent loss of nutrients to the deeps; and each lagoon would be protected by massive barriers drawing power from wind and waves. If there were a permanent 'upper' class working on the barriers, we would have a Wellsian situation like *The Time Machine*'s in reverse: a privileged aristocracy below the surface, lapsing into dilettantism, and a technical class above becoming steadily less refined and physically tougher, until the system broke down into savagery. ('Come with me and I will make you fishers of men.') To avoid that, all able-bodied people would have to take their turns on the barriers; but for physiological reasons the gravity might make division between the sexes unavoidable. Once in a lifetime, like National Service, wouldn't be enough —it would have to be every year, like military service in Switzerland.

Ultimately there might be linked bands of lagoons right round the planet, at different latitudes, rotating past each other like the present cloud belts. Quite possibly the equatorial band would be filled up before the next one was started, since each band at higher latitude would have appreciably higher surface gravity due to the polar flattening and the lesser effect of rotation. There would be polar icecaps (floating low in the water) unless the internal heat compensated for latitude—Jupiter's poles are 4600km nearer the planet's centre than the equator is. If any scheme has been devised to use the deeps, therefore, water or hydrogen, it will be run from the poles rather than from the lagoons.

A terraformed Jupiter would have a surface area about 125 times that of the Earth. Since the lagoon colonies may eventually be far more densely gathered than settlements in Earth's oceans, however, the proportion of habitable area may in reality be much greater. Eventually, convection currents will bring nutrients and trace elements back up from the deeps and huge upwellings will form, each perhaps as large as all Earth's oceans (like the 'white ovals' now), and fully populated with lagoons which no longer need underlying shells or seeding. Asimov has suggested that, if a Jovian ocean were fully claimed by life—as this one might be, with a steady flow of heat from below—the total Jovian biomass could reach one-eighth the mass of Earth's Moon. [115] Conceivably, but regrettably, the settlements might then decide to turn down the reactors and seal themselves off altogether as the surface froze: why go up into $2.5g$ if you don't have to? In *City* Clifford Simak imagined a mutaformed human race emigrating *en masse* to Jupiter, which seemed a paradise to altered senses, [116] but he never imagined anything as strange as this.

On Saturn, however, with virtually Earth-normal gravity at the surface, links to the outside Universe would remain open. Who could bear to go under the ice and lose sight of that stupendous arch, curving from one far distant horizon to the other, with the meteors falling below it from the D-ring and the curtains of the polar aurora shimmering at one's back?

XII

The Resources of the
Outer Solar System

Ye ladies wha smell o' wild rose
Think ye, for yer perfume, tae whaur a man goes ...

—Owen Hand, 'My Donald'

It's generally supposed that the Sun's influence gives way to those of the other stars at about two light-years out (approximately 120,500AU). The nearest known star system is Alpha Centauri at 4.3 ly, with its dwarf companion Proxima currently 4.2 ly from us. But A. T. Lawton pointed out in *New Worlds for Old* that, in other directions, the Sun remains dominant to much greater distances. Alpha Centauri, Sirius and Procyon are all in the same quadrant of the sky and all lie close to the Galactic Equator, as seen from here. Over the rest of the huge volume out to about 8 ly the Sun is dominant, the much less massive red-dwarf stars controlling relatively small volumes of space—just as each planet has its own sphere of influence within the much larger 'fold of the Sun'.

Beyond 2 ly, nothing could revolve about the Sun without experiencing very large perturbations. The biggest factor is the Sun-Galactic Centre L1 point, which Chebotarev calculates to be only 3.3 ly from us. As a result, a body in circular orbit around the Sun at that distance would be perturbed within 400 million years; in that time, however, the Sun goes around the Galactic Centre twice. Our stellar neighbourhood can be considered as a dynamic environment in continuous change. At present the massive neighbour stars are all behind us on the Sun's Way, adding their pulls to the Sun's in any tendency to capture material from the interstellar medium ahead of us.

We know that comets out there are firmly under the Sun's control. There's never been a comet whose velocity indicated it wasn't a member of the Solar System, and overall their orbits show no bias towards the Sun's Way. [1] There may be 100 billion comets at mean distances around 100,000AU, where perturbations by the nearby stars and chance encounters would redirect three comets on average per year towards the Sun, as is observed, while another three escaped. But, when the effects of water-ice evaporation are allowed for (a relatively new element in the calculations), the mean distance may be around 50,000AU [2] and the numbers could then be much lower. There could even be two belts of comets, one at 100,000AU and the other at only 40,000AU, with a total population of only about three million. [3]

Vsekhsvyatskiy, who predicted Jupiter would have a dust ring from volcanic outbursts on the Galilean satellites, [4] claimed that the short-period comet 'families', whose periods are linked to the giant planets', arise from Krakatoa-scale eruptions on the giant satellites; while the long-period comets would have been driven outwards by planetary flybys, just the opposite of the general view that planetary encounters draw long-period comets into shorter orbits. But Io's volcanoes are driven by sulphur chemistry, while comets passing through the inner Solar System form such huge haloes of hydrogen that their nuclei must be primarily water ice. Io's volcanoes are capable of the ejection but can't match the composition; the other three Galileans have the ices but no evidence of vulcanism. Titan's dense atmosphere rules out cometary launches, so only Triton remains a candidate, unlikely to account for all the observed comets.

But Vsekhsvyatskiy calculates that other stars pass within 100,000AU of the Sun every 250,000 years, on average; within 150,000AU every 110,000 years; and within 200,000AU every 62,000 years. [5] An external halo of comets should then disperse in at most a few hundred million years, a few Galactic Years, and so the comets we see would have to be recent in origin. Professor William McCrea suggested that comets may be formed as the Sun passes through interstellar dust clouds; [6] in its history the Sun may have traversed 135 clouds denser than 100 hydrogen atoms per cm^3, and about sixteen clouds as much as ten times denser. Even at the lower density, infalling material would compress the Solar Wind to within Earth's orbit on the approach side, and brighten the Sun appreciably. [7] If the Sun's surface is still enriched with heavier elements from the last encounter, then nuclear reactions in the core won't be quite as we suppose; this could explain the 'missing' solar neutrinos. Such encounters could maintain a cometary envelope throughout the System's history. But Bill Ramsay suggested a still simpler explanation, if comets *do* form at the same time as stars and planets: since most of the passing stars are red dwarfs, much less massive than the Sun, perhaps in most encounters the Solar System gains more comets than it loses.

Hoyle and Wickramasinghe suggest that the Earth and the other inner planets acquired their volatiles from cometary bombardment, early in their history, and perhaps *life* may have come with the falling comets. In recent years, increasingly complex organic compounds have been detected within interstellar dust clouds; so far radicals and ions of this complexity have not been observed being driven off from comets by sunlight, but there's carbon chemistry at work and the only question is how far it goes. Extremely complex compounds may be generated in the expanding shockwaves of supernovae, preserved in the frigid interstellar clouds, and taken up into comets without ever being heated enough to break down. In the USSR, Goldanskii has pointed out that at very low temperatures (some interstellar clouds are apparently at only 1 K^8,) all exothermic (energy-releasing) reactions become thermodynamically 'profitable'. Chain polymers, even biopolymers, could form on the outsides of clouds due to ultraviolet excitation, but collisions with high-energy cosmic-ray protons within dense clouds are a more likely and promising mechanism. Reaction rates would be stepped up as protostars began to form and comets, when they took shape, would be primed for life.

There seems no doubt that, when life arose on Earth, it happened swiftly. 'Microfossils' of single-celled life have been found in rocks 3.5 billion years old, and there are hints of still older traces going back almost into the bombardment phase. Yet, if Earth's primal atmosphere was oxidizing, like Venus's (see Chapter 8), the much discussed 'primal soup' of amino acids in the oceans, with proteins forming in clays or on lava at the edges, would not have been possible; and there's no evidence in the oldest sedimentary rocks of a reducing atmosphere of methane/ammonia. [9]

At ASTRA Robert Shaw had argued in the early 1970s that low-temperature life might exist in the comets; Asimov had suggested possible chemistries for such life when gas giant planets were thought to be cold throughout. [10] But Hoyle and

Wickramasinghe think that at their formation comets may have been 30% 'prebiotic materials', the remainder mostly water ice. Impact heating could form liquid water reservoirs, insulated from vacuum, already rich in 'given' compounds. There's more recent evidence for clays formed by water processes within carbonaceous chrondrites,[11] and some metallic clays were apparently 'templates' for the evolution of nucleic acids and proteins.[12] The next stages towards the evolution of life on Earth would be predetermined by their arrival, and would proceed as soon as the greenhouse effect warmed up the surface.[13]

All that was startling enough; but then the input of genetic material from space might continue to this day, entering the upper atmosphere with dust released from comets, and manifest itself as viral infections, particularly among the highest lifeform—ourselves:[14] their traditional association with comets would be genuine, and would explain widespread plagues in times when there was little movement of population. It would explain why earlier plagues, like that of Athens, appear to have no modern counterparts, while the common cold was apparently unknown until the 15th century, influenza until the 17th, and both frustrate modern medicine by apparently mutating spontaneously and rapidly: the 'mutations' would be new strains brought down by fresh infalls. Or the invaders might be not complete viruses but 'viroids', fragments of genetic material which attach themselves to existing DNA;[15] as they're tamed and absorbed, such additions could be the driving mechanism for biological evolution. Since DNA controls the manufacture of RNA, which in turn controls the manufacture of proteins, the hypothesis might fit Alan Bond's 'engineer's approach to evolution' which assesses the evolutionary state of an organism by the number of proteins it uses.[16]

But life on Earth uses only a few of the amino acids and proteins available. If all the above is true *and* if the current comets are new acquisitions, but yet organisms or viroids from them can invade our cells, cause plagues and ultimately alter our very genetic nature, then it implies that over a major segment of a galactic spiral arm, at least, comets predetermine much the same kind of life. After all, a single supernova can affect a very large volume of space (see below). An underlying assumption of my own 'Interface' stories from the early 1970s was lines of stars in the spiral arms supporting similar dominant lifeforms, due to interstellar drifts of genetic material which predetermined convergent evolution; now it seems interstellar chemistry may provide amino acids, chlorophyll, etc., while exchanges of comets between stars could share out proteins, nucleic acids, perhaps 'viroids' or even life.

In theory, then, we could adapt, with our crops and domestic animals, to the biospheres of other Earthlike worlds. The chances of finding life based on different amino acids, 'right-handed' polymers instead of our 'left-handed' ones, or completely different protein structures would be much reduced—even though these compounds are found in meteors. A large population dumped on such a world, as envisaged by Larson, might after all survive in sufficient numbers to remain viable despite the appalling casualties he foresaw.[17] A habitat group who can choose whether or not to colonize, and on what timescale, could adapt themselves by genetic engineering if desired, and the viroids needed could be gathered from the comets of the system. But that 'if desired' is a big factor: the current view is that, because of the biological hazards and general limitations of Earthlike worlds (high escape velocity, dense corrosive atmosphere), worlds supporting life aren't the places we should choose to settle.

If we didn't go into space we could continue to evolve by viroid invasion, through selection by suffering and death, as (supposedly) hitherto. By eliminating smallpox from the world, are we taking out an essential component of the next evolutionary advance?—although it may come back with a later comet pass. Cometary dust fills only the inner Solar System, so by the time we reach the giant planets we should be clear of it, unless we sought it out. Ian Downie suggested that genetic engineers would be able to assess the potential of viroids and use them under control, if we so chose. Deliberate acceleration of biological evolution might be a motive for expanding the asteroid civilization to the cometary halo; and from there, as Asimov pointed out, onward moves will be easy.[1] Even if the neighbour stars don't have comets, our comets on that side of the halo are nearer to Alpha Centauri than to the comets on the other side.

Dyson suggested that independent colonies might flee to the halo to escape increasing regimentation of the Solar System and preserve the 'city-state' culture.[18] If a habitat group claimed an outgoing comet and wasn't coming back for, say, a million years, the most dictatorial government might think it a waste of time to pursue and convert them by force, unless activities further out are forbidden by a fanatical 'only one Solar System' movement, or by authorities afraid of possible Contact with Other Intelligence. Mobile worlds expanding to the halo could ensure that the human race would survive a destructive Contact, but that's not much comfort to the inhabited planets, with nowhere to hide.

O'Neill estimates that if mirror mass is limited to twice the mass of the habitat, and Earth-normal sunlight concentration is required, then the 'Solar System shelf', analogous to the continental shelf, would be at 16 times the mean distance of Pluto.[19] But Dyson suggests that much larger quantities of sunlight could be collected by the foliage of trees planted on the comets. Rotations are fast enough (4.6 hours to 5 days[20]) to grow trees all round the nuclei. It's not certain whether comets' nuclei have cores, becoming carbonaceous Earth-grazing asteroids when their ices have been driven off,[3] but they do contain a great deal of dust:[21] silicates, metals and almost certainly organic compounds. Genetic engineering for trees in vacuum could be perfected on short-period comets, then transferred to long-period ones passing through the inner System. Retreating from the Sun, in virtual zero-*g* the trees could maintain sufficient growth of foliage to survive (but they'd better be evergreens, not deciduous!). Growing trees would be 'mining' the comet for volatiles, organics and heavier elements; and, if the settlers wanted to keep in touch and picked a comet which would return relatively soon, clippings could be sold during the next solar pass. Downie suggested that habitats working near the Sun would want cuttings to plant in external avenues flanking their windows, below the mirrors, to cut down excessive light. The trees' shade would let comets pass near the Sun without evaporation, although Bill Ramsay remarked that the trees themselves might need sunglasses.

In the outer System, Downie pointed out that CETI (Communication with Extraterrestrial Intelligence) might be a major activity—especially if it becomes real communication and not just a search programme. Far out from the Sun and the planets, with very little interference, it would be easy to operate large, low-temperature, highly sensitive antennae. Since the trees are genetically engineered, perhaps they could grow 'nervous systems' for radio waves or even gravity waves.

Bio-engineering has been suggested for CETI before: in Blish's *A Case of Conscience* the 'message tree' blended properties of organic and inorganic materials, [22] and in *Imperial Earth* Clarke proposed a design like the spines of a sea-urchin, with filaments thousands of kilometres long, for very long radio waves. [23] On a smaller scale Robert L. Forward imagined open-mesh interstellar probes in which the wires might be organic superconductors, with solid-state sensors at the junctions, possibly organic and grown with the mesh. [24] With a diameter of several kilometres, rather than the few hundred metres he envisaged, such a system could also detect gravitational waves and pinpoint the source. [25]

CETI will come up again under large-scale projects for the outer System. The masses of material available may be startling: from the numbers of observed comets, Whipple calculates that their total mass out to 40AU could be half the Earth's; by 50AU 1.3 Earth masses; and by 67,000AU 0.01 of the Sun's mass, nearly ten times that of all the known planets. [26] But as far as we know comets are too widely separated to use *en masse*, however many colonies they come to support. Harper suggested in 1973 that there might be a massive ring of asteroids, totalling 0.26 of solar mass, orbiting between 100 and 30,000AU, where he predicted the start of the cometary halo proper. [27] Kohoutek's Comet, with its poor visual display from ices but large amounts of dust, might have been such an asteroid, with its strangely close aphelion (1800AU) and corresponding orbital period of 75,000 years; [28] but then Comet West, although very dusty, had a period of 300,000 years. [21] Apparently, as ice is lost, crusts of dust form on the comets; explosive emissions of dust and gas may be from recent craters penetrating the crust, [3] and it seems that Donati's Comet of 1858 had only one active area on the nucleus. [29] If Harper's asteroids exist—closer, bigger and more rocky than the halo comets—Chiron and Phoebe may be examples, and the differences between the two groups may be analogous to those between inner and outer known asteroids.

But if Vsekhsvyatskiy's argument about lifetimes is correct, when were they formed or captured? It was suggested at ASTRA, following Lawton's lecture, that it might have been after a relatively recent supernova. From short-lived isotope products, in meteorites, there may have been a nearby supernova only a few million years before the Solar System came into being:

the shockwaves probably triggered the final contraction of the primal nebula.[30]   There's evidence from lunar samples for another such event within the last 100 million years,[31] so perhaps a new accretion disc formed in the outer System. If so, samples from comets should be much younger than known meteorites.

Of the comets trapped, by planetary flybys, into frequent returns, the biggest and most famous is Halley's. It's next due in 1986 but its retrograde orbit makes rendezvous difficult: for chemical rockets the launch window for Jupiter slingshot transfer was as early as 1978. NASA concentrated on a faster transfer by solar sail or ion-drive, and by 1979 had opted for ion-drive—but was then refused funding. ESA will have *Giotto*, named after Giotto di Bendone, who painted the comet in 1301; launch will be direct and encounter head-on at 70kps, so the probe will have an erosion shield. A Soviet 'kamikaze' mission is planned by Venus slingshot, carrying French cameras but no shield, and Japan intends to stage a more distant flyby.[32]

If Harper's right, then the postulated tenth planet which disrupted the Neptune system would be one of a large number of asteroids, mostly 150-1500km in diameter but ranging up to 6000km, with perhaps five or six, including 'X', as large as 20,000km.[27] Chiron has since been discovered, at the bottom end of the range; Phoebe, Pluto and Charon have all turned out to fit into it; and if 'X' is another low-density icy body it would indeed be at the upper end. Even Chiron-sized ones, possibly enriched by a recent supernova, could be industrial targets to make the known Asteroid Belt seem barren. Their other potential application would be in the planetary engineering which Schwiglhofer called 'orboforming': altering the rotation or the orbit of one of the known worlds.

The only thing that would change if the Moon fell into the Earth would be the precise arrangement of the masses.
                                                    —Nigel Calder[33]

If one could remove most of the Earth's orbital velocity, our planet would plunge towards the Sun. Just think of the exciting observations that could be made a few million kilometres above the solar surface!
                                                    —Robert W. Chapman[34]

Only one method of nonviolent orboforming has previously been discussed (see Chapter 9), Dyson's solar-powered EMF generator satellites, interacting with metallic windings along the lines of latitude to change the rotation of a planet with a magnetic field. In practice it's applicable only to Earth and Mercury in the Solar System. Other proposals are more drastic, and the practical ones involve close flybys or even impacts by other bodies. Fascinatingly, orbital photography shows parallel fractures in Africa and South America suggesting that the Earth's rotation altered before the two continents separated, around 600 million years ago, about the time that life emerged from the sea.[35] Considering its potential importance, there's been amazingly little discussion of what the passing body might have been or what became of it. Asimov once conjectured that we didn't acquire the Moon until about 600 million years ago, and that the new tides brought life up onto the land,[36] but there's evidence now for lunar tides in rocks more than three billion years old,[37] apparently confirmed by the formation of the *maria* about the same time; so it seems that a Precambrian orboforming body would have been smaller and closer, perhaps torn apart if it flew past within the Roche Limit. There's evidence for the break-up of a dense iron asteroid, about 200km in diameter, about 630 million years ago;[38] and the ending of the Great Precambrian Ice Age, 600 million years ago, may have been due to a change in the Earth's rotation.[39] Orboforming may already have profoundly affected our destinies.

Comets are too light to be used effectively for orboforming, and moving asteroids by mass driver would be wasteful (see page 77). Daedalus engines could move small ones but, for anything more than (say) 1-2km across, propellant requirements become extreme because the mass goes up with the cube of the radius. Cruder methods using nuclear explosions are effective only (if at all) in giving small asteroids very small course changes. Adelman investigated the possibility of orboforming Venus by 175km asteroid impacts, and found that the energies required were equivalent to those for relativistic interstellar missions—matter/antimatter-powered photon drives would be needed. Furthermore, there aren't enough asteroids of that size even to give Venus a 24-hour day, and the job would have to be finished (if possible) by running photon drives on the surface of the planet.[40] The possibility of changing the *orbit* wasn't even considered.

Shaw suggested fabricating a body of planetary mass out of asteroids whose elliptical orbits could be modified by nuclear-pulse engines to collide at low relative velocities at aphelion. The orbit of the synthetic body would be preplanned to pass close to a planet in the inner System and alter its orbit during the flyby. Archimedes said, 'Give me a long enough lever and a suitable pivot to rest it on, and I will move the Earth'; the synthetic planet is such a lever. A second flyby, or a second lever planet, would circularize the orbit of the target world at the desired distance from the Sun, but we would have also to arrange for the lever planet(s) to be broken back into controllable fragments, expelled from the Solar System, or captured by the target planet as a moon or a ring—otherwise they would remain a major threat to the orboformed world because their final orbit would intersect its new one. (If two lever planets were used, only the second one or its fragments would pose that danger; but then there would be the threat to *other* planets.) Major tidal stresses would be imposed on both bodies during flyby, and the lever planet, not properly compacted after its formation, is the more likely to break up. Major fragments could then be salvaged by fitting them with engines and moving them into safe orbits—perhaps around the orboformed world, if we couldn't arrange for that during the circularization flyby. All fragments over about 20 tonnes would have to be recovered, or they'd inflict big impacts on somebody sooner or later.

There seems to be no case for 'levering' large bodies to terraform them, since we already have an Earth-type world —Earth—and we don't want its orbit disrupted. The Sun-Earth L4 and L5 points would be the only places where large masses could share this distance from the Sun without dislodging Earth, in theory, but in practice they'd have to be small enough to be kept on station despite perturbations by the other planets. Asteroids brought sunwards could be given Earthlike atmospheres by surrounding them with transparent shells or membranes: they'd be interesting recreation centres, since gravity would be very low indeed. Mercury might be orboformed *nearer* to the Sun for industrial purposes, making it even less like Earth, but the only terraforming application might be to move the Galilean moons closer to a Jupiter being changed by 'mini-suns' (see page 239). In other planetary systems, however, with no Earthlike worlds, orbo-terraforming might be an option.

Adrian Berry proposed moving Mercury out to the orbit of Jupiter with surface nuclear explosions, [41] but as we've seen that technique isn't effective. The planet could be disrupted by Dyson's method and flown out piecemeal, which would make it (recombined) the only known lever world possibility—the total mass of the known asteroids is probably 0.01 of the Earth's at most. But only Harper's asteroids (if they exist) should be used to manufacture levers. To break up Mercury takes an element of diversity out of the Solar System to create greater uniformity elsewhere in it, a philosophy to be resisted if possible (see Chapter 13).

Looking further out of the System, there are in fact more stimulating possibilities. Lawton's first suggestion to ASTRA was that there might be a supernova-enriched disc of dust around the Solar System, in the plane of the Ecliptic. Later, taking into account the continuously changing situation, he thought there might at least be clouds at the 'balance points' between the Sun's gravitational field and those of the neighbour stars. However, I found that Professor J. D. Fernie had studied interstellar absorption around the Sun, in and around the plane of the Galactic Equator, and there's apparently *less* dust in those directions. [42] Since then the OAO satellites have established that between us and some nearby stars the density of interstellar hydrogen is also 100 times less than expected. [43] Furthermore, the directions *opposite* the neighbour stars are also relatively clear of dust, in Fernie's graphs; [42] the densest concentrations are: between us and the Galactic Centre; opposite to it; and at 100° Galactic Longitude, 32° from the Apex of the Sun's Way.

Fernie's interpretation was that the Sun was travelling into an irregular cloud of interstellar dust up to 610 parsecs (nearly 2000 light-years across (1pc = 3.258 ly). Hughes and Routledge related it to their evidence for a rare, very violent Type III supernova 30-90 million years ago, then 1000pc away; [44] but other interpretations are possible. Linda Lunan pointed out that the situation is dynamic: the Sun, the massive neighbour stars, the Chebotarev L1 point, and the Apex of the Sun's Way all lie within a disc about 20° of Galactic Latitude in thickness, centred on the Galactic Equator and cutting the

Ecliptic almost at right angles, in which the Sun is moving at nearly 20kps, and the absorption curve (the butterfly shape in the centre of fig. 22) is anything but random. At first I saw the effect as a shockwave, but at the third BIS Interstellar Conference it was pointed out that a shockwave could arise only from an *outward* flow from the Solar System, colliding with the interstellar medium. My proposed boundary was 3 ly out at its closest, hardly likely to be generated by the Solar Wind (although, having seen the estimated heliopause move out from

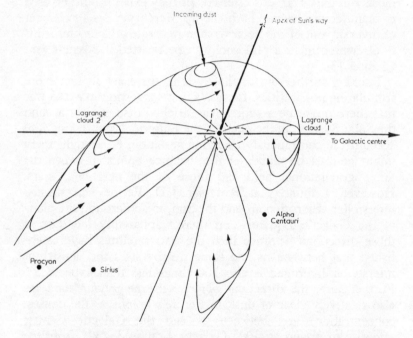

Fig. 22 The dust shockwave initially envisaged (*'New Worlds for Old'*)

5.5AU to 100AU during this project, I'm not betting). On the face of it, a pattern like fig. 23 is more likely. We can no longer tell directly the distance to the dust concentration responsible for the absorption peak at 100° Longitude but, if Hughes and Routledge are right in identifying the centre of their gas ring with it, the cloud's centre would be 250pc off and its densest part would be about 44pc across. If the supernova happened 30 million years ago, the cloud's expansion has averaged 0.723kps—slow, but not impossible—and when the Sun is level with it, in 12 million years' time, it will have grown to 62pc across and the edge will still be 100pc from us. Whether the habitats will let it pass, since the dense cloud presumably contains the really valuable isotopes, is another matter. But the faster-moving shockwaves which have passed us would be poor in such isotopes, so verifying a recent origin for comets would be more difficult and outer System industry would be more limited.

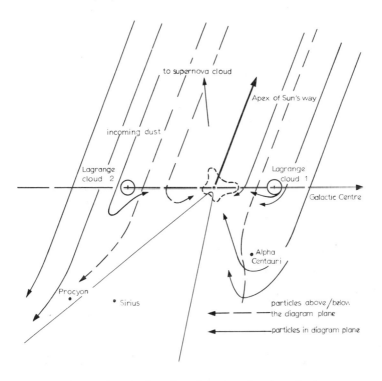

Fig. 23 A revised version of the dust-flow hypothesis

As to the other two suggested concentrations, in line with the Galactic Centre, things look a great deal better. In 1978 French scientists announced that a cloud about 40° in diameter was approaching the Solar System from the direction of the Galactic Centre. [45] Its distance is 0.01-2pc, with a corresponding diameter range from 0.01pc. It could, therefore, be centred on the Chebotarev L1 point at 1.02pc, and its apparent approach velocity (15-20kps) is very close to the Sun's velocity relative to the nearby stars. It's also the velocity of neutral hydrogen and helium entering the Solar System, according to Pioneers-10 and -11, from a source on the Ecliptic, almost due north of the Galactic Centre[46] —within the thickness of figs. 22 and 23. So the apparent approach could be illusory, and the clouds an eddy effect of our movement through the interstellar medium, as shown.

If such clouds exist they're unquestionably 'ours', controlled by the Sun's pull; but they'll disperse in time if we don't utilize them. Utilization might begin with a fleet of ramscoop vehicles, Lawton suggested, spread over the surface of a sphere within the cloud, thrusting inwards. At high velocities the ramscoop system, once favoured for interstellar propulsion, is likely to act as a brake and reflect matter from its magnetic field, but that's just what's wanted here: to compress the dust and gas until gravitational attraction takes over, and a new star is formed. Exploitating the dust clouds therefore turns the Solar System into a widely separated, multiple star system, with planets orbiting the new components as we see fit.

Surprisingly, there was relatively little interest within ASTRA in the outcome. 'Lever worlds' could be extracted for orbo-forming in the known Solar System, but there hadn't been much enthusiasm for that in the first place. Paul Benson pointed out that at least one gas-giant planet would be needed, to conserve hydrogen and helium which would otherwise be blasted out of the new system by the powerful stellar wind of the igniting sun. Ian Downie suggested an obviously artificial world as a sign to others, perhaps many millions of years later, of the system's artificiality. (And where *did* Earth get that weird Moon, anyway?) But he suggested also refraining from intervention, to observe what would happen—although the new System wouldn't be typical, since it would be relatively gas-poor. Roberts suggested that a society working on this scale wouldn't be driven by shortages of materials or energy, so its motives would in a sense be playful. The outcome would be more exciting if it were not predetermined; and in discussion it emerged (see Chapter 13) that such manufactured uncertainties and challenges may be necessary, in a few centuries' time, for the survival of the human mind.

Lawton had mentioned 'Rudge's flat comets': cometary nuclei, rotating as they coalesced, might end up disc-shaped. Certainly Donati's Comet, rotating in 4.6 hours, was close to the 3-hour value at which ice spheres would break up. [29] With plentiful hydrogen reserves for nuclear-propulsion modes, and relatively stable shapes, such comets could be the platforms for the scoops which drove the dust, ices and gas together and carved them up as required. Such control would be necessary because interstellar matter is so diffuse and patchy [43] that at first it would be hard to tell just how much there was. A collapsing body 2-3 times the mass of the Sun but rich in the heavier elements would have a strong tendency to go supernova, with disastrous consequences for the Solar System. One might imagine flat comets fitted with engines and aerodynamically shaped, circling within the manmade dust globule like cowboys preventing a stampede, splitting the embryo star into a double or triple system. Shaw thought they'd have to move at relativistic speeds, and Fitzgerald contraction might give them the aerodynamics of a boomerang.

Mentioning relativistic speeds suggests a literally more pressing danger. If the infalling dust were nearing the speed of light the fleet would have no option but to pull out—they'd have begun the creation, which no known power in the Universe could stop, of the most frightening concept of modern physics. A black hole is an object so massive (or so compressed) that no form of electromagnetic radiation can scale the sides of its 'gravity well'. The collapsing matter which brings it into being disappears over an 'event horizon' beyond which no observations can be made from outside: a black hole can be detected only by the effects of its gravitational field. But its most unnerving attribute is the mathematical proof that, if even one stellar-mass black hole exists, all the matter in the Universe must eventually fall into it.

Not all scientists are convinced that black holes exist. X-ray sources such as Cygnus X-1 might be black holes tearing up supergiant companion stars, but other explanations have been suggested. 'Gravity wave' detectors seem to show large numbers of 'events', as if the entire core of the Galaxy were falling star by star into oblivion; but such waves may instead come from neutron stars, the remnants of supernovae. The Universe appears to have considerable 'missing mass' not visible as stars, dust and gas, but there are possible explanations for the discrepancies in our Galaxy and in the Cosmos. A black hole was *not* responsible for the 'Tunguz event' (see Chapter 10). But if black holes do exist, 22nd-century civilization may not be daunted by them. If one were created, the first priority would be to throw a shield around it, imprison it in an electrostatic field and prevent it from growing any bigger. ('Meantime ...' Nemesis whispers at our backs.) John Taylor has suggested ways in which a future civilization could use the almost sheer gravity well near the event horizon as a source of power.[47] But Taylor doesn't share Adrian Berry's view[48] that black holes may provide 'star gates' allowing us to cross the Galaxy as if at speeds much faster than light.

Berry cites mathematical argument that a body entering the event horizon of a rotating black hole precisely at a tangent, at circular orbital velocity, could avoid collision with the singularity inside and emerge at some far-distant point in space. For a black hole of 10 solar masses, he quotes an event-horizon circumference of 186.76km, enough for a ship entering it not to be disrupted by tidal forces; surprising, since the radius is only 29.6km, but the calculated orbital velocity is still stranger. 'This disc ... will have a circumference of just under 116 miles. It will be rotating just as a gramophone record rotates on its turntable, but at a velocity of 1,000 complete revolutions every second. Each part of the disc will therefore be moving at a speed of 116 miles per second, or just over 400,000mph. The astronaut must travel round the disc of the black hole and precisely match its speed ... about 17 times the highest speed which the Apollo astronauts attained on their way to the Moon.'[48]

Berry corrected this later. 1000 116-mile circuits per second give a speed of 116,000 miles per second (186,760kps); 62% of the speed of light, just the velocity which could be reached by a Daedalus probe initially launched by Dyson's interstellar accelerator. It might be worth doing, if the black hole opened up instantaneous travel across the Galaxy; but there are bigger problems.

Berry has been criticized for not sufficiently emphasizing the possibility that matter collapsing into a black hole escapes the singularity condition (infinite density in zero volume) not by moving elsewhere in this Universe but by shifting into an alternate Universe where, in effect, it didn't fall into the hole in the first place—as it were! But if it does reemerge in this Universe, most theorists suppose that it must be at random, since within the black hole the known laws of physics break down. Berry assumes instead that the process is controllable so that, after emerging with the collapsed stellar matter from a white hole (a dangerous moment, one imagines), the builders can create a new, parallel black hole/white hole 'gate' to return them to the outer Solar System. But, if there are rules governing the reappearance points, surely the most likely one is materialization at the core of the next most dense concentration of matter around—the Sun, about a parsec away. Berry dismisses this as 'absurd' because computers will be so sophisticated by then but, even if they do tell us that blowing up the Sun can be avoided, can we sanction an experimental programme to find out?

'Isogravisphere' theory, as Lawton terms it, might open up other exotic forms of travel. Some years ago the poet David Godwin suggested to me that the path of a body in interstellar space, acted on by many gravitational fields of roughly equal intensity, might be truly unpredictable—a matter of probability, like the movement of an electron. If paranormal powers, particularly psychokinesis, are manipulations of probability, then the 'psionic drive' of science fiction might become a reality. There's great appeal in the image of psi powered spaceships swooping through the Galaxy at near lightspeed, following the isoclines of the multiple gravitational fields, banking round the vortices of Chebotarev points, and descending the gravity wells of their destinations on photon parachutes.

Lawton disassociated himself from that idea—like me he doubts the future of the psi powers, if they exist at all. But he thought groups working the dust clouds might have visitors —either because other civilizations may have habitats abroad in the Galaxy as mobile worlds, working the dust concentrations between the stars, or because astro-engineering on this scale is liable to attract attention. Distant observers, seeing a new star light up in a situation very different from the usual huge nebulae, would turn their instruments on it and pick up the intense communications traffic of the builders in the protoplanetary disc. The arrival of spacecraft—manned, unmanned, or indistinguishable—would be only a matter of time.

Some time before, Lawton and I had worked on a draft paper on interstellar beacons; he dropped the idea but I have continued to work on it. To attract alien attention might be a motive to build a new system, for a culture which had explored out to, say, 100 light-years without establishing Contact. Doubling the radius of exploration brings in eight times as many candidate stars and, in the time it would take to visit them all, the wave front of a beacon could reach every star within optical range. Another possibility is that two cultures 1000 ly apart (say) become aware of each other's existence, but can't meet face-to-face for 50-100,000 years, as mobile worlds work their way across the bridge, star by star, at 1% of lightspeed. In the same timescale, they could start a beacon to which any other cultures within 1000 ly or more could respond. Like watchfire beacons the movement could sweep the Galaxy in 100,000 years or less, depending on where it started; so, in about the same time that it takes for the first two to meet, all the spacefaring cultures in the Galaxy could be aware of one another and the first step towards a Kardashev-3 culture (see Chapter 13) would have been taken.

The same arguments apply to radio beacons, but the chances of success are much less. The range of radio frequencies to be searched is enormous, whereas all beings evolved on Earthlike planets are liable to have optical astronomy. Directional radio beacons are virtually a dead loss, sending briefly to many stars or indefinitely to a few; though Ian Ridpath has pointed out that, paradoxically, it's easier to broadcast to all distant civilizations in the plane of the Galaxy than to cover the whole sky for those close to you.[49] Lawton maintained that astro-engineering projects like building new stars are more effective interstellar beacons, and pointed out how short our data-base now is for any attempt to locate them. We've had telescopes for less than 400 years, photography for less than 100, and radioastronomy (in effect) for only 35. Ultraviolet, X-ray, gamma-ray and infrared satellite astronomy are in their infancy; just another century could make the activities of other civilizations very conspicuous to us. But even now there's one possibility, which I discovered while researching the paper he and I originally had in mind.

In *Les Étoiles* (1881), Camille Flammarion wrote:

... of all the celestial wonders enclosed by [Andromeda], the most marvellous is undoubtedly the beautiful triple star Gamma Andromedae. A low-power glass ... splits it into a splendid orange sun and a splendid sun shining with a transllucent emerald hue, and a more powerful instrument splits that in turn into two precious stones, an emerald and a sapphire ... This remarkable double, one of the most ravishing of the sky, was discovered on 29th January 1777 by Christian Mayer, astronomer at Mannheim, who had turned a glass on the same star the year before, without seeing it as double, although he was searching for double stars. 'That evening,' he wrote, 'I found to my great surprise a little pale companion, scarcely visible. One year later, on 27th January 1778, I was astonished to find it shining like a star of 7th magnitude.' He made no remark on the colours, which are however so striking.

If one didn't know how necessary it is to be cautious about negative observations (for not to see certain details, even having the eyes before them, does not prove that they don't exist), one could believe that the second star of Gamma Andromedae has not existed long—or at least did not become visible until 1777, because one must take account of the time the light takes to reach us. On a fine August night of 1764, the experienced observer Messier, using a Newtonian telescope $4\frac{1}{2}$ feet long, carefully compared the Andromeda Nebula with the star Gamma to measure its light: but he saw the star neither doubled nor coloured. In 1776, an 8-foot telescope likewise did not reveal the companion to Mayer, although he was *looking for* double stars. In 1777, he discovered it, with the help of the same glass, pale and barely visible, that's to say of about 9th magnitude. In 1778, he found it much more brilliant, and of 7th magnitude. Today, we see this companion as of 5th magnitude. It is difficult to believe that it has not gained in brightness ... [50]

Flammarion goes on to show that the companions can't have been eclipsed by the major sun before its discovery: their orbital period around it is at least 36,000 years. In 1842, when the rise in brightness had halted, Struve was the first to resolve the minor sun into two components, magnitudes $5\frac{1}{2}$ and 6, blue and green. As a description of one of Lawton's artificial systems lighting up it would seem hard to beat, and certainly Gamma Andromedae should be checked for other anomalies. It wouldn't ordinarily come in for such scrutiny because it's a type K giant and unlikely to have been the home of intelligent life: hypothetical builders would have to be spacefarers on an interstellar scale. According to the *Atlas Coeli* catalogue Gamma Andromedae is 162 ly from us. If that's the average separation between spacefaring civilizations, then over the next few centuries we may see the sky light up with replies.

The Philosophy of a Kardashev-2 Civilization

The conquests made by science are varied in character, sometimes seeming to promise a domain more hurtful (on the whole) than fruitful; a sort of intellectual Afghanistan.

—R. A. Proctor, 1887[1]

Intelligence may indeed may be a benign influence, creating isolated groups of philosophy-kings far apart in the heavens and enabling them to share at leisure their accumulated wisdom ... (or) intelligence may be a cancer of purposeless technological exploitation, sweeping across a galaxy as irresistibly as it has swept across our own planet.

—F. J. Dyson, 1964[2]

There are three roads to ruin: women, gambling and technicians. The most pleasant is with women, the quickest is with gambling, but the surest is with technicians.

—Georges Pompidou, c1975[3]

In the classification scheme for technological civilizations devised by Nikolai Kardashev, a Type-1 civilization controls the matter and energy resources of a planet; one of Type 2 controls the environment of a Solar System. A Type-1 civilization can communicate with other Type-1s, or with Type-2s if their technology isn't too far advanced to permit interaction. Type-2s can talk to one another as equals. A Type-3 civilization controls the environment of a galaxy, and can talk to other galactic civilizations—the timescale for exchange of signals is less, compared with the size of its own domain, than for communicating Type-2s. A Type-4, could such a thing exist, could talk only to itself—although, as Boyce suggested, beings within its sphere of influence might pray to it.

Present human civilization is generally put at about Type-0.7. (Nimmo disagreed, suggesting 0.3). We can now seek communication with other Type-1s, by radio or laser signals, although the likelihood of success depends on the separation between us and on surviving long enough to find each other. Lawton thought accidental contact with a Type-2 civilization was more likely, since they can move their solar systems or extend their presences into rewarding regions such as our hypothetical dust clouds. A habitat with tens of thousands or more inhabitants would effectively add another populated world to the Solar System. Such units might well be 'city-states' not typical of their culture as a whole, raising a new range of Contact problems not discussed in *Man and the Stars*. Clarke's *Rendezvous with Rama* barely scratches the surface of the problem, since the visiting habitat is unoccupied and has no active purpose here. [4]

Nimmo asked whether Type-3 status shouldn't be applied to stellar clusters, but it seems unlikely. Open clusters, like the Pleiades, in the plane of the Milky Way, are still too young for intelligent life to have evolved within them and, by the time it did, gravitational perturbations would have scattered the clusters; while globular-cluster stars are very old, formed out of hydrogen, a little helium and virtually no heavier elements, in the early history of the Galaxy. There seems no possibility of life, even within Jupiter-type planets—the only kind available. Supernovae within the clusters would sow them with heavier elements, but whether stars and planets could *then* form in such crowded surroundings remains to be seen. But, of course, any civilization happening to reach Kardashev-2 level when in the vicinity of a cluster would benefit.

An entirely different question is whether Kardashev status is determined by *actual* or *potential* use of available resources. If it has *full* control, culture at the Kardashev-2 level has the option of adopting conservationist policies. If it can have any kind of Solar System it wants, it can retain the *status quo*; indeed, only a culture which can exercise voluntary restraint can be said to be in control, with genuine options for future development.

In unrestrained expansion, first the accessible resources of the planets, later the entire matter and energy resources of the system, would have to be called on to maximize living area, life support, technological-systems use and material possessions.

Such utilization inevitably involves demolishing the planets, breaking them up into asteroids which can be exploited and inhabited to the full as the 'natural' ones will already have been. Dyson's demolition method[5] is feasible only for Earth and Mercury (see page 181), but the other solid worlds could be shattered by brute force. Most of the available material is concentrated in the giant worlds, however, and converting it into iron using fusion reactors[6] would be so violent that most of the gaseous mass would simply be blasted into space (see page 239).

Boyce's 'pinpoint nova' mining, although using the outer planets, would leave most of their mass untouched. But, if the technique is successful *and controllable*, it might be used to industrialize the Sun itself—at the poles, since the glare from the 'furnace mouth' might be enough to melt any of the inner planets. If factories were in Sun-synchronous orbit, the risk of any accident would be unacceptable. (As it is, reflectors of some sort would be needed—perhaps a plasma in the shaft itself, opaque to all frequencies but the lasers'—to prevent the energy already within the Sun from escaping and cooling the focus of the manufacturing beam.)

Theoretically, by such methods a quantity of usable metals equivalent in mass to Jupiter could be obtained from the Sun much faster than from Jupiter itself. That's the minimum requirement for a rigid hollow sphere around the Sun with the radius of Earth's orbit, to provide living area for a vastly expanded human race. This was Dyson's original proposal,[7] but it requires materials or techniques at present inconceivable. To hold together against tidal stresses from the Sun, no steel shell orbiting it at 1AU could be more than a million kilometres across, and a rotating shell enclosing the Sun would be out of the question; yet a nonrotating enclosing shell, unless held in place by some unforeseeable method, would be in unstable equilibrium and liable to collide with the Sun after any disturbance. The same applies to the 'alternatives to worlds' proposed by Larry Niven (ringworlds, ribbons, etc.);[8] all such things need unforeseeable materials or a wholly new technology. But there could be a shell of artificial asteroids, still trapping virtually all the Sun's energy output up to intermediate latitudes, with Jupiter-equivalent mass.[5]

Either type of Dyson civilization would be at Kardashev-2 level by definition, except for the question of control. One inherent danger is described in Bob Shaw's *Orbitsville*, where the sphere provides an environment so benign that all human effort is abandoned.[9] Nimmo argued that a Dyson civilization would maintain spaceflight because adventurers need a frontier but, as James Campbell replied, the colossal unexplored area of the sphere would keep adventurers busy for countless generations. The more the builders make it interesting, with mountains, seas and other natural barriers, the more distinct environments and cultures will develop. Nimmo thought no group would regress because communications would be too good—but how, without access to raw materials, are worn-out communicators to be replaced?

Effectively the sphere would be like the US frontier, but going on forever—and with technology so thinly spread that the overall level would soon *be* that of the Wild West, without metals. For obvious reasons, the inner planets would have been broken up and added to the sphere; and even if the giant worlds were left, with or without Jupiter, they could scarcely supply enough materials to maintain high technology all over the sphere's inner surface. There'd also be the question of energy for their exploitation, since the sphere would reradiate mostly in the infrared at the frequencies of waste heat. Outside, everything would have to be nuclear-powered and done by artificial light. With the Solar System's usable resources committed one way or the other to the sphere itself, there's little prospect of enough interstellar imports to maintain high-technology civilization—even if anyone would fly such missions when they could go hunting with bow and arrow. The biggest trap of the sphere is that it blots out the stars.

The sphere of asteroids is equally undesirable, even though this book has hailed the asteroid culture as the spearhead of civilization from the mid-21st century onward. The Dyson asteroid sphere is a lesser trap than the solid one: it might choose to scatter. Adventurers could claim an unused asteroid, convert it and move out towards other suns. But still the vast shell of asteroids, swarming around the Sun in similar orbits and cutting off one another's view of the stars, is very different from the few (by comparison) free-ranging motes bridging the vast gulfs between the worlds of the original Solar System. Adventurers might be drowned in complacency.

In any case, Schwiglhofer argued for converting Venus, Mars, Jupiter and Saturn to human habitation; huge inhabited caverns in Mercury and the major moons; and adaptation through 'mutaforming' to still more hostile environments. Forming a Dyson civilizaion would end most of these ventures; their environments could be duplicated inside asteroids, but so can any environment, so there's no challenge. For physical and mental flexibility we'd wish adaptation and cross-breeding at least as energetic as on Earth, and that's an argument for preserving the planets, where conditions can't be changed at will. Scientific and technological innovation are also vital, and perhaps the planets should be left as they are to serve as research environments—but changing them is a lesser issue than complete demolition, and human beings are likely to move into each ecological niche offered by the Solar System as soon as the technology exists to do so, under the drives which Nimmo emphasized throughout. In the desirability of environmental changes, the cutoff point would be where the proposed change narrowed the range of human experience instead of widening it. Terraforming or half-terraforming opens up the possibility of living in environments which, although habitable, are unlike anywhere people have lived before. But if the planets are split up into asteroids, then the range has been diminished because almost everybody *has* to live inside an asteroid—however different those insides may be.

Another point is that the known worlds may not be the only solid bodies within the Sun's grasp. Planets may be much more numerous than stars, with 'stray' worlds wandering through interstellar space, and Shapley predicted 'Lilliputian stars' shining only in the infrared or below, intermediate in size between Jupiter and the smallest known dwarf stars. (Some of these could have solid crusts, and maintain life by their internal heat.)[10]

Some years ago, Asimov argued that two light-years was the maximum distance at which the sun could retain a planet.[11] Lawton calculated that any planet beyond 1.9 ly at present, with a significant orbital inclination to the Ecliptic, would risk falling into the Alpha Centauri 'funnel'. Even in the Ecliptic plane, any planet beyond 2.72 ly would be menaced by the Sirius funnel; the Sun-Galactic Centre L1 point at 3.32 ly[12] is *very* close to the Ecliptic, so that seems to be the absolute limit. Even if a planet had a sufficiently large inclination and its orbital plane missed all the funnels, the influence of the other planets and nearby stars would rotate the plane until eventually it did penetrate a funnel. But with orbital periods of tens or hundreds of millions of years, and movement of their planes around the Ecliptic still slower, 'forbidden' planets might safely orbit at great distances for Galactic Years before falling into the gravitational domain of a neighbouring star. In that time the boundaries would actually change extensively due to passing stars, and we've no way of knowing where they were when the planets formed.

The fate of a 'forbidden' planet falling into another star's gravity well would depend on the star's Proper Motion relative to the Sun and distance relative to the planet. If Proper Motion is against the planet's approach to the star, then passage behind it (seen from Earth) will throw the planet back towards us; passage in front of the star would probably lead to capture by it. (Barnard's Star, whose low mass forms a gravitational 'bubble' within the Sun's isogravisphere, may have an outer planet considerably inclined to the others.) If Proper Motion is *with* the planet's approach, the accelerating and retarding effects of front and rear passage will be reversed, and the planet passing behind the star will be thrown outwards with greater velocity (relative to us) than it had before. In almost all cases, if the planet returns to the Sun's control its orbital inclination will be greater than before, and eccentricity will always be increased; but in relatively few would a planet be hurled radially away or straight towards the Sun. Flybys close enough for such drastic changes would be complicated by lesser companions (Alpha Centauri is a triple star, Sirius and Procyon are both double): a two-star flyby could send a planet virtually anywhere.

If the present situation had existed throughout, the chances of a 'stray' planet (almost certainly one of ours) entering the inner Solar System would be slight; but the situation is in fact far from permanent. Sirius is a brilliant, short-lived star which can't have existed a quarter as long as the Sun has, but in any case the relative positions of the stars around us are constantly changing. More than 10,000 stars may have penetrated the sphere of comets since the Solar System began. [13] Assuming the Sun formed as a member of an open cluster, now dispersed, the isogravisphere boundary will originally have been much closer to the Sun, although varying out to 8 ly during its lifetime to date; but at times it may have been only a funnel we pushed into someone else's sphere of influence. We might then have rendered some of their outlying planets 'forbidden', and captured or expelled them.

So stray planets in sizes all the way up to 'Lilliputian stars' may be wandering around the Sun's isogravisphere. The odds are against any of them being redirected to pass within 1AU of the Sun, but it happens to comets. Even then, the odds are against the stray's passing close enough to any of the known planets to do serious damage, or shift any of their orbits to a dangerous extent. But if we've broken up the planets and built a Dyson civilization around the Sun—solid-shell or asteroidal —it's hard to see how such an encounter could be anything but cataclysmic.

Another point is that, by Dyson's estimates, if 40% of the Sun's output could be utilized to expel Jupiter's mass from the Solar System in a directed beam, then over a million years the Sun's position in space could be altered by 3 ly. On average, another star passes within 3 ly every 100,000 years. A conservationist culture might preserve Jupiter in its present form, so that when the Sun's stable lifetime nears its end, Earth and other inhabited worlds could be transferred during a controlled flyby into orbit around a younger star.

On the other hand, the *social* evolution of a Kardashev-2 civilization might call for a steadily expanding population and make dismantling the planets essential. Boyce described a potential situation which seems to me to lead in that direction, and he felt that the technical and medical advances in question would be fully developed by the time Man claimed the outer Solar System, on the timescale this book suggests. Continuing improvement of physical and mental prosthetic devices, extension of machine intelligence into the 'symbolling' activities characteristic of human thought, and alterations to the brain itself by genetic engineering, would allow the individual's capabilities to be vastly enhanced by direct interaction with a System-wide computer net. Intellectually, we can only guess at the consequences of making all relevent knowledge available to any enquirer, in any field. Socially, all opinions would be known on all issues, and weighted according to the knowledge and understanding of the holders. In practical terms, anyone on the scene of an accident (for example) would instantly acquire total mastery of medicine and surgery, along with full telemetered knowledge of each patient's condition. A member of the net could transfer his consciousness into artificial bodies, mechanical or organic; machines exploring the outer Solar System could be subject to total human control when required. We no longer need a large colony at every site to have the necessary pool of human skills (although with mobile habitats the numbers may be on hand nonetheless). Thus the moral objections to 'mutaforming' (Chapter 5) would be answered by making the transition an excursion, not a sentence; fears of Man's future being dominated by the machine would end because the difference would have been removed by raising the machine to our level. Boyce showed with numerous examples that a member of the net could attain a far higher quality of life than anyone who rejected it. No doubt enclaves would be formed by 'pure' people who refused the link-up, but their culture would always be narrower than the whole. The wider culture would always be seductive because it did more for your mind—like the Tristan da Cunha teenagers' reaction to the modern UK.

The 'plugged-in' individual remains human because the defining trait of the relationship is still the distinctively human 'symbolling' characteristic, not possessed by present computers. However remote the setting, 'nose-picking simulations', as Boyce put it, can be provided to satisfy primal appetites. Indeed, there's a danger of large-scale 'dropping out' for endless mental circuses, and there would have to be safeguards against that and against takeovers by compulsion. The further from Earth, the more complicated the mental life such a society would need for its survival, but a Kardashev-2 culture *must* have information-handling capability beyond the present human level to maintain the necessary control of its environment.

However, Boyce thought such a society must inevitably be compartmentalized, with minds as well as bodies formed for particular tasks, and rewards in the satisfaction of larger social goals rather than the enrichment of the individual. Any number of minds can take on any number of tasks, depending on the prosthetic systems employed: 'You're never alone with a mental clone.' The human population would be streamlined in function rather than in numbers; and now the danger starts to show. Boyce himself has become aware of it since first he presented these ideas and, as he said in December 1981, 'The spirit of the beehive is in this.' The trap is that the options of increased diversification could lead to increased homogenization: to the evolution of a group-mind, a multicelled singleminded entity, with all resources used and stasis inevitable. As Ramsay put it, a Pyrrhic victory over nature.

Individual personality develops in a physical brain, in a physical body, as the 'dual aspect' of the electrochemical activity of that brain. In the net society an analogue of the brain-plus-nervous-system is entered into the computers, taking its cue from the living brain. When that analogue is switched into a machine or a synthetic body, for the individual the transition is instantaneous, even though at the speed of light the 'signal' could have taken four years to cross the cometary halo. That personality immediately begins a life of its own and couldn't be switched back into the original brain because there would be too much data and patterning to be imposed, and the physical/chemical changes would be too drastic, unless the original brain had been kept 'on ice' meantime. Reintegration of a 'mental clone' with divergent experiences, perhaps complicated by timelag, could be paralyzing.

The body could be cloned, reprogramming the brain with the new pattern, but the social problems are enormous (wife? family? property?). But then *any* mind can be programmed into the cloned brain—so duplicates of all bodies are available to duplicates of all minds and there's immortality for all. But, with intermind communication becoming steadily more efficient, with 'intellectual vampirism' by nonproducers on one hand and increasing mental specialization for productive lives on the other, without the anchor of individual bodies, 'streamlining' moves rapidly towards a group-mind situation. Leaving ethical and aesthetic questions aside, the objection in this context is that the group-mind would change its attitudes too slowly and be too inflexible to survive, unless it had a continuous influx of fresh ideas and attitudes from enough new adults to change the consensus—in other words, by maintaining such a population expansion that Dyson conversion of the Solar System would be inevitable for the Malthusian reasons Dyson originally described.

But eventually even the resources of an asteroid sphere must be exhausted, after which fragmentation of the group-mind, with asteroids cannibalizing one another, must follow ... until all that's left is a great shroud of debris which the Sun gradually smooths into a vast, peaceful equatorial ring. Meantime, in the planetary systems to which the adventurrnntuers fled long ago, events move inexorably along the same course, and the expanding culture would be one where the interior was continuously corrupting, over a scale of centuries or more, as the outer regions developed. The race would survive, spreading from star to star, but only as the technological cancer envisaged by Dyson.[2] Ultimately it would die out, leaving behind a Galaxy ruined for its successors—an image Clarke used with an analogous background in *The City and the Stars*.[14]

Ian Downie proposed that we push on—what appears now to be a dead end may not be, and we'll never know if we don't try it. What if the evolutionary goal of the human race is participation, as the equivalent of a single cell, in a cosmic being? 'What if it isn't?' is the obvious reply. The course apparently leads to the runaway Dyson situation or stasis, with eventual extinction, and we shouldn't pursue it on an offchance —although at the moment we're pursuing it blindly. Judging by past human experience, choices leading to homogenization are to be avoided, and even if Downie were known to be right we could legitimately ask whether we *want* life to evolve in such a fashion. Clarke's *Childhood's End*, which brings the physical existence of mankind to such a destination, is prefaced with the disclaimer that 'the opinions in this book are not those of the author'.[15]

Downie argued that, since we appear to be pursuing the course, it may be that all life is 'programmed' to do so once it reaches this level. If so, however, we aren't narrowing our options from choice and, if we're following a purpose, it isn't our own. Linda Lunan pointed out that the pattern of evolution so far has been infinite variations on a theme, filling all available niches. Going to a singularity (physical or mental) doesn't have good survival value. Where space technology offers us diversity, computer technology at first encourages it, then threatens it. Downie suggested that perhaps human destiny was to be diversified in space but unified in time; but only instantaneous communications would make that possible —telepathy, perhaps, but not the electromagnetic channels of the computer net. I doubt whether paranormal powers can be developed in such a way.

We can't predict the lifestyle of two or more hundred years hence in sufficient detail to suggest adequate strategies for restraint; not just physical conservation but mental restraint, unlikely because the net offers increased opportunities all the way into the trap. Restraint could be motivated only by alternative opportunities: society would have to emphasize the difference between human and machine, and the quality of life in the organic, individual, physical sense. Perception of self must be established before the individual fully joins the net —perhaps by emphasis on the arts, where success is unlikely to be achieved by consensus, and on physical competition. Rites of passage would test resilience, and options might be team efforts, physical and mental—mountain climbs, ballets or orchestras—*without* using the net. Soloists would be encouraged and a 'star' system practised: the net itself would be a status society, and encourage talent groups to pull out and go interstellar. Members of the net would be competitive, but competition doesn't have to be aggressive; and individual skills professed on the net could be 'recharged' in periods of retreat. The importance of hobbies would continue a present trend in post-industrial society, and emphasizing it would be a natural reaction to the development of the net. Boyce thought it unlikely that society would impose such disciplines on its members; but we have compulsory physical education in our schools, unpopular though it is with many children, because society believes it's important to develop the body as well as the mind.

James Campbell suggested that, if the group-mind does come into being, its resistance to change might stop the population explosion. It would then be too slow to adapt to changing circumstances, and eventually collapse—with disastrous consequences in the short term, but at least leaving the planets intact for later civilizations. However, since the group-mind arises in an exploratory context, the explorers' attitudes will survive as a major influence, so perhaps the group-mind may find the tensions unsupportable. The appropriate reaction would be to erase itself, leaving stern warnings to resist the lure of personal immortality through the computer net. But unless the entire situation is averted the years 2100-2300 may see turbulence unrivalled by anything in mankind's past.

Voluntary euthanasia isn't the only way out: Boyce suggested an active interstellar programme of self-replicating 'von Neumann probes' whose computers could house human personalities. In theory, such probes can explore the entire Galaxy in 1-2 million years, less than the present age of mankind. If they're to engage in large-scale information exchanges with other civilizations' probes as envisaged, there has to be continuous outward flow of information from central collators to which the individual probes report. (The same thing happens now with Meteosat, which gathers weather data from a large number of ground stations and retransmits them to all users.) Since the retransmissions are to probes in space, on which such a culture relies for its SETI efforts (*S*earch for *E*xtra*t*errestrial *I*ntelligence), there's no reason for such high-powered transmitters to operate in the 'waterhole' of optimum frequencies for detection through the atmospheres of Earthlike planets. NASA's plan for an orbiting SETI radiotelescope, refused all funding and allocated a Golden Fleece award by Senator Proxmire for alleged worthlessness, might in fact produce almost immediate results.

Since travel broadens the mind, the answer to the problem of stasis on the net may be what Boyce called 'the terminal transmission', transferring one's awareness to a distant von Neumann probe and erasing it from the Solar System net. Transfer would 'feel' instantaneous, and once 'in' the probe one could switch off during the boring interstellar and interplanetary transfers, 'waking' only when there's work to do or something to see. Nor would one be limited to a single probe, when the net is in effect being cast over the whole Galaxy. John Kelk calculated that, even if such a complex 'signal' had to travel by two different paths, to make sure there were no errors, it could cross the Galaxy in only three 'steps'. Boyce thought such a transition to 'Cosmic Man' would be like going from the sea to the land. Very few lifeforms have gone back to the sea, which is now merely a part of the human environment in which we don't live, although we visit it; likewise, he thought, star-travellers won't want to live on planets again.

Here too there are dangers, although on a different level. Boyce foresaw a vast net of minds between the stars, a 'supermind' evolving as in the transition from single-celled to multicelled life. Since the galaxies themselves are still evolving, the nature of intelligence and its view of the Universe may have enormous changes ahead. But the changes could be retrogressive: the processes of a 'supermind' would be very slow, limited by the speed of light across the 100,000 ly diameter of the Galaxy. A multicelled organism lives much longer than a single-celled one, but one could imagine a 'Copernicus Two' situation in which the relatively quick-thinking Magellanic Clouds took the rest of the lifetime of the Universe to convince the Milky Way that the Universe didn't revolve around it.

Much earlier, there's the problem that to the immortal minds 'in' the probes, able to switch themselves off for as long as they wish, normal individual lives would seem as transitory as mayflies and of no importance. It's not a good attitude for our Galactic envoys, and the mobile world scenario is generally more attractive. If the outer System dust clouds exist they tempt us to sally forth, possibly leading us into Contact with other civilizations, but certainly giving us a much broader base of resources on which to stabilize our society; literally the equivalent of whole solar systems to use—unexceptionably, as we see it, because they'll fill up again while the present configuration of neighbouring stars lasts. Since during its history the Sun may have had several such envelopes and lost them to passing stars, we may find left behind in the outer Solar System solid evidence that it has supported large-scale industry before.

For the isogravisphere resources to be exhausted, demand would have to be so great that other planetary systems could offer no significant relief. The only remaining step would be to blow up stars, to manufacture new dust clouds. (This was why Dyson proposed to move solar systems, to stick stars together into supernova critical masses.[5]) It would be a project approaching Kardashev-3 level, since as Lawton pointed out the detonation of a star affects a huge volume of space, the occupants of which would have to work in concert. But, if we've adopted planetary conservation and stabilized the population, we don't have an ever-growing demand for materials, and the isogravisphere resources should last out the Solar System's lifetime (up to thirty more Galactic Years). Having gathered them to prevent their loss, we might build idealized solar systems or Niven 'alternatives'[8] as stockpiles against far future needs.

It seems almost too good to be true, knowing that in geological time the situation is temporary, that so much material should be ours—incontestably ours, because ruled by our Sun—just when we need it. It would be even more remarkable if, as was suggested at ASTRA, *two* supernova shockwaves would have to interact here for the Sun to capture and condense enough material before passing stars dispersed it—or if a dust wave reached us from the Hughes-Routledge supernova just as the present situation came into being. Lawton remarked that, if the probability of one supernova granting us the dust is tiny, the probability of two combining to do so is tiny squared!—although of course any two supernova shock-waves must interact somewhere in the Galaxy, along a wide front, and the vicinity of the Solar System is no less likely than any other meeting point. The alternative would be to suggest that the supernovae were *timed*.

One of the most pessimistic arguments about the future is that all high-technology civilizations destroy themselves: other-wise, it's said, a Type-3 culture would have occupied the Galaxy by now and we'd have been absorbed or destroyed by it. There's no evidence in the sky for an industrial Type-3 civilization as Dyson described it: 'Starlight instead of shining wastefully all over the galaxy would be carefully dammed and regulated. Stars instead of moving at random would be grouped and organised. In fact, to search for evidence of technological activity in the galaxy might be like searching for evidence of technological activity on Manhattan Island ...' [5] (In 1976 the *National Geographic Magazine* showed 'a ring galaxy a billion light-years away', a ring broken by radial gaps, apparently thousands of light-years deep and *straight*. 'Only a few such galaxies have been discovered,' the caption stated. [16] The accepted explanation is that ring galaxies are created by concentric collisions between spirals. [17])

Yet if the supernova(e) creating the dust disc were timed, it could only be the work of a culture at or near the Type-3 stage. Presumably many solar systems would have been intended to benefit. It's not unreasonable to suggest that we haven't been exposed to full-scale Contact because we've been protected from it; and the lack of evidence for uncontrolled technological exploitation of the Galaxy would then imply that a conserva-tionist attitude is required for Type-3 membership. If so, the dust gives us an excellent opportunity to qualify. Shaw re-marked that other planetary systems might be easier to exploit than the dust, because the resources were concentrated, but Boyce replied that, if we tried that, we might be interrupted by a higher group. 'If you want to play, make your own toys—you have the resources.' The supernovae which gave us those resources would be the work of galactic gardeners, not industrialists. And at the point when we qualified for membership of that club—on the argument that control includes restraint—we'd find that Type-3 civilizations can, after all, talk to Type-2s, because full absorption is impossible.

In the alternative sense of full, unrestrained exploitation, a united Type-3 culture is in fact unattainable, unless by force—and if we and the other Type-1s in this area are nurtured and protected, or even if we are still alone, it doesn't suggest that violence prevails.

REFERENCES
(For key to abbreviations see p. 300)

Chapter 1: The Case for Deep Space (pp. 1-11)
1 'A Long-term Policy for Europe', *SP 21*, 12, 493-4, 518 (Dec. 1979)
2 Ian Ridpath, ed., *Stars and Space '77*, Independent Newspapers Ltd, 1976
3 David Baker, 'The NASA Budget—Fiscal Years 1979-80', *SP 21*, 8-9, 339-348 (Aug./Sept. 1979)
4 K. A. Ehricke, 'A Strategic Approach to Interplanetary Flight', *4S*
5 'Dinosaurs "Killed by Asteroid"', *DT* 7.1.'80, 15
6 V. A. Hughes, D. Routledge, 'An Expanding Ring of Interstellar Gas with Centre Close to the Sun', *Astronomical Journal* 77, 210 (1972)
7 Carl Sagan, I. S. Shlovskii, *Intelligent Life in the Universe*, Holden-Day, 1966
8 'A Nod's as Good as a Wink for the Varying Sun', *NS* 15.4.'76, 129
9 Carl Sagan, *The Cosmic Connection*, Doubleday, 1973
10 'The Sun as a Variable Star', *S&T 51*, 1, 26 (Jan. 1976)
11 'Solar Neutrino Problem May Be Remnant of the Ice Age', *NS 71.* 1015, 436
12 John Gribbin, 'The Sun and Earth's Weather', *Stars and Space '77, op cit*
13 Boris Belitsky, 'The Debate on SETI in the Soviet Union', *SP 20*, 9/10, 346-7 (Sept./Oct. 1978)
14 Duncan Lunan, 'Are Humans a Protected Species?', *Second Look 1*, 8, 13-17, 23, (June 1979)
15 'Sir Bernard Lovell Says Search for Life on Other Planets May Put Mankind at Risk', *Times* (London), 28.8.'75
16 Zdenek Kopal, *Man and His Universe*, Rupert Hart-Davis, 1972
17 N. S. Kardashev, 'Transmission of Information by Extraterrestrial Civilizations', in *Extraterrestrial Civilizations*, ed. G. M. Tovmasyan, Israel Program for Scientific Translations, 1967
18 F. J. Dyson, 'The Search for Extraterrestrial Technology', in *Perspectives in Modern Physics*, ed. R. E. Marshak, Interscience Publishers, 1966
19 Adrian Berry, *The Next Ten Thousand Years*, Cape, 1974

Chapter 2: The Rôle and Future of the Space Shuttle (pp. 13-31)
1 Curtis Peebles, 'The Origins of the US Space Shuttle—1', *SP 21*, 11, 435-442 (Nov. 1979)

2   Ibid.—2, *SP 21*, 12, 487-492 (Dec. 1979)

3   Eric Burgess, *Rockets and Spaceflight*, Hodder & Stoughton, 1956

4   David Baker, *Space Shuttle*, New Cavendish Books, 1979

5   'Tile Checks in Orbit?', *SP 22*, 1, 41 (Jan. 1980)

6   'Shuttle Programme Review', *SP 22*, 1, 27-31 (Jan. 1980)

7   'Slow Progress at the Cape', *SP 21*, 11, 460-462 (Nov. 1979)

8   'Future of Space Transportation', *SP 13*, 7, 268-270 (July 1971)

9   David Baker, 'Programming the Shuttle to Future Needs', *SP 22*, 3, 137-140, 144 (Mar. 1980)

10 'Soyuz 31 Redocks with Salyut 6', *SP 21*, 2, 72-73 (Feb. 1979)

11 'Milestones', *SP 21*, 7, 289 (July 1979)

12 Neville Kidger, 'Salyut 6 Mission Report: Part 2', *SP 22*, 3, 109-120 (March 1980)

13 '3-Year Flight for Cosmonauts', *DT* 26.6.'78; 'Stepping Stone to Mars?', *SP 22*, 1, 38 (Jan. 1980)

14 Adrian Berry, 'Asking for the Moon', *DT* 19.11.'79

15 Konstantin Tsiolkovsky, *Beyond the Planet Earth*, Pergamon Press, 1960

16 'Space Shuttle Payloads', *SP 22*, 4, 165 (Apr. 1980)

17 'Space Shuttle's First Year to Be a Busy One', *L5 News 2*, 12, 5 (Dec. 1977)

18 'Milestones', *SP 22*, 3, 97, 141 (Mar. 1980)

19 Theo Pirard, 'From Molniya to Ekran', *SP 20*, 1, 9-12 (Jan. 1978)

20 'Europe Controls US Satellite', *SP 21*, 3, 136-137 (Mar. 1979)

21 K. W. Gatland, 'Into Space by Low Technology?', *SP 20*, 1, 2-8 (Jan. 1980)

22 Arthur Wilcox, *Moon Rocket*, Nelson, 1946

23 'Milestones', *SP 21*, 7, 299 (July 1979)

24 'International Launch Center Proposed', *L5 News*, 2, 6, 1 (June 1977)

25 'Equatorial Nations Claim Geosynchronous Orbit Portions', *L5 News 2*, 4, (April 1977)

26 Dave Dooling, 'Super Skylab', *SP 19*, 7/8, 269-270 (July/Aug. 1977)

27 P. J. Parker, 'Shuttle External Tank Space Station', *L5 West European Branch Newsletter 3*, 1, 6 (Jan./Feb. 1978)

28 'O'Neill at AIAA', *L5 News 2*, 3, 7 (Mar. 1977)

29 Ben Bova, *Kinsman* (novel), Sidgwick & Jackson, 1980

30 Bob Parkinson, *High Road to the Moon*, British Interplanetary Society, 1979

31 'Shuttle Abort Procedures', *SP 21*, 7, 329-330 (July 1979)

32 'Milestones', *SP 20*, 6, 202 (June 1978)

33 'Milestones', *SP 21*, 4, 145 (April 1979)

34 P. J. Parker, 'Soviet Space Shuttle—Is It a Tip-Tank Design?', *L5 West European Branch Newsletter 3*, 8, 25 (Nov./Dec. 1978)

35 A. T. Lawton, *A Window in the Sky*, David & Charles, 1979

36 Joseph Green and Fuller C. Jones, 'The Bugs that Live at − 423°C', *ASF LXXX*, 8, 8-41 (Jan. 1968)

37 'First Test Flight of the European Ariane Launcher', European Space Agency, Centre National d'Etudes Spatiales, 1979

38 T. Nonweiler, 'Descent from Satellite Orbits Using Aerodynamic Braking', in *Realities of Space Travel*, ed. L. J. Carter, Putnam, 1957

39 *NS* 17.11.'77, 400
40 'On the Road with the Space Shuttle', *S&T 56*, 5, 372-379 (Nov. 1978)
41 R. J. Stalker, 'Laboratory Studies of Planetary Entry Aerodynamics', *Parsec (Transit* special edition) *4*, 4, 30-34 (Oct. 1973)
42 Irene Sänger-Bredt, 'The Silver Bird Story', *SP 15*, 5, 166-180 (May 1973)
43 Adrian Berry, 'US Puts off "Moon Treaty" Decision', *DT* 3.12.'80

Chapter 3: Shuttles and Launch Vehicles (pp. 32-58)
1   R. W. Johnson, 'The Lunar Colony', *Science Journal 5*, 5, 82-88 (May 1969)
2   'Moon House', *SP 12*, 1, 30-31 (Jan. 1970)
3   Don R. Ostrander, 'One-Man Propulsion Devices and their Application on Earth and in Space', *4S*
4   Dave Dooling, 'The Evolution of Skylab', *SP 16*, 1, 20-24 (Jan. 1974)
5   David Baker, 'Skylab—the Diary of a Rescue Mission', part 1, *SP 15*, 9, 334-340 (Sept. 1973)
6   David Dooling, Jr., 'Space Shuttle: Crisis and Decision', *SP 14*, 7, 242-245 (July 1972)
7   George E. Mueller, 'An Integrated Space Programme for the Next Generation', *A&A*, Jan. 1970
8   'Space Tug', *SP 12*, 8, 332 (Aug. 1970)
9   'Four-man Apollo?', *SP 12*, 5, 204 (May 1970)
10 David Baker, 'Orbital Bases', *SP 13*, 9, 318-334 (Sept. 1971)
11 P. M. Molton, 'The Nuclear Rocket', *SP 12*, 1, 390-394 (Oct. 1970)
12 'Space Manpower', *Aviation Week & Space Technology* 11.8.'69, 25
13 'Expedition to Mars', *SP 12*, 2, 67-68 (Feb. 1970)
13 David Baker, 'Saturn V', part 3, *SP 13*, 3, 100-107 (March 1971)
15 David Dooling, Jr., 'Skylab', *SP 12*, 12, 470-475 (Dec. 1970)
16 David Baker, 'A Schedule for the Shuttle', *SP 13*, 12, 454-455 (Dec. 1971)
17 K. W. Gatland, 'Europe and Post-Apollo: a Chaotic Situation', *SP 14*, 9, 322-324 (Sept. 1972)
18 'Milestones', *SP 14*, 9, 321 (Sept. 1972)
19 David Baker, 'The NASA Budget for Fiscal Year 1973', *SP 14*, 10, 362-364 (Oct. 1972)
20 'Milestones', *SP 14*, 4, 121 (Apr. 1972)
21 'Milestones', *SP 15*, 3, 81 (Mar. 1973)
22 David Baker, 'Financial Setbacks in the US Space Programme', *SP 15*, 8, 306-308 (Aug. 1973)
23 Herman Hendericks, 'A Modularised Space Station', *SP 13*, 9, 341-343 (Sept. 1971)
24 Dave Dooling, 'The Evolution of the Apollo Spacecraft', part 2, *SP 16*, 4, 127-136 (Apr. 1974)
25 David Dooling, Jr., 'The Manned Exploration of Mars', *SP 13*, 6, 198-202 (June 1971)
26 Cornelius Ryan, ed., *Man on the Moon*, Sidgwick & Jackson, 1953
27 Willy Ley and Wernher von Braun, *The Exploration of Mars*, Sidgwick & Jackson, 1956

28 Philip Bono and Kenneth Gatland, *Frontiers of Space*, Blandford Press, 1969
29 'Milestones', *SP 12*, 1, 1 (Jan. 1970)
30 Neville P. Clarke, 'Biodynamic Environments in Spaceflight', *4S*
31 'Milestones', *SP 16*, 1, 1 (Jan. 1974)
32 Reginald Turnill, *The Observer's Book of Manned Spaceflight*, Frederick Warne, 1972
33 J. E. Vanderveen, 'Nutrition for Long Space Voyages', *4S*
34 *Ibid.*, panel discussion
35 'The Soviets at Baku', *SP 16*, 3, 68, 76 (Feb. 1974)
36A 'Latest Soyuz Flights', *SP 16*, 3, 110 (Mar. 1974)
37 'Wastes to Water', *SP 14*, 10, 380 (Oct. 1972)
38 'Oxygen Reclaimed from Water Vapour', *SP 13*, 12, 460 (Dec. 1971)
39 David Dooling, Jr., 'Closed Loop Life Support Systems', *SP 14*, 4, 134-139 (Apr. 1972)
40 R. E. W. Jansson and I. Edwards, 'Theoretical Performance of Ammonia, Hydrogen and Biowaste Resistojets', *JBIS 27*, 6, 433-443 (June 1974)
41 'Skylab Food Technology', *SP 13*, 2, 52 (Feb. 1971)
42 Joseph P. Kerwin, 'Doctor in Space', *SP 16*, 8, 296-297 (Aug. 1974)
43 David Baker, 'Skylab—the Diary of a Rescue Mission, contd.', *SP 15*, 11, 409-410 (Nov. 1973)
44 James E. Fletcher, 'The Space Commitment', *SP 16*, 11, 431-432 (Nov. 1974)
45 David Baker, 'Space Station Situation Report', part 2, *SP 13*, 9, 344-351 (Sept. 1971)
46 Robert R. Gilruth, 'Manned Space Stations', *4S*
47 Frederick I. Ordway, '2001: A Space Odyssey', *SP 12*, 3, 110-116 (Mar. 1970)
48 'Artificial Gravity Experiments', *SP 14*, 4, 129-130 (Apr. 1972)
49 '"Meteoroid Bumper" Test', *SP 16*, 8, 309 (Aug. 1974)
50 David Baker, 'Report from Jupiter', *SP 16*, 4, 140-144 (Apr. 1974)
51 John W. Evans, 'The Sun', *4S*
52 P. M. Molton, 'The Protection of Astronauts from Solar Flares', *SP 13*, 6, 220-224 (June 1971)
53 Paul D. Lowman, Jr., 'Geologic Orbital Photography Experience from the Gemini Programme', *4S*
54 'The Now Frontier: Pioneer to Jupiter, part 4', GPO 791-693 (1973)
55 K. A. Ehricke, 'A Strategic Approach to Interplanetary Flight', *4S*
56 R. K. Plebuch and J. S. Martinez, 'Nuclear Propulsion Applications', *2*
57 R. Salkeld and R. Beichel, 'Reusable One-Stage-to-Orbit Shuttles: Brightening Prospects', *A&A 11*, 6, 48 (June 1973)
58 W. A. Kuhrt, 'A Survey of Future Space Propulsion Systems', *2C*
59 P. Bono and V. Gradecek, 'The Rocket-Sled Launching Technique: its Implications on Performance of Reusable Ballistic (Orbital/Global) Transport Systems,' *2C*
60 Robert Salkeld, 'Mixed-Mode Propulsion for the Space Shuttle', *A&A 9*, 8.11.'71, 52-58.

61 Robert Salkeld, 'The Space Shuttle: Some Growth Possibilities', *SP 15*, 11, 402-408 (Nov. 1973)

62 A. V. Cleaver, *A&A, 11*, 6, 50 (June 1973)

63 David Dooling, Jr., 'Space Shuttle Main Engine', *SP 14*, 2, 56 (Feb. 1972)

64 'Space Fuel Insulation', *SP 12*, 1, 31 (Jan. 1970)

65 'Testing Electric Propulsion in Orbit', *SP 12*, 6, 254-255 (June 1970)

66 'Milestones', *SP 12*, 8, 309 (Aug. 1970)

67 'SERT 2 Report', *SP 13*, 5, 163 (May 1971)

68 John S. MacKay, 'Manned Mars Missions Using Electric Propulsion', *SP 12*, 1, 41-46 (Jan. 1970)

69 'Solar Electric Propulsion', *SP 16*, 6, 214-216 (June 1974)

70 'Jupiter Fly-by: First Results', *SP 16*, 3, 107-108 (March 1974)

71 K. A. Ehricke, 'Exploration of the Solar System and of Interstellar Space', *2C*

72 Arthur C. Clarke, *The Lost Worlds of 2001*, Sidgwick & Jackson, 1972

73 David Dooling, Jr., 'Controlled Thermonuclear Fusion for Space Propulsion', *SP 14*, 1, 26-27 (Jan. 1972)

74 Heinz Gartmann, *The Men Behind the Space Rockets*, Weidenfeld & Nicolson, 1955

75 F. J. Dyson, 'Interstellar Transport', *2C*

76 'Project Daedalus, an Interim Report on the BIS Starship Study', *SP 16*, 9, 356-358 (Sept. 1974)

77 'Prospects for Laser-Triggered Fusion', *JBIS 27*, 9, 704-705 (Sept. 1974)

78 Conley Powell, 'Interstellar Flight and Intelligence in the Universe', *SP 14*, 12, 422-447 (Dec. 1972)

79 R. B. Hickley, R. C. Reid and P. E. Glaser, 'Recovery of Deuterium in the Atmosphere of Jupiter', *2C*

80 J.N. Smith and C.W. Mead, 'Mission Profiles for the Exploration of the Solar System with Nuclear Pulse Rockets', *2C*

81 'Shuttle Crews to Get Tasty, Varied Meals', *ARC* 78-176 (24.11,'78)

82 J. M. Vogel, 'Bone Mineral Measurement: Skylab Experiment M-078', *AA 2*, 1/2, 129-139 (Jan./Feb. 1975)

83 S. L. Kemsey *et al.*, 'Skylab Experimental Results: Hematology Studies', *ibid.*, 141-154

84 P. C. Johnson *et al.*, 'Postmission Plasma Volume and Red-Cell Mass Changes in the Crews of the First Two Skylab Missions', *AA 2*, 3/4, 311-317 (Mar./Apr. 1975)

85 Neville Kidger, 'Salyut 6: The Long-Stay Cosmonauts', *SP 21*, 5, 212-214 (May 1979)

86 R. L. Johnson *et al.*, 'Skylab Experiment M-092: Results of the First Manned Mission', *AA 2*, 3/4, 265-296 (Mar./Apr. 1975)

87 'Keeping Fit in Orbit', *SP 21*, 1, 36-37 (Jan. 1979)

88 Gordon R. Hooper, 'Missions to Salyut 6', part 8, *SP 21*, 8/9, 359-363 (Aug./Sept. 1979)

89 'Milestones', *SP 20*, 6, 202 (June 1978)

90 'Stepping Stone to Mars?', *SP 22*, 1, 38 (Jan. 1980)

91 '3-Year Flight for Cosmonauts', *DT* 19.11.'79

92 Edwin 'Buzz' Aldrin and Wayne Warga, *Return to Earth*, Random House, 1973

93 James B. Irwin and W. A. Emerson, Jr., *To Rule the Night*, Hodder & Stoughton, 1973

94 Edgar D. Mitchell, 'Space Experiment in ESP, *SP 14*, 1, 20-21 (Jan. 1972)

95 Andrew Wilson and D. J. Shayler, 'Return to Apollo', *SP 22*, 1, 7-21 (Jan. 1980)

96 H. Bücker and G. Honeek, 'The Biological Effectiveness of HZE-Particles of Cosmic Radiation Studied in the Apollo 16 and 17 Biostack Experiments', *AA 2*, 3/4, 247-264 (March/Apr. 1975)

97 M. O. Burrell, 'The Risk of Solar Proton Events to Space Missions', NASA TN D-6379, *GPO* June 1971

98 *Ibid.*, pp. 2-3

99 Leland F. Belew, ed., 'Skylab, Our First Space Station', NASA SP-400, *GPO* June 1971

100 David M. Rust, 'Warming Up for the Solar Maximum Year', *S&T*, 58, 4, 315-318 (Oct. 1979)

101 T. Kiang, 'Recent Astronomical Research in China', *S&T 54*, 4, 260-263 (Oct. 1977)

102 'Cerenkov Radiation Caused Apollo Flashes', *NS 72*, 1021, 14 (7.10.'76)

103 Robert Edgar, 'Skylab Experimental Results', *SP 18*, 2, 59-67 (Feb. 1976)

104 T. A. Heppenheimer, *Colonies in Space*, Warner Books, 1977

105 Dave Dooling, 'Space Factories in 1997', part 1, *SP 19*, 10, 342-347 (Oct. 1977)

106 M. W. Jack Bell, 'Advanced Launch Vehicle Systems and Technology', *SP 20*, 4, 135-143 (Apr. 1978)

107 Robert Piland, 'Results of Recent Studies of the Space Solar Power Concept', *L5 (WE)*

108 'Powersat, an Astronautical Energy Solution', *SP 19*, 3, 82-89 (Mar. 1977)

109 'Boeing Designers Answer Questions about Satellite Solar Power', *L5 News 2*, 5, 6-9, 17-20 (May 1977)

110 Kenneth Gatland, *Missiles and Rockets*, Blandford Press, 1975

111 Charles P. Vick, 'The Soviet Super Boosters', part 2, *SP 16*, 3, 94-104 (Mar. 1974)

112 'Milestones', *SP 18*, 7/8, 237 (July/Aug. 1976)

113 Phillip S. Clark, 'The Proton Launch Vehicle', *SP 19*, 9, 330-333, 340 (Sept. 1977)

114 'SERT II Restarts', *SP 17*, 2, 62-63 (Feb. 1975)

115 'Sailing the Silent Main', *L5 News 2*, 7, 1 (July 1977)

116 'Solar Sail Loses Out to Ion Drive', *L5 West European Branch Newsletter 2*, 6, 5 (Sept./Oct. 1977)

117 'Solar-Electric Drive for Comet Rendezvous', *SP 19*, 9, 314-315 (Sept. 1977)

118 Robert L. Forward, 'Comet Catcher', *Omni 2*, 5, 55-58, 60, 97 (Feb. 1980)

119 'Ion Propulsion for Spacecraft', NASA Lewis Research Centre, *GPO* (1977-757-070/6307 Region No. 5-11)
120 Phillip J. Parker, 'Space Industrialisation—American Style', *SP 19*, 7/8, 291-297 (July/Aug. 1977)
121 *Project Daedalus*, ed. A. R. Martin, *JBIS Supplement*, 1978
122 Gregory L. Matloff, 'Utilisation of O'Neill's Model 1 Lagrange Point Colony as an Interstellar Ark', *JBIS 29*, 12, 775-785 (Dec. 1976)

Chapter 4: All Done By Electricity (pp. 59-77)

1   P. E. Cleator, *Into Space*, Allen & Unwin, 1953
2   *Soviet Moon Rockets*, Soviet Booklets, Dec. 1959
3   Arthur C. Clarke, *The Exploration of Space*, Temple Press, 1951
4   R. C. Parkinson, 'Take-off Point for a Lunar Colony', *SP 16*, 9, 322-326 (Sept. 1974)
5   G. Harry Stine, 'The Third Industrial Revolution: The Exploitation of the Space Environment', *ibid.*, 327-334
6   Adrian Berry, *The Next Ten Thousands Years, op cit*
7   E.A. Steinhoff, 'Importance of the Use of Extraterrestrial Resources to the Economy of Space Flight Beyond Near-Earth Orbit', *4S*
8   'Boeing Designers Answer Questions about Satellite Solar Power', *op cit*
9   *NS* 22.4.'76, 163
10 Gerard K. O'Neill, *The High Frontier*, Cape, 1977
11 T. A. Heppenheimer, *Colonies in Space, op cit*
12 P. M. Molton, 'The Protection of Astronauts from Solar Flares', *op cit*
13 'Radio Astronomy Explorer', *Parsec* (*Transit* special edition) *4*, 4, 35-38 (Oct. 1973)
14 Jane McClure, 'Instead of Frictionless Elephants', in *Space Colonies*, ed. Stewart Brand, Penguin, 1977
15 'O'Neill Fund Appeal', *L5 News 2*, 9, 16
16 'The Colony Column', *L5 West European Branch Newsletter 3*, 1, 9 (Jan./Feb. 1978)
17 D. A. Evans, 'Asteroids and the Mass Driver' (letter), *SP 20*, 8, 317 (Aug. 1978)
18 Michael McCollum, 'The Disposal of Nuclear Waste in Space', *ASF* XCVIII, 3, 35-49 (March 1978)
19 Duncan Lunan, letter, *ASF* XCIX, 3, 177-178 (March 1979)
20 Norman M. Tallon, 'Materials Sciences', in *1978 Yearbook of Science and the Future*, Encyclopedia Britannica, Inc., 1977
21 Jerry Pournelle, 'Halfway to Anywhere', *Galaxy 34*, 7, 94-101 (Apr. 1974)
22 Peter Glaser, 'Environmental Implication of SPS', *L5 News 3*, 5, 9-11 (May 1978)
23 R. J. Rosa, 'How to Design a Flying Saucer', *ASF* XC, 1, 64-71 (Sept. 1972)
24 Eric Drexler, 'Laser Propulsion to Geosynchronous Orbit', *L5 News 3*, 7, 8-10 (July 1978)
25 F. Winterberg, 'Launching of Large Payloads into Earth Orbit by Intense Relativistic Electron Beams', *JBIS 31*, 9, 339-343 (Sept. 1978)
26 Roger Arnold and Donald Kingsbury, 'The Spaceport', part 1, *ASF* XCIX, 11, 48-67 (Nov. 1979)

27 Edwin 'Buzz' Aldrin, 'Line of Sight Guidance Techniques for Manned Orbital Rendezvous', Massachusetts Institute of Technology, Jan. 1963

28 Wernher von Braun, *Space Frontier*, Muller, 1968

29 Arnold & Kingsbury, 'The Spaceport', part 2, *ASF* xcix, 12, 61-77 (Dec. 1979)

30 Hans Moravec, 'Cable Cars in the Sky', in *The Endless Frontier*, ed. Jerry Pournelle, Ace, 1979

31 Jerome Pearson, 'The Orbital Tower: a Spacecraft Launcher Using the Earth's Rotational Energy', *AA 2*, 9-10, 785-799 (Sept./Oct. 1975)

32 Charles Sheffield, *The Web between the Worlds* (novel), Ace, 1979

33 Arthur C. Clarke, *The Fountains of Paradise* (novel), Gollancz, 1979

34 Charles Sheffield, 'How to Build a Beanstalk', in *Vectors*, Ace, 1979

35 Brian W. Aldiss, *Hothouse* (novel), Faber, 1962

36 Jerome Pearson, 'Anchored Lunar Halo Satellites for Cislunar Transportation and Communication', *L5(WE)*

37 James Blish, *Earthman Come Home* (novel), Faber, 1956

38 Saunders B. Kramer, 'Problems of Asteroid Capture' (letter), *SP 20*, 8, 319 (Aug. 1978)

Chapter 5: The Development of the Moon (pp. 78-110)

1 C. P. Vick, 'The Soviet Super Boosters', part 2, *op cit*

2 K. A. Ehricke, 'A Strategic Approach to Interplanetary Flight', *op cit*

3 'Moon House', *SP 12*, 1, 30-31 (Jan. 1970)

4 'Lecture on "The Lunar International Laboratory"', *SP 12*, , 4, 184-185 (Apr. 1970)

5 E. A. Steinhoff, *op cit*

6 'Lunar Water Process', *SP 13*, 4, 131 (Apr. 1971)

7 D. T. Schowalter, T. B. Malone, *The Development of a Lunar Habitability System*, NASA CR-1676, *GPO* Feb. 1972

8 Hermann Oberth, *Man into Space*, Weidenfeld & Nicolson, 1957

9 A. V. Cleaver, 'European Space Activities Since the War: a Personal View', *SP 16*, 6, 220-238 (June 1974)

10 G. Harry Stine, 'The Third Industrial Revolution', part 2, *ASF* xc, 6, 94-115 (Feb. 1973)

11 Arthur C. Clarke and R. A. Smith, *The Exploration of the Moon*, Muller, 1954

12 Arthur C. Clarke, *Earthlight* (novel), Muller, 1955

13 Kenneth F. Weaver, 'The Moon, Man's First Goal in Space', *NG 135*, 2, 206-230 (Feb. 1969)

14 Richard R. Vondrack, 'Creation of an Artificial Lunar Atmosphere', *Nature 248*, 657-659 (19.4.'74)

15 E. C. Walterscheid, 'Plowshare Today', *ASF* LXXIII, 4, 8-16, 81-84 (June 1964)

16 V. S. Safronov, Ye. L. Rushkol, 'History of the Lunar Atmosphere and the Possibility of Ice and Organic Compounds Existing on the Moon', NASA TT F-232, *GPO* Sept. 1964

17 J. W. E. H. Sholto Douglas, 'Farming on the Moon', in *Man and the Moon*, ed. R. S. Richardson, World Publishing Co., 1961

18 M. O'Day, 'Power for a Lunar Colony', *ibid*

19   G. Simmons, *On the Moon with Apollo 17*, NASA EP-101, *GPO* Dec. 1972

20   *Astronautics & Aeronautics, 1970: Chronology on Science, Technology and Policy*, NASA SP-4015, *GPO* 1972

21   Adrian Berry, *The Next Ten Thousand Years, op cit*

22   John S. Rinehart, 'Basic Design for Moon Building', in *Man and the Moon, op cit*

23   V. A. Firsoff, *Strange World of the Moon*, Hutchinson, 1959

24   *Apollo 15—Preliminary Science Report*, NASA SP-289, *GPO* 1972

25   T. L. Page, 'The Third Lunar Science Conference', part 1, *S&T 43*, 3, 145-154 (March 1972)

26   Robert A. Heinlein, 'It's Great to be Back!' (short story) in *The Green Hills of Earth*, Sidgwick & Jackson, 1954

27   Jonathon Norton Leonard, *Flight into Space*, Sidgwick & Jackson, 1953

28   Arthur C. Clarke, 'A Meeting with Medusa' (short story) in *The Wind from the Sun*, Gollancz, 1972

29   R. A. Heinlein, *The Moon Is a Harsh Mistress* (Novel), Dobson, 1967

30   Isaac Asimov, *The Gods Themselves* (novel), Gollancz, 1972

31   R. A. Heinlein, 'The Menace from Earth' (short story) in *The Menace from Earth*, Dobson, 1966

32   Fritz Leiber, *A Spectre Is Haunting Texas* (novel), Gollancz, 1969

33   Isaac Asimov, 'Waterclap' (short story) in *The Science Fictional Solar System*, ed. Asimov, Greenberg and Waugh, Sidgwick & Jackson, 1980

34   Alexei Panshin, *Heinlein in Dimension*, Advent, 1968

35   Arthur C. Clarke, 'Out of the Cradle' (short story) in *Tales of Ten Worlds*, Gollancz, 1963

36   Ernest Taves, 'Mayflower One' (novelette), *Galaxy 33*, 3 (Nov./Dec. 1972); 'Mayflower Two', Nov. 1973; 'Mayflower Three', Jan. 1973

37   John W. Macvey, *Journey to Alpha Centauri*, Macmillan, 1965

38   James Blish, *Earthman Come Home*, (novel) *op cit*

39   Cordwainer Smith, *The Planet Buyer* (novel), Pyramid Books, 1965

40   Francis Godwin, 'The Man in the Moone' (1638) in *The Man in the Moone*, ed. F. K. Pizor, T. A. Comp, Sidgwick & Jackson, 1971

41   Isaac Asimov, *The Naked Sun* (novel), Michael Joseph, 1958

42   A. T. Lawton, 'Photometric Observation of Planets at Interstellar Distances', *SP 12*, 9, 365-373 (Sept. 1970); letters, *13*, 8, 315 (Aug. 1971)

43   E. H. Wells, 'Small Optical Telescopes on the Moon', *SP 14*, 3, 90-94 (Mar. 1972)

44   David A. Smith, letter, 'Radio Astronomy on the Moon', *SP 16*, 11, 436 (Nov. 1974)

45   G. Harry Stine, 'The Third Industrial Revolution: the Exploitation of the Space Environment', *op cit*

46   Graham Chedd, 'Colonisation at Lagrangea', *NS 64*, 920, 247-249 (24.10.'74)

47   T. A. Heppenheimer, *Colonies in Space, op cit*

48   G. L. Matloff and A. J. Fennelly, 'A Superconducting Ion Scoop and its Application to Interstellar Flight', *JBIS 27*, 9, 663-673 (Sept. 1974)

49   Bob Parkinson, 'Small High-Technology Communities on the Moon', part 2, *SP 19*, 3, 103-108 (Mar. 1977)

50   Peter Voke, 'The Role of Selenostationary Orbits in Cislunar Settlements', *L5 (WE)*

51   Fred Hoyle, *The Nature of the Universe*, Blackwell, 1960

52   James Blish, *The Seedling Stars* (short stories), Faber, 1957

53   John W. Campbell, Jr., 'The Simple Way', *ASF* LXXXIII, 4, 5-7, 174-178 (June 1969)

54   Larry Niven, 'Becalmed in Hell' (short story) in *Inconstant Moon*, Gollancz, 1972

55   Anne McCaffrey, *The Ship Who Sang* (novel), Andre Deutsch, 1971

56   Harlan Ellison, 'I Have No Mouth and I Must Scream' (short story), *If* 17, 3, 24-36 (Mar. 1967)

57   Arthur C. Clarke, *The Sands of Mars* (novel), Sidgwick & Jackson, 1951

58   Adrian Berry, 'Pharmaceuticals to be Made in Space by 1987', *DT* 25.9.'81

59   Ted White, 'Junk Patrol' (short story), *Amazing Stories 45*, 3, 10-17, 108 (Sept. 1971)

Chapter 6: Space Colonies and Space Ships (pp. 111-137)

1   Leonard Cottrell, *The Bull of Minos*, Evans, 1955

2   Konstantin Tsiolkovsky, *Beyond the Planet Earth*, Pergamon, 1960

3   J. D. Bernal, *The World, the Flesh and the Devil*, Cape, 1970

4   G. Harry Stine, *Earth Satellites and the Race for Space Superiority*, Ace, 1957

5   L. R. Shepherd, 'Interstellar Flight', in *The Complete Book of Outer Space*, ed. Jeffrey Logan, Maco Magazine Corp., 1953

6   Arthur C. Clarke, *Rendezvous with Rama* (novel), Gollancz, 1973

7   Gerard K. O'Neill, *The High Frontier, op cit*

8   H. Hornby, W. H. Allen, 'Mission to the Libration Centres', *A&A* July 1966, 78-82

9   P. E. Schmid, *Lunar Far-side Communications Satellites*, NASA TN D-4509, *GPO* June 1968

10   R. W. Farquhar, *The Control and Use of Libration-Point Satellites*, NASA TR R-346. *GPO* Sept. 1970

11   A. T. Lawton and S. J. Newton, 'Long-Delayed Echoes: the Search for a Solution', *SP 16*, 5, 181-187, 195 (May 1974)

12   George Sassoon, 'A Correlation of Long-Delay Radio Echoes and the Moon's Orbit', *SP 16*, 7, 258-264 (July 1974)

13   James Strong, *Flight to the Stars*, Temple Press, 1965

14   Duncan Lunan, 'Long-Delayed Echoes and the Extraterrestrial Hypothesis', *Journal of the Society of Electronic and Radio Technicians*, 10, 8, 180-182 (Sept. 1976)

15   Robert Piland, 'Results of Recent Studies of the Space Solar Power Concept', *op cit*

16   Peter E. Glaser, 'Development of the Satellite Solar Power Station', *SP 18*, 6, 198-208 (June 1976)

17   Adrian Cowderoy, 'Biological Effects as a Factor Affecting a High Power Microwave Transmission-Reception System', *L5 (WE)*

18   Richard D. Johnson and Charles Holbrow, *Space Settlements, a Design Study*, NASA SP-413, *GPO* 1977

19 T. A. Heppenheimer, *Colonies in Space, op cit*
20 Cornelius Ryan, ed., *Across the Space Frontier*, Sidgwick & Jackson, 1953
21 Mark M. Hopkins, 'A Preliminary Cost Benefit Analysis of Space Colonisation', *JBIS 30*, 8, 289-300 (Aug. 1977)
22 Eric Cabot Hannah, 'Radiation Protection for Space Colonies', *ibid.*, 310-313
23 D. J. Sheppard, 'Concrete on the Moon', *SP 17*, 3, 91-93, 120
24 D. J. Sheppard, 'Concrete Space Colonies', *SP 21*, 1, 3-8 (Jan. 1979)
25 'Products from Basalt', *SP 17*, 2, 63 (Feb. 1975)
26 Frank D. Hess, 'Demeter: Island in Space', *SP 21*, 10, 393-396 (Oct. 1979)
27 Ian Richards, 'Area Requirements for Food Production on Space Colonies', *L5(WE)*
28 Nigel Calder, *Spaceships of the Mind*, BBC, 1978
29 C. E. Singer, 'Sources of Volatile Materials for a Space Manufacturing Facility', *L5 (WE)*
30 M. W. Jack Bell, 'Advanced Launch Vehicle Systems and Technology', *op cit*
31 Bob Parkinson,, 'Superfuels', *SP 18*, 10, 348-350 (Oct. 1976)
32 Steward Brand, 'Is the Surface of a Planet Really the Right Place for an Expanding Technological Civilisation?', in *Space Colonies, op cit*
33 A. V. Cleaver, 'On the Realisation of Projects: with Special Reference to O'Neill Space Colonies and the Like', *JBIS 30*, 8, 283-288 (Aug. 1977)
34 'Space Solar Power', *L5 News, 1*, 16, 2-3 (Dec. 1976)
35 'Space Beam Builder', *SP 20*, 11, 388 (Nov 1978)
36 'Space Construction Tools', *SP 21*,7, 309 (July 1979)
37 'Robot Space Arm', *SP 20*, 8, 295-296 (Aug. 1978)
38 Cover and p. 305, *SP 19*, 9
39 'Powersat, an Astronautical Energy Solution', *op cit*
40 Dave Dooling, 'Outlook for Space', *SP 18*, 12, 422-425 (Dec. 1976)
41 G. Harry Stine, 'Riposte to Pournelle', *ASF* c, 3, 115-118 (March 1980)
42 G. Harry Stine, 'The Third Industrial Revolution', *op cit*
43 M. M. Hopkins, 'Recent Developments in the Economies of Power from Space', *L5 News 1*, 14, 8 (Oct. 1976)
44 J. Peter Vajk, 'NASA Ames 1976 Summer Study', *L5 News, 1*, 13, 3-5 (Sept. 1976)
45 T. A. Heppenheimer, 'Two New Propulsion Systems for Use in Space Colonisation', *JBIS 30*, 8, 301-309 (Aug. 1977)
46 *SA* Aug. 1974, p. 19
47 Arthur C. Clarke, *Interplanetary Flight*, Temple Press, 1950
48 'The Stability of L5', *JBIS 30*, 1, 20 (Jan. 1977)
49 Bob Parkinson, 'Small High-Technology Communities on the Moon', part 1, *SP 19*, 3, 42-47 (Feb. 1977)
50 G. Vulpetti, 'Fission Engine Model: Data Processing and Improvement', *JBIS 29*, 2, 113-135 (Feb. 1976)
51 *Project Daedalus, op cit*
52 Bob Shaw, *Orbitsville*, Gollancz, 1975
53 K. A. Ehricke, 'A Strategic Approach to Interplanetary Flight', *op cit*

54 Isaac Asimov, 'After Apollo, What?', in *Today and Tomorrow and ...*, Abelard-Schuman, 1974

55 David B. S. Smith, 'Off Planet Industry', *L5 News 5*, 3, 2-5 (Mar. 1980)

Chapter 7: The Exploration of Mars (pp. 138-163)

1 Percival Lowell, *Mars*, 1895; History of Astronomy Reprints, 1978

2 James B. Pollack, 'Mars', *SA 233*, 3, 106-117 (Sept. 1975)

3 Ludek Pesek and Peter Ryan, *Solar System*, Allen Lane, 1978

4 'Mars, Phobos and Deimos', *JBIS 29*, 12, 819 (Dec. 1976)

5 B. C. Clark *et al.*, 'Inorganic Analysis of Martian Surface Samples at the Viking Landing Sites', *Science 194*, 4271, 1283-1288 (17.12.'76)

6 J. Kelly Beatty, 'Viking 1 Lands on a Very Red Planet', *S&T 52*, 3, 156-161 (Sept. 1976)

7 J. Kelly Beatty, 'Vikings Rest during Mars' Conjunction', *S&T 52*, 6, 404-409 (Dec. 1976)

8 Everly Driscoll, 'Viking 2: Tests for Life', *SP 18*, 12, 435-436 (Dec. 1976)

9 M. M. Averner and R. D. MacElroy, *On the Habitability of Mars: an Approach to Planetary Ecosynthesis*, NASA SP-414, National Technical Information Service, 1976

10 'Simulating Martian Soil', *SP 18*, 10, 371 (Oct. 1976)

11 'Clues to Life on Mars?', *SP 20*, 5, 176-177 (May 1978)

12 'Still Looking for Life on Mars', *NS* 17.11.'77, 399

13 *Science*, 1.10'76, 68

14 Stewart Brand, 'Controversy Is Rife on Mars', in *Space Colonies, op cit*

15 ' "Cockroach" on Mars', *SP 17*, 1, 15 (Jan. 1975)

16 'NASA's Smart Robot', *ibid.* 16-17

17 Arthur C. Clarke, *The Lost Worlds of 2001, op cit*

18 'Milestones', *SP 20*, 6, 201 (June 1978)

19 'Milestones', *SP 20*, 8, 281 (Aug. 1978)

20 S. W. Greenwood, 'Extraterrestrial Atmospheric Transportation Considerations', *JBIS 27*, 2, 144-147 (Feb. 1974)

21 Willy Ley and Wernher von Braun, *The Exploration of Mars, op cit*

22 'A New Concept in Planetary Probes—the Mars Penetrator', *SP 18*, 12, 432-434 (Dec. 1976); 'Space Research "Down Under" ', *SP 19*, 6, 205-6 (June 1977)

23 Paul Brickhill, *The Dam Busters*, Evans, 1951

24 Robert L. Staehle *et al.*, 'Mars Polar Ice Sample Return Mission', part 1, *SP 18*, 11, 383-390 (Nov. 1976)

25 *Ibid.*, part 2, *SP 19*, 11, 399-409 (Nov. 1977)

26 *Ibid.*, part 3, *SP 19*, 12, 441-445 (Dec. 1977)

27 Geraint Day, 'Martian Dust Storms—A Mechanism for Transportation of Life?', *SP 20*, 3, 83-88 (Mar. 1978)

28 ' "Oases" on Mars?', *SP 21*, 12, 499 (Dec. 1979)

29 Norbert Giesinger, 'Water on Mars' (letter), *SP 20*, 8, 316-317 (Aug. 1978)

30 *NS 83*, 23.8.'79, 1169

31 The Kettering Group, 'Observations of 1977-66A, Cosmos 928', *SP 20*, 9/10, 353-355 (Sept./Oct. 1978)

32 'Milestones', *SP 21*, 10, 385 (Oct. 1979)

33 Norbert Giesinger, 'Manoeuvres of Cosmos 929' (letter), *SP 21*, 3, 140-141 (Mar. 1979)

34 Robert D. Christy, 'Orbits of Soviet Spacecraft at 51°.6 Inclination', *SP 22*, 2, 80-81 (Feb. 1980)

35 Phillip J. Parker, 'Bigger Salyut?' (letter), *ibid.*, 92

36 Nicholas L. Johnson, 'The Prospect of Soviet Orbital Construction in the Summer of 1977', *SP 21*, 12, 517-518 (Dec. 1979)

37 McKereghan and Friedlander, 'Nuclear Manned Missions to Mars in the 1980s', *A&A*, Jan. 1970

38 J. T. Taylor, S. W. Wilson, *A Minimum-Energy Mission Plan for the Manned Exploration of Mars*, NASA TN D-5502, GPO Nov. 1969

39 E. A. Willis, Jr., '*Comparison of Trajectory Profiles and Nuclear-Propulsion Module Arrangements for Manned Mars and Mars-Venus Missions*, NASA TN D-6176, GPO, Feb . 1971

40 Martin Caidin, *Worlds in Space*, Sidgwick & Jackson, 1954

41 Martin Caidin, *Rockets Beyond the Earth*, McBride Company, Inc., 1952

42 John Wyndham and 'Lucas Parkes', *The Outward Urge* (short stories), Penguin, 1962

43 Arthur C. Clarke, 'Transit of Earth' (short story) in *The Wind from the Sun, op cit*

44 Charles Chilton, *The World in Peril* (novel), Herbert Jenkins, 1960

45 J. M. Deerwater and S. M. Norman, *Reference System Characteristics for Manned Stopover Missions to Mars and Venus*, NASA TN D-6226, GPO Mar. 1971

46 C. A. Syvertson, *Research Problems in Atmosphere Entry and Landing from Manned Planetary Missions*, NASA TN D-4977. GPO Jan. 1969

47 E. A. Willis, Jr. and J. A. Padrutt, *Round-trip Trajectories with Stopovers at Both Venus and Mars*, NASA TN D-5758, GPO Jan. 1970

48 K. A. Ehricke, 'A Strategic Approach to Interplanetary Flight', *op cit*

49 James F. Brady, *Study of Physiological and Behavioural Response to Transitions between Rotating and Nonrotating Environments*, NASA CR-2130, GPO Nov. 1972

50 Robert S. Richardson, *Mars*, Allen & Unwin, 1965

51 Richard Goody, 'Weather on the Inner Planets', in *New Science in the Solar System*, IPC Magazines Ltd, 1975

52 'Surface of Mars', *SP 15*, 1, 22 (Jan. 1973)

53 'Martian Surface and Wind Conditions', *SP 14*, 9, 354 (Sept. 1972)

54 E. Mitchell and M. Burns, *Preliminary Study of Advanced Life-Support Technology for a Mars Surface Module*, NASA CR-1083, GPO June 1968

55 Hubertus Strughold, 'Planetary Environmental Medicine (Mars)', *4S*

56 Arthur C. Clarke, *The Exploration of Space, op cit*

57 Arthur C. Clarke, *The Sands of Mars, op cit*

58 Robert Silverberg, *The Feast of St. Dionysius* (novel), Gollancz, 1976

59 R. A. Lafferty, *The Reefs of Earth* (novel), Dobson, 1968

60 Joseph Veverka, 'Phobos and Deimos', *SA 236*, 2, 30-37 (Feb. 1977)

61 S. F. Singer, 'The Martian Satellites', in *Physical Studies of Minor Planets*, ed. T. Gehrels, NASA SP-267, GPO 1971

62 'Zooming in on Phobos and Deimos', *S&T 54*, 6, 469 (Dec. 1977)
63 'Zooming in on Phobos', *SA 236*, 4, 57 (Apr. 1977)
64 *NS* 7.4.'77, 19
65 'Mapping the Martian Satellites', *S&T 49*, 6, 368-369 (June 1975)
66 J. Veverka, P. Thomas and T. Duxbury, 'The Puzzling Moons of Mars', *S&T 56*, 3, 186-189 (Sept. 1978)
67 'Striations of Phobos', *S&T 54*, 4, 269 (Oct. 1977)
68 Eric Burgess, *To the Red Planet*, Columbia University Press, 1978
69 'The Moons of Mars', *S&T 57*, 1, 11 (Jan. 1979)
70 R. C. Parkinson, 'Planetary Spacecraft for the 1980s', *SP 17*, 10, 346-351 (Oct. 1975)
71 Dandridge M. Cole and Donald W. Cox, *Islands in Space: The Challenge of the Planetoids*, Chilton, 1964
72 Ray Bradbury, *The Martian Chronicles* (short stories), Rupert Hart-Davis, 1951
73 Edgar Rice Burroughs, *The Gods of Mars* (novel), Methuen, 1920
74 Frederik Pohl, *Man Plus* (novel), Gollancz, 1976
75 Carl Sagan, O. B. Toon and P. J. Gierach, 'Climatic Change on Mars', *Science 181*, 1045-1049 (1977)
76 J. A. Cutts *et al.*, 'North Polar Region of Mars: Imaging Results from Viking 2', *Science 194*, 4271, 1329-1337 (Dec. 1976)
77 Adrian Berry, *The Next Ten Thousand Years*, op cit
78 Eric Burgess, 'Mars—A Water Planet?', *NS 72*, 1023, 152-153 (21.10.'76)

Chapter 8: Venus as the Abode of Life (pp. 164-176)

1 R. A. Proctor, *The Expanse of Heaven*, Longmans, Green and Co., 1886
2 Carl Sagan, *The Cosmic Connection*, op cit
3 'Early Findings from Pioneer Venus', *ARC* 79-06 (8.2.'79)
4 Garry Hunt, 'Venus', in *New Science in the Solar System*, op cit
5 Fred Hoyle and Chandra Wickramasinghe, *Lifecloud*, Dent, 1978
6 Charles Petit, 'Data from Venus Show Why It Isn't Like Earth', *San Francisco Chronicle*, 7.11.'81
7 'New Findings about Venus', *ARC* 6.10.81
8 Philip Latham, 'The Aphrodite Project', *ASF* VI, 12 (British Edition), 35-41 (Oct. 1949)
9 J. P. Kirton, 'The Problem of the Gyroscopic Earth', *ASF* LXXIII, 3, 8-16, 81 (May 1964)
10 J. Kelly Beatty, 'Pioneers' Venus: More than Fire and Brimstone', *S&T 58*, 1, 13-15, 27 (July 1979)
11 NASA Staff, 'Venus Unveiled?', *SP 20*, 12, 413-419 (Dec. 1978)
12 'Milestones', *SP 21*, 7, 299 (July 1979)
13 'New Light on Venus', *SP 22*, 1, 34-35 (Jan. 1980)
14 Jim Loudon, 'Pioneer Venus: a First Report', *S&T 57*, 2, 119-123 (Feb. 1979)
15 Gordon R. Hooper, 'Missions to Salyut 6', part 8, *SP 21*, 8/9, 359-363 (Aug./Sept. 1979)
16 'Conditions on Venus', *SP 21*, 6, 278-279 (June 1979)
17 'Venus Rift Valley', *SP 21*, 8/9, 337 and Cover (Aug./Sept. 1979)
18 Nicholas L. Johnson, 'Soviet Atmospheric and Surface Venus Probes', *SP 20*, 6, 224-228 (June 1978)

19 'Milestones', *SP 21*, 3, 97-98 (Mar. 1979)
20 'Milestones', *SP 21*, 5, 193 (May 1979)
21 R. J. Stalker, 'Laboratory Studies of Planetary Entry Aerodynamics', *op cit*
22 S. W. Greenwood, 'Extraterrestrial Atmospheric Transport Considerations', *op cit*
23 C. A. Syvertson, *op cit*
24 Bob Buckley, *World in the Clouds* (novel), *ASF* c, 3, 4 & 5 (March/April/May 1980)
25 Carl Sagan, 'The Planet Venus', *Science 133* (24.3.'61)
26 T. Ransome, 'Periodic Interplanetary Orbits', *SP 13*, 2, 72-73 (Feb. 1971)
27 M. M. Averner, R. D. MacElroy, *On the Habitability of Mars, op cit*
28 A. J. McIlroy, 'Venus Shows Wonders to us Spacecraft', *DT* 29.5.'80, 19
29 'The Surface of Venus from Pioneer', *ARC* 80-48, 28.5.'80
30 'Radar Map of Venus', *S&T 59*, 6, 463 (June 1980)
31 NASA Staff, 'Four-Planet Meteorology', *SP 21*, 6, 255-259 (June 1979)
32 Adrian Berry, *The Next Ten Thousand Years, op cit*
33 Jack Vance, *The Blue World* (novel), Mayflower, 1976
34 Henry Kuttner, *Fury* (novel), Mayflower-Dell, 1963
35 Christopher Priest, *Inverted World* (novel), Faber, 1974
36 Joseph Ashbrook, 'The Next Transit of Venus', *S&T 58*, 4, 324-325 (Oct. 1979)

Chapter 9: The Workshop of the Solar System (pp. 177-182)
1 Bruce Murray, Eric Burgess, *Flight to Mercury*, Columbia University Press, 1977
2 P. Ryan and L. Pesek, *Solar System, op cit*
3 Isaac Asimov, 'Just Mooning Around', in *Asimov on Astronomy*, Macdonald & Jane's, 1974
4 'Was Mercury a Moon of Venus?', *NS 71*, 1019, 641 (23.9.'76)
5 William K. Hartmann, 'The Significance of the Planet Mercury', *S&T 51*, 5, 307-311 (May 1976)
6 James Strong, *Search the Solar System*, David and Charles, 1973
7 Robert Edgar, 'Payloads for the Shuttle', *SP 18*, 9, 327-330 (Sept. 1976)
8 Bruce C. Murray, 'Mercury', *SA 233*, 3, 58-68 (Sept. 1975)
9 J. F. Culver, 'The Human Eye in Space Exploration', *4S*
10 *JBIS 26*, 1, 52 (Jan. 1973)
11 C. A. Cross, 'The Planet Mercury', *SP 20*, 11, 363-370 (Nov. 1978)
12 G. R. Hollenbeck, D. G. Roos and P. S. Lewis, *Ballistic Mode Mercury Orbiter Mission Opportunity Handbook*, NASA CR-2298, GPO Aug.1973
13 Fred Hoyle and Chandra Wickramsinghe, *Lifecloud, op cit*
14 F. J. Dyson, 'The Search for Extraterrestrial Technology', in *Perspectives in Modern Physics, op cit*
15 Adrian Berry, *The Next Ten Thousand Years, op cit*

Chapter 10: Your Considerate Stone (pp. 183-198)
1 'Dinosaurs "Killed by Asteroid"', *op cit*

2 J. E. Enever, 'Giant Meteor Impact', *ASF* LXXVII, 1, 61-84 (Mar. 1966)
3 F. Yu Zigel, *The Minor Planets*, NASA TT F-700 *GPO* May 1972
4 Carl Sagan, *The Cosmic Connection, op cit*
5 'Earthquakes and the Earth's Magnetism', *JBIS 27*, 2, 150 (Feb. 1974)
6 Bevan M. French, *The Moon Book*, Penguin, 1977
7 John Baxter, *The Hermes Fall* (novel), Panther, 1978
8 Brian O'Leary, 'To Catch a Falling Star', in *The Endless Frontier, op cit*
9 Isaac Asimov, 'The Rocks of Damocles', in *Asimov on Astronomy, op cit*
10 Keith Hindley, 'Fireball Networks—A Mixed Blessing', *NS 72*, 1032, 695-698 (23/30.12.'76)
11 Ian Ridpath, *Messages from the Stars*, Fontana/Collins, 1978
12 Fletcher G. Watson, *Between the Planets*, Harvard University Press, 1956
13 Luigi G. Jacchia, 'A Meteorite that Missed the Earth', *S&T 48*, 1, 4-9 (July 1974)
14 Arthur C. Clarke, *Rendezvous with Rama* (novel), Gollancz, 1973
15 H. Alven and G. Arrhenius, 'Arguments for a Mission to an Asteroid', in *Physical Studies of Minor Planets, op cit*
16 Richard Beeston, ' "Spacewatch" Plan to Attack Meteors with H-bombs', *DT* 13.2.'81, 19
17 D. M. Cole and D. W. Cox, *Islands in Space, op cit*
18 'A New Interior Planet', *S&T 51*, 3, 158 (Mar. 1976)
19 A. C. Macey and J. Nichoff, 'Sample-Return Missions to the Asteroid Eros', in *Physical Studies of Minor Planets, op cit*
20 'Eros', *JBIS 30*, 6, 234 (June 1977)
21 Clark R. Chapman, 'The Nature of Asteroids', *SA 239*, 1, 24-34 (Jan. 1975)
22 David Morrison, 'Diameters of Minor Planets', *S&T 53*, 3, 181-183 (Mar. 1977)
23 'The Missing Planet?', *SP 21*, 2, 62 (Feb. 1979)
24 T. Gehrels, Introduction, *Physical Studies of Minor Planets, op cit*
25 L. Kresak, 'Orbital Selection Effects in the Palomar-Leiden Asteroid Survey', *ibid*
26 A. F. Cook, '624 Hektor: A Binary Asteroid', *ibid*
27 '532 Herculina as a Double Asteroid', *S&T 56*, 3, 210 (Sept. 1978)
28 David W. Dunham, 'Celestial Calendar', *S&T 57*, 3, 272-275 (Mar. 1979)
29 Thomas W. Hamilton, letter, *S&T 57*, 4, 333 (Apr. 1979)
30 'Shapes of Asteroids', *JBIS 27*, 8, 628 (Aug. 1974)
31 T. Kiang, 'Recent Astronomical Research in China', *op cit*
32 K. Aksnes, 'Manmade Objects—a Source of Confusion to Asteroid Hunters', in *Physical Studies of Minor Planets, op cit*
33 James Strong, *Search the Solar System, op cit*
34 G. Harry Stine, 'The Third Industrial Revolution: the Exploitation of the Space Environment', *op cit (SP)*
35 Garry Hunt, 'Venus', *op cit*
36 G.P. Vdovykin, *Carbonaceous Matter in Meteorites (Organic Compounds, Diamonds, Graphite)*, Nauka Press, Moscow 1967; trans. NASA TT F-582, *GPO* April 1970

37 G. Harry Stine, 'The Third Industrial Revolution', part 2, *op cit* *(ASF)*
38 Jerry Pournelle, 'Those Pesky Belters and their Torchships', *Galaxy* *35*, 5, 105-113 (May 1974)
39 D. J. Sheppard, 'Concrete Space Colonies', *op cit*
40 Isaac Asimov, 'The World, Ceres', in *The Tragedy of the Moon*, Coronet, 1975
41 F. J. Dyson, 'Human Consequences of the Exploration of Space', in *Men in Space*, ed. Eugene Rabinowitch and Richard S. Lewis, Medical & Technical Publishing Co., Ltd., 1970
42 Brian Aldiss, *The Eighty-Minute Hour* (novel), Cape, 1974
43 Saunders B. Kramer, 'Problems of Asteroid Capture', *op cit*

Chapter 11: Taming the Giants (pp. 199-244)
1 Arthur Koestler, *The Sleepwalkers*, Hutchinson, 1959
2 Jerry Pournelle, 'Jove!', *Destinies 1*, 5, 93-107 (Dec. 1979)
3 R. D. Enzmann, 'Introduction to the Section on Environments', *2C*
4 Anthony R. Martin, 'The Detection of Extrasolar Planetary Systems', part 1, *JBIS 27*, 9, 643-659 (Sept. 1974)
5 'The Sodium Cloud of Io', *S&T 54*, 6, 479-480 (Dec. 1977)
6 NASA Staff, 'Discovering Jupiter—2', *SP 19*, 1, 21-28 (Jan. 1977)
7 J. Kelly Beatty, 'Voyager's Encore Performance', *S&T 58*, 3, 206-216 (Sept. 1979)
8 *NS 83*, 1170, 657 (30.8.'79)
9 Wm. K. Hartmann, 'The Smaller Bodies of the Solar System', *SA 233*, 3, 142-159 (Sept. 1975)
10 'Milestones', *SP 21*, 6, 242 (June 1979)
11 Edwin Morgan, 'The Moons of Jupiter', in *Star Gate*, Third Eye Centre, Glasgow, 1979
12 Peter Hedervari, letter, *S&T 59*. 1, 14 (Jan. 1980)
13 *Mission to Jupiter/Saturn, Issue Number Two: Satellites of the Outer Planets*, NASA JPL-Coml., s-22-82, 11/'77
14 'Jupiter's Biggest Moon', *SP 22*, 2, 72-76 (Feb. 1980)
15 J. Kelly Beatty, 'The Far-Out Worlds of Voyager 1', part 1, *S&T 57*, 5, 422-427 (May 1979)
16 *Ibid.*, part 2, *S&T 57*, 6, 516-520 (June 1979)
17 *SP 21*, 11, 433 and Cover (Nov. 1979)
18 'Moons of Jupiter—Callisto', *SP 22*, 4, 162-163 (Apr. 1980)
19 'The Surface of Venus from Pioneer', *op cit*
20 Nigel Calder, *Spaceships of the Mind*, *op cit*
21 R. C. Parkinson, 'The Resources of the Solar System', *SP 17*, 4, 124-128 (Apr. 1975)
22 'Discovering Jupiter—3', *SP 19*, 2, 73-74, 80 (Feb. 1977)
23 'Galileo to Jupiter', NASA JPL 400-15 7/79, *GPO* 1979-691-547
24 'Appointment with Jupiter', *SP 21*, 3, 108-109 (Mar. 1979)
25 R. O. Fimmel, Wm. Swindell, Eric Burgess, *Pioneer Odyssey*, NASA SP-396, revised edition, *GPO* 1977
26 'Discovering Jupiter—2', *op cit*
27 David Baker, 'Report from Jupiter', part 2, *SP 17*, 3, 102-107 (Mar. 1975)

28   Jerry Pournelle, 'Those Pesky Belters and their Torchships', *op cit*
29   Jerry Pournelle, 'This Generation of Wonder', *Galaxy 35*, 7, 116-123 (July 1974)
30   Ben Bova, '1974—The Year that Was', *ASF* XCIV, 5, 5-11 (Jan. 1975)
31   D. M. Cole and D. W. Cox, *Islands in Space, op cit*
32   Richard D. Johnson, ed., *Space Settlements: A Design Study, op cit*
33   J. E. Gore, *The Worlds of Space, op cit*
34   'Space Report', *SP 21*, 12, 498-499 (Dec. 1979)
35   Garry Hunt, 'Space Exploration of the Jovian Atmosphere', *JBIS 30*, 1, 15-19 (Jan. 1977)
36   R. B. Hinckley, R. C. Reid and P. E. Glaser, *op cit*
37   Anthony R. Martin, 'Missions to Jupiter—2', *SP 14*, 9, 325-332 (Sept. 1972)
38   'Preliminary Pioneer 10 Findings', *JBIS 27*, 6, 473-474 (June 1974)
39   R. C. Parkinson, 'Propellant Acquisition Techniques', in *Project Daedalus, op cit*
40   Hal Clement, *Mission of Gravity* (novel), Hale, 1955
41   'Air Turbulence Warning Now Possible', *ARC* 76-80 (11.11.'76)
42   R. C. Parkinson, 'The Colonisation of Space', *SP 17*, 3, 88-90 (Mar. 1975)
43   Isaac Asimov, 'The Element of Perfection', in *View from a Height*, Dobson, 1964
44   Frederick I. Ordway, '2001; a Space Odyssey', *op cit*
45   'Jupiter's Sulphur Ring', *S&T 59*, 2, 120-121 (Feb. 1980)
46   R. A. Proctor, *Other Suns than Ours*, W.H. Allen, 1887
47   'Two New Jovian Moons Photographed by Voyager 1', *S&T 60*, 1, 12 (July 1980)
48   G. L. Matloff and A. J. Fennelly, *op cit*
49   'Pioneer 11: Through the Dragon's Mouth', *S&T 49*, 2, 72-78 (Feb. 1975)
50   'Pioneer Saturn Discoveries', *ARC* 1980
51   P. Ryan and L. Pesek, *Solar System, op cit*
52   Isaac Asimov, 'The Universe and the Future', in *Is Anyone There?*, Ace, 1967
53   'Milestones', *SP 22*, 1, 45 (Jan. 1980)
54   K. A. Ehricke, in *2C, op cit*
55   R. A. Freitas, 'A Self-reproducing Interstellar Probe', *JBIS 33*, 7, 251-264 (July 1980)
56   Willard F. Libby, 'Space Chemistry in the '70s', *4S*
57   James Blish, 'Bridge' (short story), in *Jupiter*, ed. Carol and Frederik Pohl, Ballantine, 1973
58   'Metallic Xenon', *SP 21*, 3, 137 (Mar. 1979)
59   'Producing Metallic Hydrogen', *SP 19*, 5, 175 (May 1977)
60   'Milestones', *SP 20*, 2, 47 (Feb. 1978)
61   Alan Bond, 'Problems of Interstellar Propulsion', *SP 13*, 7, 245-252 (July 1971)
62   F. J. Dyson, 'The Search for Extraterrestrial Technology', *op cit*
63   A. F. O'D. Alexander, *The Planet Saturn*, Faber, 1962
64   'Pioneer Saturn Encounter', *ARC* Sept. 1979
65   J. Kelly Beatty, 'Rendezvous with a Ringed Giant', *S&T 61*, 1, 7-18 (Jan. 1981)

66 J. Kelly Beatty, 'Voyager at Saturn, Act II', *S&T* 62, 5, 430-444 (Nov. 1981)

67 'Voyager 1 Pictorial Update', *S&T 62*, 1, 8-12 (July 1981)

68 Kit Weinrichter, 'The Last Picture Show?', *ASTRA Spacereport 4*, 2 (Jan. 1982)

69 R. A. Proctor, *Flowers of the Sky*, Chatto & Windus, 1889

70 W. M. Higgins, *Researches in the Solar Realm*, Hall, Virtue & Co., 1852

71 Ian Brodie, 'Voyager Finds a Misshapen Moon', *DT* 26.8.'81

72 M. S. Dobrov, *The Rings of Saturn*, Nauka Press, Moscow; trans. NASA TT F-701, *GPO* June 1972

73 M. M. Waldrop, 'Voyager 1 at Saturn', *Science 210*, 1107-1111 (5.12.'81)

74 Ian Brodie, 'Lightning Bolts on Saturn', *DT* 1.9.'81

75 John T. Lloyd, letter, *DT* 29.11.'80, 18

76 Arthur C. Clarke, *The Sands of Mars, op cit*

77 'NASA Report to Educators', Winter 1980

78 James Blish, 'How Beautiful with Banners' (short story) in *Best Science Fiction Stories of James Blish* (revised edition), Faber, 1973

79 'Meteoroid Impacts on the Earth/Moon System', *JBIS 27*, 1, 68-69 (Jan. 1974)

80 'Pioneer 10 at "Silver AU" Describes Sun's Atmosphere', *ARC* 81-39 (26.7.'81)

81 'Pacific Astronomers Convene', *S&T 48*, 3, 143-147 (Sept. 1974)

82 J. P. Kirton, *op cit*

83 'Changes in Uranus Atmosphere', *SP 21*, 1, 29 (Jan. 1979)

84 'Appointment with Jupiter', *SP 21*, 3, 108-109 (Mar. 1979)

85 'Reports on Uranus and Neptune', *S&T 53*, 6, 429-430 (June 1977)

86 NS 27.10.'77, 221

87 'Uranus and Neptune: Diamond-Studded Interiors?', *S&T 62*, 4, 317-318 (Oct. 1981)

88 'Rings of Uranus', *SP 21*, 4, 153 (Apr. 1979)

89 'More on the Rings of Uranus', *S&T 62*, 5, 418 (Nov. 1981)

90 'Voyager, Mission to the Outer Planets', NASA Facts NF-87/10-77, *GPO* 1977

91 Wm. Graves Hoyt, *Planets X and Pluto*, University of Arizona Press, 1980

92 Joseph W. Chamberlain, 'The Outer Solar System—Focus on the Future', *A&A* Jan. 1972, 22

93 'Miranda', *JBIS 27*, 8, 629 (Aug. 1974)

94 S. K. Vsekhsvyatskiy, *The Nature and Origin of Comets and Meteors*, Prosveshcheniye Press, Moscow, 1967; trans. NASA TT F-608, *GPO* Apr. 1970

95 'Snowballs at the Outer Limits II: No Methane Atmosphere on Triton?', *S&T 62*, 4, 316 (Oct. 1981)

96 Vernor Vinge, Arthur Sorkin, 'Titan as a Gravitational Brake', *JBIS 27*, 2, 129-131 (Feb. 1974)

97 Wm. K. Hartmann, 'A 1974 Tour of the Planets', *S&T 48*, 2, 78-81 (Aug. 1974)

98 F. L. Whipple, *Earth, Moon and Planets*, 3rd edition, Penguin, 1971

99 *NS 73*, 1039, 303 (17.2.'77)

100 'Neptune's Third Satellite', *S&T 62*, 4, 317 (Oct. 1981)

101 'Kirkwood's Gaps and Neptune's Rings: Resonance at Work?', *S&T 62*, 6, 541 (Dec. 1981)

102 Isaac Asimov, 'Beyond Pluto', in *Asimov on Astronomy, op cit*

103 'Charon Update', *S&T 61*, 3, 198 (Mar. 1981)

104 'How Large Is Pluto?', *S&T 59*, 3, 209 (Mar. 1980)

105 R. S. and B. J. Harrington, 'Pluto: Still an Enigma after 50 Years', *S&T 59*, 6, 452-454 (June 1980)

106 'Pluto's Atmosphere', *S&T 60*, 6, 483 (Dec. 1980)

107 *NS 83*, 1171, 733 (6.9.'79)

108 Joseph L. Brady, 'The Effect of a Trans-Plutonian Planet on Halley's Comet', *Pub. Astron. Soc. of the Pacific 84*, 314-322 (Apr. 1972)

109 Ian Ridpath, 'The Mini-Planet', *NS* 17.11.'77, 406-407

110 A. T. Lawton, 'Asteroid Chiron—The First of a Few?', *SP 20*, 8, 312-313 (Aug. 1978)

111 'Past and Future Orbit of Chiron', *S&T 57*, 3, 249 (Mar. 1979)

112 Charles T. Kowal, letter, *S&T 55*, 3, 195 (Mar. 1978)

113 A. T. Lawton, 'Charon—A Companion to Pluto', *SP 20*, 12, 428-429 (Dec. 1978)

114 Adrian Berry, *The Next Ten Thousand Years, op cit*

115 Isaac Asimov, 'By Jove!', in *View from a Height, op cit*

116 Clifford D. Simak, *City* (novel), Weidenfeld & Nicolson, 1954

Chapter 12: The Resources of the Outer Solar System (pp. 245-263)

1 Isaac Asimov, 'Steppingstones to the Stars', in *Asimov on Astronomy, op cit*

2 'The Origin of Comets', *JBIS 27*, 6, 467 (June 1974)

3 David Hughes, 'The Direct Investigation of Comets by Space Probes', *JBIS 30*, 1, 3-14 (June 1977)

4 G. Lovi, R. Kracht, S. Vsekhsvyatskiy, letters, *S&T 58*, 1, 16-17 (July 1979)

5 S. K. Vsekhsvyatskiy, *The Nature and Origin of Comets and Meteors, op cit*

6 'Solar Neutrino Problem May Be Remnant of Ice Age', *op cit*

7 'Consequences of Meeting a Dense Interstellar Cloud', *S&T 54*, 3, 193 (Sept. 1977)

8 Adrian Webster, 'The Cosmic Background Radiation', *SA 231*, 2 26-33 (Aug. 1974)

9 Fred Hoyle and Chandra Wickramasinghe, 'Does Epidemic Disease Come from Space?', *NS* 17.11.'77, 402-404

10 Isaac Asimov, 'Not As We Know It', in *View from a Height, op cit*

11 'Findings Suggest New Theory on Origin of Solar System Bodies', *ARC* 81-52 (25.9.'81)

12 'Key Mechanism in the Origin of Life Apparently Found', *ARC* 78-25 (16.6.'78)

13 Fred Hoyle and Chandra Wickramasinghe, *Lifecloud, op cit*

14 Fred Hoyle and Chandra Wickramasinghe, *Diseases from Space*, Dent, 1979

15 Adrian Berry, '"Viroids" Drive Evolution, Say Professors', *DT* 27.3.'80, 3

16 Alan Bond, 'On the Improbability of Intelligent Extraterrestrials', 3rd BIS Interstellar Studies Conference, Sept. 1979

17 Carl A. Larson, 'Strong Poison', part 2, *ASF* LXXXIX, 4, 72-84 (June 1972)

18 F. J. Dyson, 'Human Consequences of the Exploration of Space', *op cit*

19 G. K. O'Neill, *The High Frontier, op cit*

20 Norman Sperling, 'Northeast Region, Astronomical League', report, *S&T 56*, 4, 310, 312 (Oct. 1978)

21 'Comet West's Fine Performance', *S&T 51*, 5, 312-321 (May 1976)

22 James Blish, *A Case of Conscience* (novel), Faber, 1959

23 Arthur C. Clarke, *Imperial Earth* (novel), Gollancz, 1975

24 Robert L. Forward, 'A Programme for Interstellar Exploration', *JBIS 29*, 10, 610-631 (Oct. 1976)

25 'Comets, Galactic Chemistry and Other Matters', JBIS *29*, 7/8, 523-524 (July/Aug. 1976)

26 George W. Harper, 'Styx and Stones: And Maybe Charon Too', *ASF* XCII 3, 64-81 (Nov. 1973)

27 George W. Harper, 'Kohoutek; A Failure that Wasn't', *ASF* XCIII, 5, 40-51 (July 1974)

28 'Rotation of a Comet Nucleus', *S&T 55*, 3, 214 (Mar. 1978)

29 'Traumatic Birth', *SA 238*, 1, 66, 68 (Jan. 1978)

30 JBIS Nov. 1972, 673

31 Mark Washburn, 'In Pursuit of Halley's Comet', *S&T 61*, 2, 111-113 (Feb. 1981)

32 Nigel Calder, *Einstein's Universe*, BBC Publications, 1979

33 Robert W. Chapman, 'NASA's Search for the Solar Connection', *S&T 58*, 3, 223-227 (Sept. 1979)

34 'The World Is a Bit Cracked', *NS 73*, 320

35 Duncan Lunan and John Braithwaite, 'Gravitational Telescopes' (paper in preparation)

36 Isaac Asimov, 'The Triumph of the Moon', in *The Tragedy of the Moon, op cit*

37 Bevan M. French, *The Moon Book*, Penguin, 1977

38 'Climate in a Spin', *NS 83*, 1173, 894 (20.9.'79)

39 Edward Boswell, review, 'Comets, Asteroids, Meteorites', *S&T 57*, 2, 173-175 (Feb. 1979)

40 Saul J. Adelman, 'Can Venus Be Transformed into an Earth-like Planet?', *JBIS 35*, 1, 3-8 (Jan. 1982)

41 Adrian Berry, *The Next Ten Thousand Years, op cit*

42 J. D. Fernie, 'Interstellar Absorption in the Galactic Neighbourhood of the Sun', *Astronomical Journal 67*, 4, 224-228 (May 1962)

43 Bruce Morgan and Stuart Bowyer, 'Extreme-Ultraviolet Astronomy from Apollo-Soyuz', *S&T 50*, 1, 4-9 (July 1975)

44 V. A. Hughes and D. Routledge, 'An Expanding Ring of Interstellar Gas with Centre Close to the Sun', *op cit*

45 Alfred Vidal-Madjar, C. Laurent, P. Bruston and J. Audouze, 'Is the Solar System Entering a Nearby Interstellar Cloud?', *Astrophys. J. 223*, 589-600 (15.7.'78)

46 'Is the Solar System Heading into an Interstellar Cloud?,' *S & T, 56*, 3, 211-212 (Sept. 1978)

47   John Taylor, *Black Holes: The End of the Universe?*, Souvenir Press, 1973
48   Adrian Berry, *The Iron Sun*, Cape, 1977
49   Ian Ridpath, *Messages from the Stars, op cit*
50   Camille Flammarion, *Les Etoiles*, Paris, 1881

Chapter 13: The Philosophy of a Kardashev-2 Civilization (pp. 264-278)

1   R. A. Proctor, *Other Suns than Ours, op cit*
2   F. J. Dyson, *SA* April 1964
3   *Prism 2*, 3; Spectrum Group, London, 1975
4   Arthur C. Clarke, *Rendezvous with Rama, op cit*
5   F. J. Dyson, 'The Search for Extraterrestrial Technology', *op cit*
6   Adrian Berry, *The Next Ten Thousand Years, op cit*
7   F. J. Dyson, 'Search for Artificial Stellar Sources of Infra-red Radiation', in *Interstellar Communication*, ed. A. G. W. Cameron, Benjamin, 1963
8   Larry Niven, 'Alternatives to Worlds', *Speculation 32*, Spring 1973; reprinted as 'Bigger than Worlds', *ASF* xciii, 1, 65-79 (Mar. 1974)
9   Bob Shaw, *Orbitsville*, Gollancz, 1975
10   Harlow Shapley, 'Crusted Stars and Self-Heating Planets', *Matematica y Fisica Teorica Serie A 14*, 69-75 (1962)
11   Isaac Asimov, 'Harmony in Heaven', *Fantasy & Science Fiction 28*, 2, 81-91 (Feb. 1965)
12   D. D. Meisel, 'Exploration of the Outer Solar System', *2C*
13   S. K. Vsekhsvyatskiy, *The Nature and Origin of Comets and Meteors, op cit*
14   Arthur C. Clarke, *The City and the Stars* (novel), Muller, 1956
15   Arthur C. Clarke, *Childhood's End* (novel), Sidgwick & Jackson, 1954
15   Kenneth F. Weaver, James P. Blair, 'The Incredible Universe', *NG 145*, 5, 589-625 (May 1974)
17   'Ring Galaxies', jbis *30*, 3, 115 (Mar. 1977)

Key to Abbreviations used for Publications

AA - *Acta Astronautica*
A & A - *Astronautics and Aeronautics*
ARC - NASA Ames Research Centre
ASF - *Astounding Science Fiction,* later *Analog Science Fiction / Science Fact*
DT - *The Daily Telegraph*
GPO - *U.S. Government Printing Office*
JBIS - *Journal of the British Interplanetary Society*
NG - *National Geographic Magazine*
NS - *New Scientist*

SA - *Scientific American*
SP - *Spaceflight*
S & T - *Sky & Telescope*
2C - *Second Conference on Planetology and Space Mission Planning, Ann. New York Academy of Sciences, 163,* Article 1, pp. 1-558.
L5 (WE) - *Proceedings of the L5 Society (Western Europe) Conference,* L5 Society, Tucson, Arizona
4S - *Fourth International Symposium on Bioastronautics and the Exploration of Space,* ed. Roadman, Strughold and Mitchell, Aerospace Med. Divn., (AFSC), Brooks AFB, Texas, 1968.

INDEX